DAVID D. BEDWORTH, Ph.D., Purdue University, is Professor of Engineering at Arizona State University. A Professional Engineer, Dr. Bedworth has served as a consultant for the Process Computer Division of General Electric Company and Semi-Conductor Products Division of Motorola, Inc., primarily in the field of digital computer control. He is a Contributing Editor of the *Production Handbook, Third Edition,* published by The Ronald Press Company. Dr. Bedworth is a member of the editorial board of *AIIE Transactions* and a contributor to *Industrial Engineering,* both publications of the American Institute of Industrial Engineers. He is National Executive Secretary of Alpha Pi Mu, the industrial engineering honor society.

INDUSTRIAL SYSTEMS

SYSTEMS

—

PLANNING, ANALYSIS, CONTROL

DAVID D. BEDWORTH

ARIZONA STATE UNIVERSITY

THE RONALD PRESS COMPANY • NEW YORK

Library of Congress Catalog Card Number: 72-96967
PRINTED IN THE UNITED STATES OF AMERICA

DEDICATED TO THE STUDENT

*There are more men ennobled
by study than by nature.*
CICERO

Preface

This textbook is designed for courses emphasizing quantitative techniques in the planning, analysis, and control of industrial systems. Though oriented toward industrial systems, the application of these techniques is shown to extend beyond the traditional production functions. Thus a particular course need not be restricted to the narrow confines of manufacturing systems to make effective use of this text.

The book is self-contained; all essential material related to the topics covered has been defined and derived within pedagogically sound boundaries. For his part, the student is expected to bring an introductory background in calculus and statistics. A level of maturity one would expect of senior and first-year graduate engineering and business students is assumed.

In order to introduce a program of action, a plan must be developed, its implementation optimized by the use of appropriate analytical tools, and its performance monitored by suitable controls. The organization of this book parallels such a sequence of functions. Part I covers the planning function from a systems viewpoint. Fully documented case problems are used here, as throughout the book, to stress particular applications and demonstrate effective problem-solving procedures. The concepts of network planning and forecasting are the main areas treated quantitatively. It is recommended that both business and engineering courses cover this material in its entirety. For the class with minimal optimization foundation, the chapter assignments can be arranged so that optimization (Chapter 5) is covered before statistical forecasting (Chapters 3 and 4).

Part II is devoted to analysis, primarily that of the scheduling function. The basic aim is to develop a proper foundation in the subject upon which the student can later build through advanced study and research. Fundamentals are emphasized and a wide range of scheduling problems are investigated. While topics in this

v

Part are considered essential for most course presentations, a thorough coverage of optimization would depend on the mathematical background of the class as a whole.

Finally, Part III is concerned with control. It is this function that sees to it that actual performance conforms with prior planning and analysis. Although the chapter on adaptive control is the last one concerned with quantitative methods, subsequent chapters do provide material for a more rounded picture of the control functions. The final two chapters of the book take the student beyond present techniques into the realm of future uses of automated planning, analysis, and control of industrial systems.

To say that the persons who assisted with the development and preparation of this text are too numerous to mention, is to throw out a tired cliché; but it would also be a true statement. To the many students who suffered, contributed, and received knowledge during the growing pains of this project goes my sincere appreciation. To the academic chairmen at Arizona State University under whom I have served goes a special debt of gratitude: C. B. Gambrell, my first chairman, and H. H. Young, who succeeded him—each in his own way contributed to the atmosphere and relationships so necessary and conducive to professional growth. To my peer group, the industrial engineering faculty at Arizona State University, let me tender a word of appreciation for allowing me to mature with them. Special thanks must also be given to those persons who helped with the manuscript preparation: Mrs. Pat Jones, for typing, correcting, sometimes editing, always contributing to the final manuscript; Mrs. Karen Langdon, for typing manuscript revisions; Glenn Dunlap, for painstakingly reading and editing the original manuscript; Mrs. Shirley Aman, for performing many tasks related to the duplication of the manuscript.

To my family goes a debt of gratitude that never can be repaid; no words can describe their aid during the agony of text writing. Absent hours were accepted without complaint and tired rebukes suffered with patience. Thomas Jefferson expressed my feelings completely when he said, *"The happiest moments of my life have been the few I have passed at home in the bosom of my family."*

David D. Bedworth

Tempe, Arizona
March, 1973

Contents

PART II • ANALYSIS

I

PLANNING

1

Interactive Systems and Planning

Advise well before you begin, and when you have maturely considered, then act with promptitude.

SALLUST

1-1. FOUNDATION

Historically many qualitative procedures and quantitative techniques have been evolved for facilitating the production process. While the development of these techniques and procedures is laudable and their acceptance gratifying there is no doubt that the outlook, which is from a *production planning and control* point of view, has been narrow. The spectrum of utilization should be far broader than the production connotations.

The philosophy that serves as a foundation for this text is that the theory for planning, analyzing, and controlling complex production systems is equally applicable to systems other than those of production. Basically, production planning and control techniques can be loosely divided into the three functions of *forecasting, scheduling,* and *inventory control.* This does not take into consideration quality control, facility planning, and information control; but forecasting, scheduling, and inventory analysis provide the heart of the production process. The three functions are applicable to hospital operation, transportation analysis, airplane auto-landing systems, bank processes, university

3

planning, and so on. The limitation to the production process is not correct—neither in theory nor in current application.

As an example, it might be interesting to look at the analogies (from a system overview) that exist between the traditional production cycle and an auto-landing device designed to land a Boeing 747 at London's fogged-in airport.

The possible relationship between the two systems is depicted schematically in Figure 1–1. Both the production and the flight control systems require a prediction of required characteristics. From a production point of view this would entail forecasting sales for some future period of time. The analogous condition in flight control would be in calculating the required plane position in order to get the airplane touched down at the correct location at the correct time. After these *planning* functions are completed, action is taken to get the plan accomplished in the optimum manner. In production, a schedule is developed which may be optimized by some *analysis* technique, possibly linear programming. The schedule is then implemented in the production environment, and products are produced. The analogous relationship in the flight system is in the control/actuate controller sequence. The automatic controllers will "schedule" corrective action to allow the airplane to arrive at its correct position. Correction may be proportioned to the change required or may be an integral or derivative-type correction, depending on the size and urgency of the change. An ultimate function of the control may be to smooth corrective action so that the flight downward is relatively free of oscillations and quick changes. Similarly, the production scheduling function may smooth forecasts so that a permanent work force may be maintained at a specified level, not requiring continuous hiring and layoff (continuous in this instance refers to monthly fluctuations).

Environmental conditions act on both systems which prevent the desired condition from being perfectly attained. Consumer whims, for example, will cause random fluctuations about a particular sales trend, assuming such a trend exists, which is used in the forecast of sales. Changes in competition and economic conditions are also typical of the production environmental conditions. In the flight control process these unusual conditions could be air pockets, wind resistance, storm activity, and so on. The correction for these unusual conditions would be a *control* activity.

If one ultimate goal in the production system is to smooth work force, then the control operation will be a fluctuating inventory level that

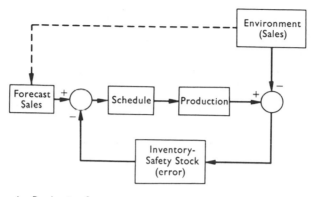

A. Production System

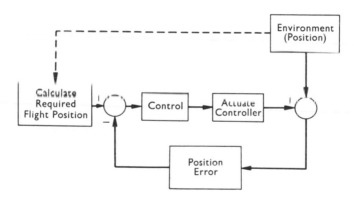

B. Flight Control System

Figure I-I. Analogies in production and flight control systems.

takes care of excessive demand. Extra inventory is produced when demand is low to take care of later sales peaks, and a properly designed system will allow for an expected cyclic inventory situation. An alternate goal might be to smooth inventory, which in turn would necessitate oscillations in work force requirements.

In both production and flight systems, the latest timely data are required on which to base the next action. It can be seen that in both, there exists a continuous dynamic interaction of planning, analysis, and control. In general, the production/sales situation would be a *discrete* case, while the flight control would be an example of a *continuous* process. As earlier stipulated, the philosophy of this text is that the planning, analysis, and control functions are applicable to a wide variety of industrial systems. A plan of action should always be conceived prior to taking action. After a plan has been developed, implementation of the plan is desired in the optimum manner with criteria of optimality being a function of the problem and the solver. Once optimization is achieved, control is maintained to insure satisfactory solution of the problem by the developed procedure. This philosophy of planning, analyzing, and controlling being a common systems approach to a variety of problem areas will be the assumption in subsequent material which will be presented in light of a variety of problems, many of which will fall into the production category, but some of which will be considered in a much broader field of application.

Just as a wide variety of industrial problem areas should benefit from research aimed primarily at the more traditional production planning and control, so should production planning and control benefit from problem solutions from other disciplines.- Topics of autocorrelation analysis applied to sales forecasting and adaptive control used for improving forecasting techniques are typical of how production control can benefit from other disciplines.

This introductory chapter will initially be concerned with presenting a few key definitions pertinent to the text material. Then we will consider that the interaction of system components might nullify the theory that forecasting, scheduling, and inventory control should be considered as autonomous items for simplicity of analysis. Finally, the *systems approach* will be presented as the key to attacking large interactive systems.

1-2. DEFINITIONS

Definitions will be given where needed within the body of the text. However, a few terms have been used on the assumption that they are familiar to all readers, so at this point we will give firm definitions of key terms on which most of this text is based so that everyone will be working on the same foundation.

System. The word *system* will be considered in its broadest sense to cover large-scale problems which have interacting components. Semantically, one now gets into trouble with the word *problems.* A flight control *problem*, for example, will be a complex system consisting of an airplane, pilot, flight controller, airport, flight control section coordination, and many other interacting components. A production *problem* can be a complex system comprising marketing, manufacturing, engineering, management, and service functions, all interacting. The analysis of a system, because of its complexity, usually has to be accomplished in terms of analysis of its components.

Project. A *project* will consist of a series of jobs that individually have to be completed in order for the project itself to be satisfactorily culminated. A *system* will consist of one or more projects. The design of a new automobile may be one individual project. Similarly, so might the development of the manufacturing facility for building the automobile. Setting up a marketing operation can be described as another project. Combined, they can be thought of as the new automobile production *system.*

Forecast. The scientific prediction of future events will constitute a forecast. The usual connotation is that of forecasting expected sales demand for a particular business. However, *forecast* has a much wider spectrum of use. In a flight control system, determination of airplane position trends will allow a forecast of future position to be made. On the basis of this forecast and a knowledge of where the airplane is required to be at some future time, corrective action can be made to insure that the desired time/position will be attained.

Process. The term *process* will be used loosely and not in its usual *process industry* application. *Process* will denote certain dynamic characteristics of a system being studied. A series of sales data used for forecasting will constitute a *sales process.* Similarly, a scheduling procedure that is not rigid in its makeup will be thought of as a *scheduling process.*

Network. In order to visualize a complex system as an entity, graphical arrow diagrams will be developed to represent the system. Such a graphical diagram will be designated a *network.* In general, the text will deal with project networks, with arrows in the network representing components of the project such as *jobs* to be accomplished in a scheduling network.

Optimization. When a system is analyzed, an attempt will be made to *optimize* the system. This will imply operation of the system at some *best* or *optimal* condition. The criteria for optimization have to be a function of the system. For example, it may be possible to maximize profit, maximize production, and minimize costs, but probably will not be possible to optimize all three. Also, optimization of sub-components of a system may lead to optimization of the system but will not necessarily optimize the system.

Control. The term *control* will refer to the process whereby a set of conditions determined for a system by planning and analysis are maintained, even though uncertain characteristics operate upon the system.

Deterministic. For a condition to be *deterministic* implies that predicted characteristics for the condition will be correct. For example, a linear deterministic demand situation in a sales process assumes that the demand will indeed have a constant increase over time.

Stochastic. On the other hand, a *stochastic* sales demand is one that can deviate from a predicted pattern with some probabilistic characteristics. Needless to say, the stochastic situation is the one most closely approaching the real-world case, but it is also the most difficult to analyze mathematically. In general, most of the systems analyzed in this text will be assumed deterministic.

1–3. SUBSYSTEMS AND SYSTEM OPTIMIZATION

Optimization of large systems is difficult, if not impossible, because of their complexity. One approach to the problem is low-order optimization, or subsystem optimization. Components of the overall problem are analyzed as autonomous categories rather than as a whole. For example, consider the interaction between quality control and inventory control. Both are part of the production planning and control system, but each is invariably analyzed as a separate entity. However, depending on the specific quality control approach utilized, decisions from the quality control analysis can directly affect the inventory situation.

To clarify this a little, suppose incoming raw material is subject to a sampling inspection. Assuming that a contractual agreement has been reached with the supplier to the effect that incoming lots will be shipped back to the supplier upon failure of the lot to satisfactorily pass the sampling inspection, it is apparent that there should be sufficient inventory on hand to offset any delay in receipt of the new shipment. Therefore, any economic model that describes the inventory picture, and is optimized to allow overall minimum costs commensurate with maintaining satisfactory production conditions, should include the quality control incoming inspection plan.

Typically, this is not so, because of the mathematical complexity of optimizing the two subsystems as a unified entity. Rather, the approach is to optimize the incoming sampling plan by itself, balancing inspection costs against allowable defectives. The inventory control procedure will similarly attempt to minimize costs by analyzing holding charges and purchase order costs. This latter approach is certainly a step toward overall optimization, but it should be realized that the ultimate in optimization may not be achieved. The obvious benefit is that at least a good solution will be reached.

Forecast/Schedule/Inventory Interaction

From an industrial point of view the easiest large-system interaction problem would be that involving forecasting, scheduling, and inventory. Each of these functions will be discussed in depth later in this book.

The *forecasting* function will attempt to determine customer requirements at some short-term point of time in the *future*, say two months. This point in time might be of some *duration*, such as a month. On the basis of the forecast, a production *schedule* will be evolved to meet the forecasted demand. The schedule will indicate how resources, such as machines and men, will be utilized during the month for which the demand is predicted in order to meet the demand. Of course, this process is dynamic and will continue indefinitely from time period to time period even though only one time period is being considered in this discussion.

When sales are tallied for the month in question, it is doubtful that they will equal the forecasted values, and so an error value is created. This in turn will cause either an increase or a decrease in *inventory* levels. Logically, feedback is required from various conditions within the system to allow better initial decisions to be reached. A simplified possible schematic of this dynamic process is represented in Figure 1–2. The schematic will be discussed with reference to the numbers given in pertinent locations on the diagram. It should be pointed out that, for simplicity, no reference is made on the schematic to differences in time. It should be realized that the forecast, schedule, and sales demand might be displaced from each other by one time period. Similarly, forecast errors are determined by comparing sales demand for a particular period with the forecast that predicted the sales for that period, even though the forecast itself might have been made at least two time periods previous.

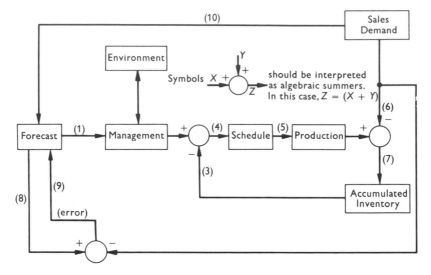

Figure I–2. Simplified forecast/schedule/inventory system.

Initially, a forecast is made—in this situation it will be assumed that the forecast is made by extrapolating trends from past sales data to the future. The forecast is submitted to management (1). Logically, a time-series prediction by itself is not the actual value scheduled for a particular time period. The inventory levels of the particular product should be examined to see if partial or whole satisfaction of the expected demand could be met from inventory (3), leaving at least some minimum inventory safety level for the next period. Also, the real-world environment (2) should be evaluated to determine demand changes that would be affected by other than time-series trends. Imminent new contracts, potential recessions, computer changes, etc., may be typical of conditions that the time-series evaluation may not catch. A composite of (1), (2), and (3) is then used to schedule production for the next period (4). This is implemented into the production process (5), which actually evolves the products. Sales (6) are subtracted from production with a net result that either raises or lowers current accumulated inventory (7). It is this inventory (3) which feeds back to assist in the scheduling decision. The latest sales demand (10) should be fed back to the forecast to allow the time-series evaluation to be made on the basis of the most current set of data. The data will be used to define the forecast *model*. However, the difference between sales demand and the forecast for a particular time period should be used as an error term to allow better model parameters to be evolved or, for that matter, more responsive models to be determined.

Even the rather unsophisticated forecast/schedule/inventory model discussed points up how a simple system composed of three sub-systems can be quite complex when analyzed as a total system. Interactions between the components can become unwieldy. It should be emphasized again that even though complete system optimization would be desirable, this might not be feasible. Sub-optimization is at least a step in the right direction.

Decision Theory Approach to the Forecast/Schedule Interaction*

The forecast/schedule/inventory model just presented does not take into account the fact that a known probability distribution for sales demand can be used to improve a dollar return. A hypothetical problem will be discussed to show how a schedule might be manipulated to some value other than the forecasted amount based on these distributions. It will be apparent that the problem is too simple for reality and that the results are almost ridiculous. However, the problem is given in this introductory material to attempt to imbue a philosophy in the reader that known imperfections and interactions within systems analysis might be used to advantage.

Consider a retail store that has a customer demand (Z) for one of its products that is known to be 1 per time period with a probability of 0.6, and 2 per time period with a probability of 0.4. The profit for a particular stock (X)/demand combination is as shown in Table 1–1.

In addition to the profit values, data have been maintained on the accuracy of forecasts in the past. From these data conditional probabilities have been determined for the probability of a particular forecast value (F) knowing the demand. These probabilities, with γ representing a perfect forecast, are shown in Table 1–2.

Table 1-1

Profit per Period for Specific
Stock/Demand Combinations

Stock Quantity (X)	Demand (Z)	
	1	2
1	$3.50	$3.50
2	2.00	7.00

* This approach was suggested by H. E. Thompson and W. Beranek.[8]

Table 1-2

Conditional Probabilities for a
Particular Forecast Amount
Given a Known Demand

Forecast	Demand (Z)	
Quantity (F)	1	2
1	γ	$1 - \gamma$
2	$1 - \gamma$	γ

Four possible scheduling strategies for product stocking are available. Using the notation $S(i, j)$, where i represents the amount stocked if one unit is forecast and j represents the amount if two is forecast, then these four strategies are:

a. $S(1, 1)$: Do not forecast, always stock one unit.
b. $S(2, 2)$: Do not forecast, always stock two units.
c. $S(1, 2)$: Always stock as forecast.
d. $S(2, 1)$: Believe the forecast always incorrect, so stock an amount contrary to that forecast.

The strategy to use is dependent on the probability of a perfect forecast, γ, and on the return equations. The first two strategy returns, $S(1, 1)$ and $S(2, 2)$, are only dependent on the demand probabilities of 0.6 for 1 unit and 0.4 for 2 units, as forecast values are not considered. If the expected returns for a strategy are defined by $E[S(i, j)]$, then $S(1, 1)$ and $S(2, 2)$ will have respective returns as follows, using Table 1–1:

a. $E[S(1, 1)] = (0.6)(3.50) + (0.4)(3.50) = \$3.50$
b. $E[S(2, 2)] = (0.6)(2.00) + (0.4)(7.00) = \$4.00$

An interpretation of this can be made by saying that if forecasting is *not* going to be used, always stock or schedule two units per period.

The expected returns for $S(1, 2)$ and $S(2, 1)$ are a little more complex to calculate. Table 1–2 probabilities have to be considered in line with the profit values of Table 1–1. For each strategy, the expected returns for demand of 1 unit and also the expected returns for 2 units have to be determined. These are then treated like the non-forecasted cases using the two probabilities of 0.6 and 0.4. For example, if $E(Z)$ denotes the expected return for one or two units, $E[S(1, 2)]$ may be evaluated as:

a. $E(1) = (3.50)(\gamma) + (2.00)(1 - \gamma) = (1.50)(\gamma) + 2.00$
b. $E(2) = (3.50)(1 - \gamma) + (7.00)(\gamma) = (3.50)(\gamma) + 3.50$

   c. $E[S(1, 2)] = (0.6)[E(1)] + (0.4)[E(2)] =$
$(0.6)[(1.50)(\gamma) + 2.00] + (0.4)[(3.50)(\gamma) + 3.50]$, which reduces to $(2.30)(\gamma) + 2.60$.

Similarly, $E[S(2, 1)]$ can be found to be $4.90 - (2.3)(\gamma)$.

Before deciding which strategy to employ for a given γ value, it might be interesting to look at the validity of $S(1, 2)$. The maximum return for $(2.30)(\gamma) + 2.60$ is realized when γ has a value of 1. This gives a return of \$4.90. If γ is 1, this is a condition of perfect forecasting. Considering only Table 1–1, perfect forecasting gives a return of \$3.50, with a probability of 0.60, and \$7.00, with a probability of 0.40. These figures rise from the fact that with perfect forecasting, if 1 unit is forecast, then 1 will be the demand figure. The same reasoning applies to a forecast and demand of 2 units. The expected return from Table 1–1 would then be. $[(3.50)(0.6) + (7.00)(0.4)] = \$4.90$. This, of course, corresponds to the strategy result.

Plotting expected returns against γ for the four strategies gives Figure 1–3 with the expected returns for the strategies:

   a. $E[S(1, 1)] = \$3.50$
   b. $E[S(2, 2)] = \$4.00$
   c. $E[S(1, 2)] = \$[(2.30)(\gamma) + 2.60]$
   d. $E[S(2, 1)] = \$[(4.90) - (2.30)(\gamma)]$

The results shown in Figure 1–3 are a little peculiar, to say the least. We can get as good a return if the forecasting is always incorrect ($\gamma = 0$) as we do if forecasting is always correct ($\gamma = 1$). Why is this possible? If we have only *two* products and *know* that the forecast is always wrong, then we can reverse the forecast and get a perfect forecast. This will only be correct for two products. Two major points can be deduced from this naive example:

1. Knowing the *distribution* of an *imperfect* forecast allows a strategy to be employed that allows the schedule to negate some of the effects of a bad forecast.

2. Forecasting, even bad forecasting, is almost always better than no forecasting. For γ values of 0.39 to 0.61, this is not correct. For a larger number of products this γ range would become smaller.

The moral of the example is simple. Sub-systems considered in an interactive phase will benefit the total system. However, this is only true if good historical data are maintained. In this case, data relating the forecast to actual demand were needed. Also, statistics would have had to be maintained to allow the determination of probability of demand during any given period. This would be available if the data

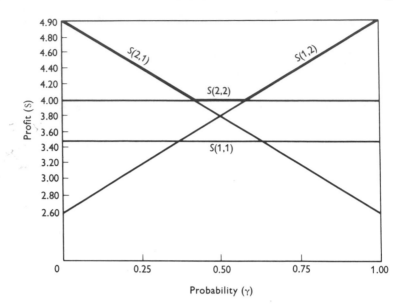

Figure I–3. Optimum schedule strategy for values of γ.

relating forecast to demand were maintained. The major problem encountered in evaluating or improving particular situations such as forecasting or scheduling or inventory is usually attributable to lack of data. So, plan ahead and determine what data are required, and then maintain this in as efficient a manner as possible.

I–4. SYSTEMS PLANNING

The need for careful planning should be obvious when large and complex systems are being considered. In fact, careful planning should be incorporated into small, seemingly straightforward problems. The degree of planning required would be dictated by the complexity and size of the project requiring planning. The need for major improvements in planning was foreseen by a Space Committee[7]* which stated:

Space activities are so unbelievably expensive and people working in this field are so imaginative that the space program could easily grow to cost many more billions of dollars per year. . . .

Our review of the United States space program has disclosed a number of organizational and management deficiencies as well as problems of staffing and direction which should receive prompt attention from the new administration.

* These numbers identify references at the end of each chapter.

These include serious problems within NASA, within the military establishment, and at the executive and other policy-making levels of the Government. . . .

There is urgent need to establish more effective management and coordination of the United States space effort. . . . This cannot be done without major improvements in the planning and direction of the program.

The latter sentence of course is the important one. It was observed that *effective planning and directing* are the key to *managing* and *coordinating* a highly complex project.

The need for planning in complex projects was pinpointed extremely well in a *Time* magazine cover article entitled *America the Inefficient.*[10] Commenting on the Bay Area Rapid Transit (BART) system, discussed later in Chapter 13 from a systems point of view, *Time*[10] said:

Among its ludicrous inefficiencies, BART has somehow managed to lose 100 lamp-posts, a total of 200,000 lbs of metal costing $150,000. Workmen pulled them from a street that was being torn up for a new subway line, and BART's managers just cannot find them.

Commenting further on private enterprise problems, and the building industry in general, *Time* stated:

When workmen put in the concrete floor of the Dorothy Chandler Pavilion at the Music Center of Los Angeles County, someone forgot that space was supposed to be left for parts of the air-conditioning system. Result: the concrete had to be broken up with air hammers. Another odd thing happened one year after construction started on Chicago's 100-story John Hancock Building: it began to sink into the ground. Air pockets had developed in the concrete caissons on which "Big John" rested, for reasons that the courts are being asked to determine. Workers spent the next five months tearing down two stories of steel framework and refilling the caissons. Cost: $1,000,000.

Time indicates that the root of these and similar problems is the nation's startling growth and the lack of planning to cope with it.

Again, that mystical word *planning* crops up. The population growth and associated problems is just another example, though it be extreme, of a complex systems problem. A possible means to alleviate some of the problems associated with complex systems has to be the so-called *systems approach* in planning.

I–5. SYSTEMS AND THE SYSTEMS APPROACH

Many definitions may be found for the word *system*. Typical, in the context we are interested in, are the following:

A regularly interacting or independent group of items forming a unified whole.[11]

In OR (Operations Research) language, a "system" is a set of interacting variables, but each system is part of a larger system.[4]

A specific combination of elements operated in conjunction with one another to accomplish some particular objectives.[5]

A very general definition of *system* was given in Section 1–2, indicating that "the word *system* will be considered in its broadest sense to cover large-scale problems which have interacting components." Typical examples given were a flight control *problem* and production *problem*. Looking at the three quoted definitions, *problem* would be analogous to *system*, which has interacting aspects in each of the definitions. We will stick to the earlier definition as this text is oriented toward the *solution* of complex *problems*. The complexity of the problems will be found to be created by the fact that several variables are *interacting*. In all the definitions given, the common aspect has to be that of *interacting* items.

Davidson's definition indicates that interaction of components is in accordance with some objective desired. It will be assumed that the *planning* function, or *system approach* to planning, will have as its first stipulation the *determination of objectives*. As will be demonstrated, if the objectives are not clearly defined then planning cannot reasonably be accomplished.

Alford and Beatty[2] tell us that the rise of *scientific management* started about 1890. As indicated in Alford's text, ". . . as industries grew and expanded, as the technical and personnel problems to be faced and solved become greater in number and more complex in character, the need for men with better training for leadership became apparent. To meet this need, technically trained men, especially engineers, were employed and given executive and managerial responsibilities. This move was particularly prominent in the years following 1890." The rise of *scientific management* led to the evolvement of the *scientific method*. Paraphrasing from Alford, the scientific method evolving from the leaders of the scientific movement has as its procedural steps:

1. Generate a *clear* and *complete* statement of the problem.
2. Gather *all* facts, past and present, which pertain to the problem.
3. Analyze these facts with the Why, What, When, Where, Who, and How criteria.
4. Synthesize the results of the analysis into statements of fundamental principle or law.
5. Apply these fundamental principles to the problem facts to arrive at an improved way of accomplishing the result.
6. Test the new result to determine its adequacy. If inadequate, repeat the procedure until an adequate solution is achieved.

The feedback concept for improvement is apparent from item number six. For a research project, Ackoff[1] feels there are six phases:

1. Formulating the problem.
2. Constructing the model.
3. Testing the model.
4. Deriving a solution from the model.
5. Testing and controlling the solution.
6. Implementing the solution.

Churchman, Ackoff, and Arnoff,[3] in their classical operations research text, classify these same six phases as the major phases of an *operations research* project, except that model is restricted to *mathematical* model.

The feedback characteristic in the scientific methodology is demonstrated in Figure 1–4 with the objective being to develop the best representative model possible. A new term, *model*, has been introduced. It will be used widely in certain sections of this text and so should be defined, even though the word might be self-explanatory. A *model* is a *representation* of something. We are all familiar with railroad train models. They may be exact scale models, differing externally from the real primarily only by a reduction in size. A two-year-old child playing with a wooden train replica also has a model, but one that is not so exact. The latter is much less expensive than the former, but both are examples of *physical models*. The cement plant schematic shown later

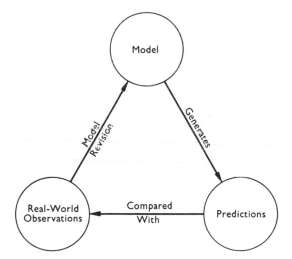

Figure 1–4. Scientific methodology in model building. (From Samuel B. Richmond, *Operations Research for Management Decisions*, copyright © The Ronald Press Company, 1968.)

is an example of a *pictorial* or *schematic* model. It represents the real cement plant and one can deduce basic operating and flow characteristics of a cement plant from it. The chemistry of cement is not apparent though, and would require a *mathematical* model for clarification. The equation for a vibrating string defines the characteristics for that string and is a *mathematical model* of the string system. We will primarily be concerned with mathematical models.

1–6. SYSTEMS APPROACH

Pritsker[6] has defined the systems approach as being the process of attempting to answer the following questions:

1. What is the system to accomplish?
2. How is it going to be accomplished?
3. Who is going to accomplish it?
4. When should it be accomplished?

As Pritsker suggests, if the approach is to simply answer four questions then there is nothing to it. However, the trick is in the approach to answering these questions with the hope of providing some optimal answer. In summarizing the results of the Railway Systems and Management Association conference just referenced, Pritsker concluded that the steps in the systems approach are

1. Structure the system.
2. Determine the key components.
3. Study the key components in depth.
4. Integrate key components into a descriptive model of the system.
5. Apply systems analysis—experimentation.

Then, what the system approach accomplishes is that it

1. Describes the system.
2. Shows interdependence and interaction of the units of the system.
3. Shows how a change in one unit affects the total system.

The *forecasting* material discussed in Chapter 3 is an excellent example of utilizing the systems approach. Time-series prediction requires an analysis of past data from which to predict future conditions. Cyclic and growth characteristics may be prevalent within these historical data. The key components of the system (historical data) will then be analyzed separately to get the best curve fit possible. Projections are made for each component and are added to form the prediction.

Experimentation is required to determine the best parameter fits for the growth and cyclic effects.

The boundary conditions for the system were set considering only the historical data. For many process control prediction systems this may be feasible. In business forecasting this is not so. Environmental conditions would have to be added to the system. These would include items affecting the forecast such as business climate, competition, market and production capacities, and so on. Of course, in this example, the difficulties arise in separating components out of so-called noisy data and then determining the optimum system parameters for these components.

The systems approach implies that the overall system (macro-view) be broken down into basic components (micro-view). The components are analyzed with regard to their system contribution and then synthesized to allow system objectives to be realized. It is important to realize that the *overall system* should be considered initially, not the components. An Arizona State University colleague, Dr. Charles Hoyt,* tells a story to explain this. A certain photographer mounted a camera which had a wide spectrum of accessories. He pointed his camera at a local mountain and installed a 20-mm lens, then a 50-mm, a 100-mm, and finally a 400-mm, taking a separate picture with each. After development, he found that the shortest lens captured the scene in only its grossest, or macro aspects, and barely showed the difference between rock and sky. But as he used the higher powered magnifiers he was able to resolve finer and finer detail in the scene in successively smaller fields of view. Finally, with the 400-mm lens and supplementary lens, his picture was down to one small pebble. Now the mountain could not be seen. The pebble could have come from any mountain. As Dr. Hoyt said, the photographer had demonstrated that as the degree of detail resolution goes up, the cost, in terms of breadth of view, also goes up. In addition, the series of pictures viewed as a *set* comprised a *model* of the mountain. In order to realize the importance of the pebble it is necessary first of all to see the mountain as a whole, and that the mountain as a whole consists in part of a large number of such pebbles. A systems analyst analyzes the system of interest in its *macro* aspects before proceeding to the micro aspects and does this sequentially using

* Reproduced by permission of Dr. Hoyt, with minor changes, from an unpublished report, "The Faculty of Industrial Engineering at Arizona State University—An Organization in Transition," Arizona State University, Tempe, Arizona, January 23, 1970.

Table 1-3

Planning Matrix Based on Possible
Objective for a Technical Society Seminar

	Planning Considerations			
	Theme	Speakers	Site	Time
1. Make money	General and popular; possibly dinner-dance.	Good drawing power; hopefully expenses will be offset.	Popular resort type; golf affiliation?	Best weather type; spring in Phoenix, for example; Saturday golf.
2. Re-tread members	Technical—geared to maximize benefit to whole group.	Professional educators—consultive fees.	Functional—university orientation.	Off-summer; greatest potential for most members; night-oriented few weeks?
3. Boost membership	General—geared to potential benefits of the society.	Top people in the society; good presentation capability.	Popular resort type; hopefully golf orientation.	Best weather time; Saturday for golf.

system. One mechanism for visually representing the system as a whole so that these interdependencies may be clarified in the planning stage is the *arrow network*. It is a key aid in the *systems approach* and in *fundamental planning* and so merits at least a cursory overview in this chapter before being dealt with in depth in Chapter 2.

Davidson[5] states that from his experience a "strategic plan" is the crucial factor in the successful employment of the systems analysis technique. The function of this strategic plan is to

1. Prescribe specific objectives and the expected payoffs;
2. Outline the general plan of action, the timetable, and selection of techniques (tactics);
3. Estimate resources required to support the plan.

The first function was discussed in light of Thuesen's series of problem solution steps. Formulation of a *planning* network greatly facilitates the latter two items. Typical advantages of the planning network include:

1. The complex system can be considered as a whole—the required initial macro-view.

2. Evolvement of the network forces an in-depth study of the component units—potential micro-items.

3. Interdependence can be graphically shown.

4. Potential bottlenecks in problem formulation can be foreseen in advance, which, with judicious planning, should aid in their elimination.

5. A time schedule can be evolved for system solution and for each independent unit.

6. Resource problems can be minimized. This will be a topic covered in Chapter 6.

As a network example, consider the technical seminar discussed in Section 1–7. One possible hypothetical network for the planning phase for the seminar might be as shown in Figure 1–5. This simplified network is predicated on the fact that the seminar will be one where papers are solicited from the society membership. The circles in the network indicate points in time (starting and ending times for jobs, or units of the system), while arrows indicate jobs to be accomplished. We will identify jobs by their circle notation. For example, job (5-6) is the job of evaluating abstracts. Many more jobs could be included. After determining objectives (1-2), it may be found that a dinner-dance is the answer. We will assume a technical seminar with papers to be presented being obtained through a call for abstracts, culled by a screening committee.

Estimating time requirements for *each unit*, or job, allows an estimate to be determined for the lead time required for the *complete* system. This may dictate either the earliest time possible for the seminar or, working backwards, the excess time available, if any, for getting the seminar on the road. Also, estimating resource requirements (members of the society) needed for each job, the required "volunteer" total can be determined. Forcing the precedence requirements as they stand insures, for example, that a site be firmed, speakers and topics be known, and fees evaluated before releasing advertising material. Assuming a certain number of days and membership volunteer help requirement for each unit, the schedule requirements given in Figure 1–6 are realized. For simplicity, jobs are defined only by their start and finish time numbers. Looking at *parallel* resource requirements, it is seen that a *minimum* of *five* members, in addition to the ten directors, could do the job. From an "ego-involvement" point of view, it would probably be better to get more. Assigning calendar dates, starting with the seminar date, makes it possible to get a good working schedule.

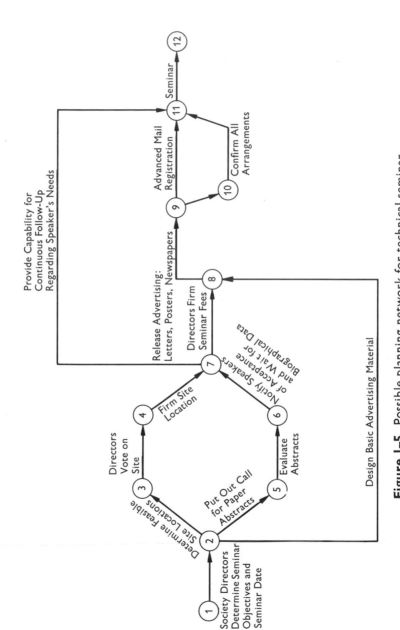

Figure I-5. Possible planning network for technical seminar.

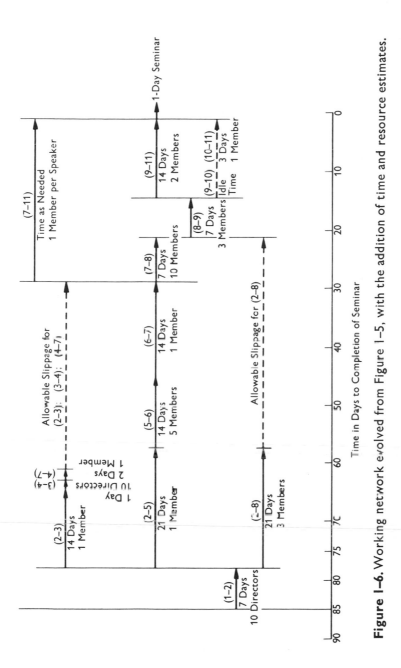

Figure 1-6. Working network evolved from Figure 1–5, with the addition of time and resource estimates.

1–9. CASE PROBLEM

Flintstone Cement Company is located in a metropolitan area which is enforcing strict new anti-pollution regulations. The cement company received a notice from the anti-pollution enforcing agency to the effect that Flintstone is introducing excess particulate matter into the atmosphere. This is primarily from open conveyors, poor crushing equipment and associated housing, poor storage facilities, and outdated quarry procedures. Succinctly, the anti-pollution notice informed Flintstone Cement that they would receive a court order requiring them to cease operations within a specified period of time unless they demonstrated that appropriate measures were being taken to combat the pollution problem, also within some appropriate time period.

Flintstone's board of directors cogitated for a while, but not too long as they only had one plant. They decided that they would modernize the plant to eliminate the pollution problem but unfortunately, due to the age of the plant, they decided to rebuild the entire operation, operating the old equipment as long as possible. Also, in looking at cement plant competition, they realized that to stay competitive they had to do what their peer group across the United States had been doing—*automate*. This case problem will analyze, in its most gross details, the systems planning function that the plant production engineer would have to direct in order to get the automation project rolling. The words "most gross details" were utilized to insure that we will not get bogged down in intricate details regarding cement production, components feasible for cement automation, instrumentation needed for automation, and so on.

For general interest, a cement plant operation is as shown in Figure 1–7. Basic material (limestone) is quarried, crushed, and mixed (blended) with other materials required for cement manufacture. These other materials include shale, iron ore, and silica sand. The blending has to be very exact in order to satisfy high Portland cement specifications. The blended material then goes through a second most critical operation, that of kiln burning. The blended material goes through a chemical change while undergoing the kiln burning process. It is transformed through an isothermic reaction to cement clinker, which looks somewhat like coke. This clinker is mixed with gypsum, crushed and then packed and shipped. The kiln operation is highly critical. If the temperature gets below a narrow temperature band then the proper isothermic reaction will not take place. If the temperature gets too high it is possible that molten fire-brick will come out at the

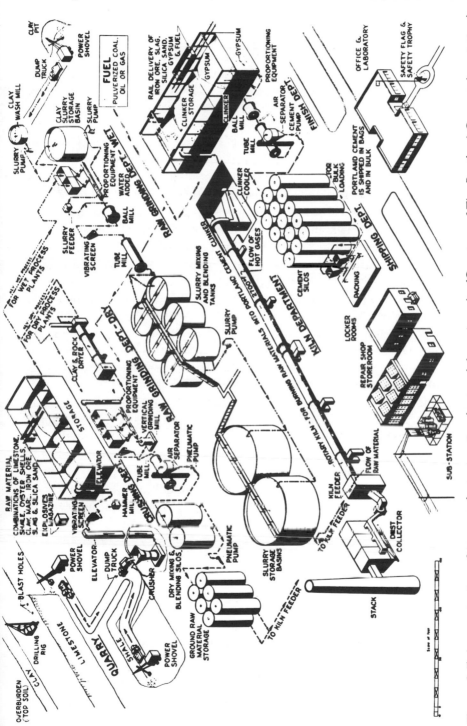

Figure 1-7. Isometric view of cement plant operation (wet and dry process).   (Courtesy of The Portland Cement Association.)

clinker end. Both cases require a lengthy downtime for cleaning and/or re-bricking. The temperature is affected by many interacting variables which would include amount of fuel used and type of fuel, rate of flow of the material through the kiln, and rotation rate of the kiln itself. Environmental conditions, such as rain and snow, would have a bearing on the manufacture process.

After contemplating possible *objectives* as regards the automation system, Flintstone Cement decides that their objective is to stay in business while still effectively meeting or beating their competitive cement manufacturers' relative profit levels. They decide that the most effective way for meeting this objective is automation by *control digital computer* (process computer). However, exactly what to have the computer accomplish, and how to remodel the plant, is another matter. Chapter 13 should provide an insight into some of the advantages to be obtained through automation by control digital computer. Suffice it to say at this time that a control digital computer has the same characteristics as a scientific or business digital computer. In *addition* it is able to operate in *real time* through an internal clock system, and it is able to communicate and interpret, through judicious programming, the conditions of plant instrumentation. Then through programming of control routines, the computer is able to adjust and control required instruments within the plant. Since it has the same characteristics as a general-purpose computer, plant conditions can be monitored for management reporting and for operator notification of alarm conditions.

As an aside, one way for Flintstone to solve their problem would be to rebuild in an area where pollution requirements are not so stringent. This is not feasible for two reasons. Pollution will be curbed in all locations in the future, so Flintstone would be delaying the inevitable. Second, a cement plant locates close to its material source (quarry) due to high material handling charges.

In *all* phases of the system automation project, Thuesen's sequence given earlier will have to be maintained:

1. Specify objectives.
2. Determine strategic factors and means for overcoming them.
3. Evaluate alternatives.
4. Evaluate economic significance of the alternatives.
5. Use items 3 and 4 to arrive at an "optimum" solution.

The overall objective for Flintstone Cement has been formulated. However, there will also be objectives for the components of the automation system. For example, one major component will be control digital computer *programming*. What is its objective? Probably to program developed control procedures and other functions to work in as efficient a manner as possible in conjunction with the remainder of the system. Limiting factors might be lack of manpower and memory limitations. Overcoming lack of manpower can be achieved by hiring more programmers or maybe utilizing a consulting firm. An economic evaluation of the alternatives in conjunction with the long-term implications could reveal a satisfactory solution.

Now to the actual planning function, using a systems approach. The steps discussed as generally comprising the *systems approach* were:

1. Structure the system—set definable limits.
2. Determine the significant components of the system.
3. Perform a detailed study in the workings of the components.
4. Evaluate component's contribution to the system and synthesize into the system.
5. Experiment.

It is in this framework that we will evolve the rough planning function. The end product will be a planning network developed through step number four:

The overall system to be planned is that of automating and renovating a cement plant. By management dictum this automation will be accomplished using a control digital computer. A glance back at Figure 1–7 reveals that a large number of functions are automatic already and computer control will not offer substantial benefits. Clinker storage and final cement packing fall into this category. The quarry is another area probably not amenable to control by computers. However, the computer may be beneficial in monitoring packing weight accumulations and clinker storage availability. Off-line linear programming calculations may indicate quarry digging locations in order to maximize long term profit figures. After all, once the quarry is depleted, that is it for the cement plant. An analysis of quarry material in conjunction with the cost of buying mix ingredients could be rather beneficial.

The *system structuring* would require an analysis of the *entire plant* to see what is required to allow conformation with anti-pollution requirements. This would be an "in-house" function, possibly with the aid of an engineering consulting firm. An analysis of all the *possible* functions that would benefit through computer control would have to be made. Computer manufacturers would make surveys and recommendations. The results of these would allow a series of possibilities, going in stepping-stone fashion from a purely *monitoring* system up to *complete control*, to be generated. Economic evaluation of the return possible from these and in-between conditions will allow a system to be structured that is *financially realizable*. For our purposes, the broad boundary conditions of the system will be

1. Plant *renovation* to conform to required anti-pollution regulations.
2. Computer *control* restricted to material blending and kiln operation only.
3. Monitoring limited to material weights, power consumption, and critical alarm conditions as specified by plant personnel.
4. *Computer size* to be limited due to financial constraints. This will limit the overall system conditions. Other feasible computer functions will be clarified when requirements of control and monitoring are realized.

It should be noted that setting the system boundaries will require a large amount of study, not the least of which will be financial. Quite a bit can be accomplished internally but external expert assistance will also be required. However, one person internally has to be able to make final decisions regarding the overall system.

The determination of the system components is another large-scale problem. What order of fineness of the components to take would be a major consideration. They would only be as fine as necessary to give *workable* interactive components. It would be beneficial to work down one order at a time, as in the mountain photography example, until the feasible minimum is attained.

For example, in the planning function for a project such as is being described, a gross breakdown is

Within these five functions we have a fine breakdown. One way to determine all required functions would be to get a team together consisting of all applicable in-house personnel, computer manufacturer representative, instrument manufacturer representative, and so on. A brain-storming session could bring out all possible functions which would be later cut down to all *reasonable* functions. We might end up with a gross taxonomy out of the five functions as follows:

A. *Plan.*

    A-1 Set overall system boundary conditions
    A-2 Determine financial boundary conditions.
    A-3 Designate in-house project team.

A-4 Determine computer functions required.
A-5 Determine instrumentation requirements.
A-6 Determine plant renovation requirements.
A-7 Evaluate computer/plant/instrument interface.

B. *Production.*

B-1 Renovate plant.
B-2 Order computer.
B-3 Order instruments.
B-4 Develop control procedures.
B-5 Program for computer.
B-6 Control room construction.

C. *Installation.*

C-1 Install computer.
C-2 Install cabling.
C-3 Install instruments.
C-4 Interface instruments/cabling/computer.
C-5 Check out instruments.
C-6 Check out computer and programs.
C-7 Check out process.
C-8 Check computer/instrument/plant operation.

D. *Implementation.*

D-1 Start-up plant (manual or computer?)
D-2 Test manual control in conjunction with *entire* system.
D-3 Test computer control in conjunction with *entire* system.
D-4 Train operators.

E. *Improvement.* (Continuous after implementation)

E-1 Refine control procedures—requires parameter adjustment and result monitoring.
E-2 Evaluate need for existing computer functions, computer timing, computer memory availability.
E-3 Add and test functions as required.

Each of these items might have a finer breakdown which should be considered. For example, "order instruments" would require specifications to be developed, bids let, and so on. Ordering the computer would require proposals to be requested from computer manufacturers, input/output specifications to be made, etc. The results would have quite a bearing on the functions to be included. For our purposes we will consider only the twenty-eight specified sub-functions, though in reality a one-order-lower taxonomy should be developed. (And after that one more order might be found to be desirable.)

Every one of the components should be analyzed in light of its contribution to the system. This should insure that satisfaction of the

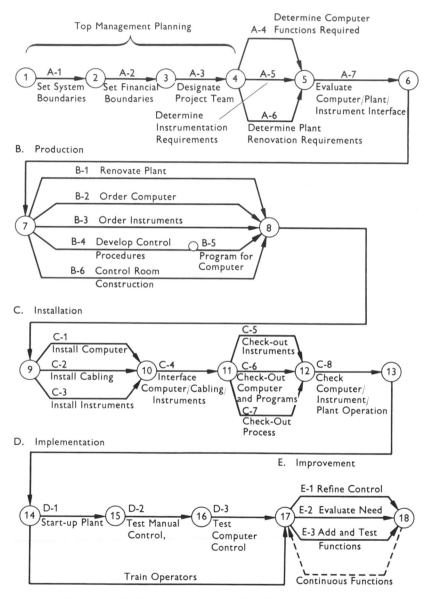

Figure I–8. Planning network for Flintstone cement.

component objectives will not be to the detriment of the whole system. As an example, installation of the instruments should not be scheduled such that later cabling installation is impossible. *All* should be considered as a sub-system. Ordering of the computer, instruments, cabling, and process renovation should not *each* be accomplished in its own vacuum. All have to be *compatible*. If digital instrumentation is utilized that has a coding incompatibility with the computer then interface equipment will be needed. Insuring overall compatibility in the initial specification will probably minimize *overall costs*, though not necessarily some of the *individual component* costs.

The overall relationships between components will be more readily apparent if a *network* of the system is evolved. The results of this activity, with its associated time schedule and resource development may require cycling back through the systems steps to simplify the project. A possible network for the Flintstone system is given in Figure 1–8. Timing and resource estimates are not included though with real-world problems they would have to be considered in order to get entire system requirements.

Continuous consideration of improvement of the system should be made. Reasonability of existing conditions and proposed functions should be evaluated. The *systems approach* is *dynamic*, not static.

This concludes the initial planning considerations. The planning function can itself be a major project, but it will reflect savings in many ways in the overall system, of which it is a part.

REFERENCES CITED

1. ACKOFF, R. L., *Scientific Method*, John Wiley and Sons, Inc., New York, N.Y., 1962.
2. ALFORD, L. P., and BEATTY, H. R., *Principles of Industrial Management*, The Ronald Press Company, New York, N.Y., 1951.
3. CHURCHMAN, C. W., ACKOFF, R. L. and ARNOFF, E. L., *Introduction to Operations Research*, John Wiley and Sons, Inc., New York, N.Y., 1957.
4. DALE, ERNEST, *Management Theory and Practice*, McGraw-Hill Book Company, New York, N.Y., 1969.
5. DAVIDSON, H. O., "Technique of Systems Analysis—A Survey," *Large Scale Systems Study*, Railway Systems and Management Association, Chicago, Illinois. 1963.
6. PRITSKER, A. A. B., "Background and Development of the Systems Approach," *Large Scale Systems Study*, Railway Systems and Management Association, Chicago, Illinois, January 1963.
7. *Science, Technology and Management*, ed. F. E. Kast and J. E. Rosenzweig, McGraw-Hill Book Company, New York, N.Y., 1962.

8. THOMPSON, HOWARD E. and BERANEK, WILLIAM, "The Efficient Use of an Imperfect Forecast," *Management Science*, Vol 13, No. 3, November, 1966.
9. THUESEN, H. G., FABRYCKY, W. J., and THUESEN, G. J., *Engineering Economy*, 4th ed. Prentice-Hall, Inc., Englewood Cliffs, N.J., 1971.
10. *Time* Magazine, March 23, 1970, Vol. 95, No. 12, pp. 72–80. [Feature article titled "America the Inefficient" gives credence to the theory that complex systems need sound planning.]
11. *Webster's New College Dictionary*, G. and C. Merriam Company, Springfield, Mass., 7th ed. 1967.

FURTHER READING

CHESTNUT, H., *Systems Engineering Methods*, John Wiley and Sons, New York, N.Y., 1967.
CHURCHMAN, C. W., *The Systems Approach*, Delacorte Press, New York, N.Y., 1968.
SAVAS, E. S., *Computer Control of Industrial Processes*, McGraw-Hill Book Company, New York, N.Y., 1965. [Chapter 7, "Planning a Computer Control Project," is highly pertinent.]

PROBLEMS

1. Sale price for a particular product is $10. Cost for stocking an item for a unit of time is $4. Cost of goodwill when items could be sold but are not available is estimated to be $5 per unit. The conditional probabilities of forecasts given a demand of 2, 3, and 4 units are given below:

Forecast Quantity (F)	Demand for Period (Z)		
	2	3	4
2	γ	$\frac{(1-\gamma)}{2}$	0
3	$(1-\gamma)$	γ	$1-\gamma$
4	0	$\frac{(1-\gamma)}{2}$	γ

The demand quantities of 2, 3, and 4 have been found to have respective probabilities of demand that are 0.4, 0.4, and 0.2, respectively. Management considers only six scheduling strategies to be feasible where $S(i, j, k)$ denotes scheduling i units when 2 are forecast, j units when 3 are forecast, and k units when 4 are forecast. The feasible strategies are: $S(2, 2, 2)$; $S(3, 3, 3)$; $S(4, 4, 4)$; $S(2, 3, 4)$; $S(3, 4, 4)$; and $S(3, 3, 4)$.

A. Evolve a profit matrix for the nine feasible combinations of schedule and demand.

B. Determine the expected returns for the six allowable strategies.

C. Plot the six strategies as functions of γ, for values of γ varying from 0 to 1.

D. If γ is found to be 0.65, what strategy would you employ? Repeat for γ values of 0.4 and 0.8.

E. Is forecasting valid in this situation?

2. Give examples of system feedback diagrams similar to Figure 1–1 for (1) hospital operating room daily schedules, and (2) developing a new product.

3. Discuss the benefits of *system* optimization in the systems discussed in Problem 2, emphasizing the pitfalls that might ensue if sub-optimization is employed.

4. Review the historical writings of Taylor, Emerson, Gantt, and Gilbreth. Evaluate their contribution to the *scientific method* and indirectly, their possible contribution to the *systems approach*.

5. Evaluate the *systems engineering* concept as it applies to the *systems approach*. Review current definitions of *systems engineering, systems analysis,* and *systems approach*. Develop your own definition for each based on similarities in those definitions you found in the literature. Is there validity in *one* definition for all three? If so develop one.

6. Take a complex system in your academic sphere of interest and develop the initial planning for this system using the *systems approach*. Be sure to develop a network to show the interrelationships between the system components.

2

Project Planning

Amid a multitude of projects, no plan is devised. PUBLIUS SYRUS, Maxim 319

2-1. INTRODUCTION

The emergence of the digital computer as a "management tool" in the 1950's led to the development of certain techniques geared to facilitate large-project planning. Prior to the evolving of these systematic planning techniques, which will be classified generally as network techniques, the planning of large projects was hampered a great deal by the complexity of the projects themselves. This is not to say that the projects were not brought to a successful fruition. Rather, there was no guarantee that the utilization of resources, such as time, manpower, money, and equipment, was accomplished in a fashion approaching optimality. Also, the combination of all the sub-components, or jobs, of the project tended to be treated as separate entities in the planning stage, rather than as a total system. The combination of the computer and network techniques, along with some criteria of optimality, will certainly allow a most satisfactory plan to be devised to allow the happy culmination of a project, or multitude of projects.

The goal of this chapter is to describe key project planning network approaches and evaluate their benefits and fallacies. As an example, the Critical Path Method (CPM) will be found to give a range of project schedules which themselves will present a range of direct costs. Combining these direct costs with applicable indirect costs will indicate, from a planning point of view, those schedules which will accomplish project objectives with minimum total cost expenditures. However, a drawback to the Critical Path Method approach is that it is strictly deterministic and so does not consider the fact that components, or jobs, within the project will not be accomplished as planned due to unforeseen stochastic effects. In all probability, the only known large project that was accomplished in *exactly* the planned manner according to a developed schedule has been well described in Genesis.

The Project Evaluation and Review Technique (PERT) will be presented as an attempt to alleviate the deterministic restrictions of CPM. The fact that restrictive assumptions within the PERT probabilistic technique prohibit realistic application will be presented and evaluated. Following PERT, the Graphical Evaluation and Review Technique (GERT) will briefly be introduced as a stochastic network approach that offsets most of the PERT fallacies.

On the assumption that the CPM deterministic approach has the most advantages for large-scale project *planning*, a case problem will be presented to allow CPM to be utilized for a realistic, though hypothetical, U.S. Army Corps of Engineers low-cost billet-housing project. This same project will later be evaluated in Chapter 6 where certain CPM scheduling fallacies will be offset by limited-resource analysis.

2–2. EVOLUTION OF NETWORK PLANNING TECHNIQUES

Historically, network analysis procedures had their inception with the traditional Gantt chart, or bar chart, originally developed by Henry L. Gantt during World War I. It is probably a rather unsatisfactory comment, but one beneficial outcome of war has been the development of significant production procedures and techniques. It is doubtful that anything else should be said about the benefits of war. The Gantt chart is still widely used today and is quite useful in analyzing the feasibility of a CPM optimum-cost schedule, as will be seen later. A typical Gantt chart is shown in Figure 2–1. The historical interest lies in the Gantt chart's *graphical* representation of jobs to be accomplished, with length of a bar on the chart, such as A-1 in Figure 2–1 being an analog of the time required to accomplish activity, or job, A-1. Typical benefits of the Gantt chart would include:

1. All jobs are graphically displayed in one easily understood chart.
2. By having the workers, or foreman, shade in the percentage of bar chart that corresponds to the percentage of job completed each basic

Job (Activity)	Date Scheduled June											
	3	4	5	6	7	10	11	12	13	14	17	18
A-1												
A-2												
B-1												
B-2												
C-1												
C-2												
D-1												

Figure 2–1. Typical Gantt planning chart.

work period, it is possible to check the overall progress of the system of jobs at any point in time. For example, Figure 2–2 shows the progress on June 7, with jobs A-1, B-1, B-2 completed; jobs A-2 and C-1 behind schedule. Unfortunately, the conventional Gantt chart does not indicate any possible cause of the problem existing with jobs A-2 and C-1.

3. When resources required are limited, the Gantt chart allows an initial evaluation of the planned use of these resources, as will be seen at the end of this chapter, as well as in Chapter 6.

The evolution from the Gantt chart to a network probably came in the late 1940's, with the advent of the Navy's *milestone method.*[6] This is a modification of the Gantt chart whereby key time periods called milestones, occurring in the duration of jobs, are indicated on the Gantt chart. Interrelationships between milestones are shown by connecting the affected milestones by solid lines. Obvious milestones for any job would be the starting time of the job and the required

	Date Scheduled June											
	3	4	5	6	7	10	11	12	13	14	17	18
A-1												
A-2												
B-1												
B-2												
C-1												
C-2												
D-1												

Figure 2–2. Progress evaluation on Gantt planning chart.

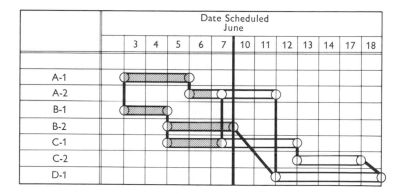

Figure 2–3. Milestone Gantt chart.

completion point. Other milestones would be appropriate at significant points within a job, such as completion of a sub-batch of parts that would then allow the start of another job. The milestone at the completion of the sub-batch and the starting milestone of the second job would be an example of an interrelationship between milestones, showing one job's *precedence* over another job.

Figure 2–3 shows the Gantt chart example with milestones added. For this naive example it is now readily apparent that the culprit in activities A-2 and C-1 slippage is activity A-2, as a large portion of C-1 cannot be started until a milestone on A-2 has been achieved, which has not. As with the Gantt chart, the milestone procedure is laudable as regards its aims, but is only of somewhat passing interest except for its position in the evolutionary process leading to the planning network.

2–3. CPM AND PERT

Now we come to the two techniques that initially added some criteria of optimality to the project scheduling function. Both were developed concurrently but independently. The Critical Path Method (CPM) evolved as a joint venture between Remington Rand and Du-Pont. The first public notification of the technique probably was made by Morgan R. Walker and James E. Kelley, Jr., in a paper titled "Critical-Path Planning and Scheduling," listed in the 1959 Eastern Joint Computer Conference.[4] The criterion of optimality inherent within CPM is the determination of a schedule that *minimizes* total project cost. The Project Evaluation and Review Technique (PERT), in addition to being developed concurrently with CPM, evolved a very similar graphical or network philosophy. PERT first came to the public eye through two brochures published by the Navy in 1958. Its criterion of optimality, if optimality is the correct word, would be in determining a time schedule for a particular project that would have a stipulated probability of successful completion within the particular time constraint. For example, in a research and development operation, management may wish to know for planning purposes what schedule would have a 95 percent probability of being met. PERT attempts to achieve this aim.

Many comments could be made concerning the attributes and deficiencies of CPM and PERT. These will be discussed in separate sections of this chapter when each technique is more fully discussed in its own right. Suffice it to say for the moment that CPM and PERT are both *computer-oriented* techniques, and that both defined the concept of an *arrow* network diagram, and that both defined the concept of a *critical path*. A conglomerate of definitions has evolved from the network-oriented techniques for common characteristics.

However, the *most* significant contribution would probably be the concept of the *arrow* network and the associated *critical path*. Such a network is depicted in Figure 2–4, for the same set of activities and associated precedence relationships given for the milestone Gantt chart. Arrows now represent the jobs or activities. Each arrow has listed above it its coded designation followed by its duration time. The longest path through the network is called the critical path, and in Figure 2–4 is indicated by double-line activities. The dotted line is used to denote a non-time activity that denotes *precedence only*. Finally, activities A-2 and C-1 are each split into two activities to allow satisfaction of the milestone characteristics given earlier in Figure 2–3.

CPM was designed strictly for the deterministic project problem. PERT attempted to allow evaluation of the stochastic research and development situation. However, PERT, while commendable, has many shortcomings and limitations due to computational simplification. These will be discussed more fully in the PERT section of this chapter. The Graphical Evaluation and Review Technique (GERT) built on developments by S. E. Elmaghraby[1] and A. A. B. Pritsker[7] satisfactorily eliminates most of the PERT limitations, but does pose some mathematical computation problems. It is, however, probably the most significant of the network scheduling approaches given in the evolutionary process.

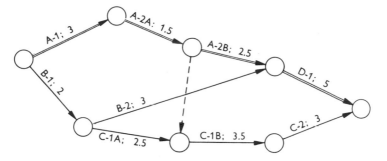

Figure 2–4. Arrow network corresponding to milestone Gantt chart of Figure 2–3.

The three major network approaches of CPM, PERT, and GERT will be discussed in some detail in subsequent sections. Prior to that, a few key definitions will be presented to allow a common foundation for this, and later work.

2–4. DEFINITIONS

Only those items pertinent to *all* techniques discussed in this chapter will be briefly defined at this point. Definitions limited to local applications will be given with the specific discussion of those applications. It is realized that some of these terms have been used under the assumption of general understanding. Now we will formalize their definitions for the common foundation.

    a. *Project:* A large-scale system comprising several tasks which have to be coordinated and scheduled to allow successful attainment of a project objective. The design of a University registration procedure, for example, may be considered a *project.*

    b. *Job* (Activity): One of several self-contained *tasks* that make up the project. It is these *jobs* that have to be coordinated and scheduled. In the registration project typical jobs might be payment of fees and the advisement process, to name just two out of many.

    c. *Arrow:* A graphical representation of one job. There will be at least as many arrows as jobs in the graphical representation of a project.

    d. *Node* (Event): Time points between which activities may be scheduled. Nodes will graphically be displayed as circles, and will be used for arrow connectors in the overall project graphical presentation.

    e. *Network* (Graph): The graphical representation of the overall project, consisting of the arrow-node relationships. Figure 2–4 is, of course, typical of a network.

f. *Resource:* Anything required to aid in the successful attainment of the project. Typical resources will be men, equipment, money, and time, among others. If available resources are unlimited then the satisfaction of the project is not affected by problems in resource scheduling. However, the interesting case is one of *limited* resources, which then have to be taken into consideration in the scheduling and coordinating of the project.

g. *Critical Path:* The longest path(s) through the arrow network, from beginning of the project to the expected completion of the project. If there are no time breaks within the network then the sum of the expected job times on the critical path will equal the expected project duration.

2–5. CRITICAL PATH METHOD (CPM)

The fundamental objective of CPM is to evolve a project schedule which minimizes the total expected cost for the project, or to evolve a project schedule, or series of schedules, which fall into an allowable project cost range. From a planning point of view, CPM has many desirable features, a few of which would be:

1. The development of the necessary network allows a large-scale project to be seen as a complete system. Interaction of activities comprising the project can be seen at a glance, and can be evaluated in light of their effect on other jobs. Without going through any optimization analysis, it is possible to foresee and eliminate potential bottlenecks before the project actually gets underway. Many users of network scheduling contend that this actual development of the network, allowing system interactions to be observed graphically, is the most beneficial aspect of CPM.

2. A *cost range* can be determined iteratively for a project that is dependent on a feasible range of schedule times. In turn, the cost range can be used to determine the economic feasibility of the particular project. A side benefit accrues from having to evolve *good* estimates of *time* and *cost* for each job so that the cost range and ultimately, the *minimum* cost schedule, can be determined.

3. Using a combination CPM network schedule and Gantt chart procedure, *resource* requirements for a particular schedule, or series of schedules, can be determined. Conversely, the effect of scarce resources as regards the cost range can be evaluated. This topic will be treated more fully in Chapter 6.

As indicated in Section 2–2, the CPM technique is *computer* oriented, though small projects may be hand-evaluated. A *normal* schedule is first determined based on job *normal* times. The *normal* time for a job is defined as that time required under so-called normal conditions. A *normal direct cost* for the project is determined by summing all the job *direct costs* evolved for each job *normal time*. The computer orientation comes through an iterative approach whereby the *project* schedule is now reduced from the normal schedule, probably by one time unit such as days or weeks, in a fashion that *minimizes* the *increase* in project direct costs that arise due to the increase in resource requirements required to accomplish the reduction in project time. Logically, only jobs on the *critical path(s)* are considered for reduction, or *crashing*, as crashing any other job would not reduce the overall project time. Iteration is continued until the shortest duration, or *crashed*, schedule is achieved. Adding the indirect costs, which decrease with a reduction of project duration time, to the direct costs, which increase with project duration time reduction, gives the schedule of project total costs.

Needless to say, this brief introduction does not give the assumptions inherent in the CPM technique, nor does it give the method for finding the *minimum* increase in direct costs as the project duration is reduced. These will be accomplished in terms of a small example. A larger case problem will be given at the end of this chapter.

Initially, the project has to be broken down into self-contained jobs. Cost and time estimates have to be made for each job. In both cases, cost and time, *normal* and *crash* estimates are required. The normal condition indicates values which would normally be expected if everything went as planned. Crash values are determined for the *minimum*, or crash, times that it is estimated the particular jobs can take. This would be under the assumption of overtime or utilizing extra resources as available. Also, it is required that a network be constructed showing the interrelationships between jobs based on a knowledge and study of the precedence conditions existing between activities. For example, assume that the data in Table 2–1 has been evolved for a CPM study. The first step is to construct the CPM network. We have glibly assumed certain precedence conditions with the data for Table 2–1, but it should be mentioned that correct network development is probably the most difficult of the CPM procedure. Since jobs *A*, *C*, and *G* have no immediate predecessors, they emanate from one starting node, as shown in Figure 2–5. Jobs *A* and *C* *immediately* precede jobs *D* and *F*, so it seems logical to connect jobs *A* and *C* to a common node, from which subsequently branch jobs *D* and *F*. Only jobs *B* and *E* remain to be assigned. *B* is dependent on job *A*, so we will add this to our network,

Table 2-1

Data for CPM Example Problem

Job (Activity)	Time (days)		Cost (dollars)		Immediate Precedence Relationship*
	Normal	Crash	Normal	Crash	
A	6	4	100	120	0
B	4	3	80	93	A
C	5	4	95	110	0
D	7	7	115	115	A and C
E	4	2	64	106	B and D
F	8	6	75	99	A and C
G	18	13	228	318	0

*Activities in this column have to *immediately* precede the activities in the same row, first column.

as shown in the third step in Figure 2–5. Finally, job E has as immediate predecessors both jobs B and D. These are then fed to a common node from which we evolve job E. To close the network, all jobs not now leading to a node are fed to an ending common node, culminating in the final network of Figure 2–5. Unfortunately, this network is incorrect from a precedence point of view! What went wrong? Job B, from the final network, has *both* jobs A and C as immediate predecessors. The relationship required in Table 2–1 is that only job A immediately precede job B. If a schedule were implemented with the erroneous network as a guide, slippage on job C work would force a delay in the start of job B—a delay that is not justifiable. The way out of this dilemma would be to separate jobs A and C by having them enter different nodes. Job B would follow the job A final node, and jobs D and F would be subsequent to the job C final node. A pseudo-job, P, is then drawn from the job A node to the node where job C ends, denoting that job A *has to precede* jobs D and F. Obviously, activity P has no time or cost values. The correct network for this rather simple case is now depicted in Figure 2–6.

2–6. COST INCREASE MINIMIZATION

Now we can attack the question concerning which schedule will minimize the project total costs. First we will look at the direct cost picture. The values given in Table 2–1 are the job *direct costs*. The

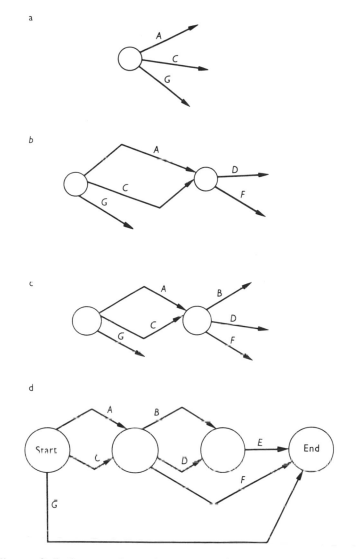

Figure 2–5. Steps in formulating example network (incorrect).

first CPM assumption, and this certainly could be waived in small hand computations, is that a linear relationship exists for each job, between the normal and crash situation. For example, from Table 2–1 it is seen that the range of allowable times for job A is 2 days and the cost range is \$20. The linear cost change per day is then \$10 which indicates an assumed cost for a 5-day schedule would be the normal cost plus \$10.

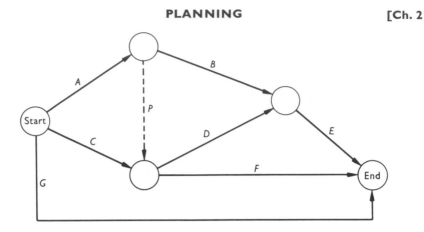

Figure 2–6. Correct CPM network for the precedence data given in Table 2–1.

This linear relationship is depicted in Figure 2–7 and follows the equation

$$\text{Cost Change/Unit Time} = \frac{[\text{Crash cost} - \text{Normal cost}]}{[\text{Normal time} - \text{Crash time}]} \quad (2–1)$$

The Cost Change/Unit Time (CCUT) for each job, from Table 2–1, is given in Table 2–2, and this will be the basis for cost increase minimization, thus reducing schedule time by crashing. The general procedure

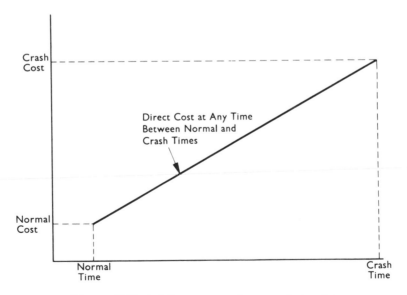

Figure 2–7. Job linear cost change relationship.

Table 2-2

**Cost Change/Unit Time for Each Job
Comprising the Network of Figure 2-6**

Job (Activity)	Cost Change/Unit Time[*]
A	$\dfrac{(120 - 100)}{(6 - 4)} = \$10$
B	$\dfrac{(93 - 80)}{(4 - 3)} = \$13$
C	$\dfrac{(110 - 95)}{(5 - 4)} = \$15$
D	No allowable change— can not be crashed.
E	$\dfrac{(106 - 64)}{(4 - 2)} = \$21$
F	$\dfrac{(99 - 75)}{(8 - 6)} = \$12$
G	$\dfrac{(318 - 228)}{(18 - 13)} = \$18$

*Based on Equation 2-1, with data from Table 2-1.

to follow in determining the minimum cost per schedule is as follows:

a. Determine the *project normal schedule;* that is, the project schedule with normal times for all jobs.
b. Determine the *critical path(s)* for the normal schedule.
c. Determine the Cost Change per Unit Time (CCUT) for all jobs.
d. *Direct cost* for the normal schedule is the sum of the job normal costs.
e. Reduce (crash) the schedule by one time unit. Only those jobs on the critical path(s) are considered for crashing. Only *one* job on each critical path is crashed. This should be obvious, as crashing two jobs on one path would crash the project by two time units. The job on each path that is crashed is the one that will achieve a *minimum* CCUT for *all* paths to be crashed.
f. Direct cost for the new schedule is the previous schedule's direct cost plus the CCUT for each crashed job leading to the new schedule.
g. Perform steps a and b for the *reduced* time schedule.
h. Procedures e, f, and g are continued until a critical path(s) is realized that has all its jobs at the crash, or minimum time. The minimum project time has now been realized, with the project minimum direct costs for each schedule falling between the normal and crash schedules.
i. The minimum total cost for each schedule is obtained by summing the schedule's minimum direct cost to that schedule's indirect cost. The

indirect costs would be those costs charged *per day* on an overhead basis, as contrasted to *direct* costs which are primarily the labor and materials that are directly chargeable to the project.

j. The minimum of the minimum total costs realizes the "optimum" schedule.

It can be seen that steps e, f, g, and h are iterative in nature. Also, since projects may entail a thousand or more jobs, it should be apparent that the problem of determining the job(s) that realize the minimum CCUT for each project can get very complex, especially when several critical paths are involved. The problem, therefore, is highly adaptable to digital computer solution.

The CPM steps will now be clarified by a solution to the example problem. The network of Figure 2–6, and the data given, or calculated, in Tables 2–1 and 2–2, will be utilized in this solution. The sequence of steps will be subtitled to correspond to the sequence just presented.

Step a. The project *normal schedule* is found by determining the *minimum* time that each node can occur, and still allow the project to be completed, assuming the project starting time is zero. Mathematically, this may be designated by

$$T_n = \max[(T_{n-1})_i + J_i] \qquad (2\text{–}2)$$

where $(T_{n-1})_i$ is the *i*th *immediate predecessor* node time to T_n.

An *immediate predecessor* node is one which has *one* job leading from that node into the node under consideration.

J_i is the time duration of the job leading from the *i*th immediate predecessor node into the one under consideration.

If we number Figure 2–6 network's five nodes as shown in Figure 2–8, then Equation 2–2 yields the results in Table 2–3 for T_n. The project normal time is found to be 18 days.

Step b. It is seen from the results that this was formed by job G emanating from node 1. This was the only path leading to a total of

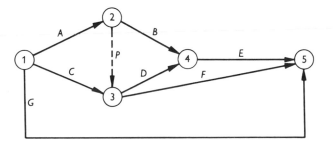

Figure 2–8. Node numbers for example problem.

Table 2-3

Determining Earliest Time, T_n, Possible to Schedule
Each Node (n) in the Network

Node (n)	$(T_{n-1})_i$		J_i		$(T_{n-1})_i + J_i$	T_n
1	None		None		None	0
2	$i = 1$;	0	A;	6	$0 + 6 = 6$	6
3	$i = 1$;	0	C;	5	$0 + 5 = 5$ ⎫	6
	$i = 2$;	6	P;	0	$6 + 0 = 6$ ⎭	
4	$i = 2$;	6	B;	4	$6 + 4 = 10$ ⎫	13
	$i = 3$;	6	D;	7	$6 + 7 = 13$ ⎭	
5	$i = 1$;	0	G;	18	$0 + 18 = 18$ ⎫	18
	$i = 3$;	6	F;	8	$6 + 8 = 14$ ⎬	
	$i = 4$;	13	E;	4	$13 + 4 = 17$ ⎭	

18 days. Therefore, the *initial critical path* is job G. Also, it can be seen from Table 2–3 that the next longest path length in the project will be 17 days. This means that if a job on the critical path is crashed one day, and that job is *not* on the next longest path (A-P-D-E), then two critical paths will exist for a schedule of 17 days. These will be G and A P-D-E.

Step c. The Cost Change per Unit Time (CCUT) values were calculated in Table 2–2.

Step d. The normal schedule *direct cost* is simply the sum of all the job direct costs for Table 2–1, and yields a value of $757.

Step e. Crashing the network to 17 days can only be accomplished by crashing *activity G*, as that *is* the critical path. G goes to 17 days, as does the project.

Step f. The 17-day direct cost is $757 + (CCUT for G), or $757 + $18 = $775.

The reduction to 17 days creates two critical paths, as mentioned earlier. These would be path G and path A-P-D-E. In order to reduce the project one time period, it is necessary to insure that *both* paths are reduced one day, with a *minimum total* increase in CCUT. The first approach would be to find a job that is on both paths to crash. None exists for G and $APDE$. To go to 16 days then, G would have to be crashed with the job A, D, or E that has the minimum CCUT. This would be A for path $APDE$. The increase in cost would be $10 for A added to $18 for G, which gives a total increase of $28. The iterative procedure continues for steps g and h until a project minimum is

Table 2-4

Iteration Steps in Determining Direct Cost Range for CPM Example Problem

Iteration	Critical Path(s)	Job(s) Crashed and (New Time)	Added Direct Cost (CCUT) (dollars)	Direct Cost (dollars)	Project Time (days)	Activities Now at Minimum Time
0	(G)	—	—	757	18	D
1	(G)	G (17)	18	775	17	D
2	(G) (APDE)	G (16) A (5)	18 10	803	16	D
3	(G) (APDE) (CDE)	G (15) E (3)	18 21	842	15	D
4	(G) (APDE) (CDE)	G (14) E (2)	18 21	881	14	D,E
5	(G) (APDE) (CDE)	G (13) A (4) C (4)	18 10 15	924	13	D,E,G,A,C*

*Paths *G, APDE,* and *CDE* are now all at their crashed minimum—the project is, therefore, at its minimum.

reached. These iterative steps are summarized in Table 2–4. A few comments are in order concerning the results given in Table 2–4:

1. Iteration three has three critical paths. Since path G (Job G) is not associated with the other two paths, it follows that G has to be crashed. In considering paths $APDE$ and CDE, the following possibilities are available for crashing (D is already at its limit):

   A and C: CCUT is \$10 + \$15 = \$25
   A and E: CCUT is \$10 + \$21 = \$31
   C and E: CCUT is \$15 + \$21 = \$36
   E: CCUT is \$21

   Obviously, G and E are the jobs to crash.
2. Considering iteration five, which has the same three critical paths, jobs D and E are at their limit. The next minimum CCUT from the above four possibilities would be to crash A and C. Since path G also has to be crashed, the minimum increase is obtained by crashing G, A, and C.
3. Upon reaching a schedule of 13 days we are now constrained by jobs D, E, G, A, and C, all of which are at their minimum times. This means that paths G, $APDE$, and CDE are all at their minimum times,

and so the project is restricted to 13 days. The allowable project time range is 18 to 13 days with a direct cost range of $757 to $924.

Several computer programs are available for solving the CPM problem, and these would certainly be desirable for complex projects. Figure 2–9 gives a sample General Electric computer printout for the 16-day schedule, that *will be* found to be optimum in steps i and j. Also, a computer summary of schedules is given. One interesting point concerning the summary is that no cost is given for day 15. Recalling the iterative steps in Table 2–4, going from day 16 to day 15, and day 15 to day 14, both required crashing jobs G and E. Obviously, the cost increase for day 16 to day 14 is linear and the direct cost for day 15 can be found by splitting the difference between days 14 and 16 direct cost—$842, which is verified later in Table 2–5. Steps a through h in the CPM procedure have now been completed. All that remains is to obtain the *minimum total cost schedule* with steps i and j.

Step i. Logically, project *indirect costs* have to be obtained through accounting procedures. We will assume for our example that indirect costs equal $500 plus ($30) (schedule time). If this is the case, then the schedule total costs are as calculated in Table 2–5.

Step j. The minimum total cost schedule is found to be $1,783 for the 16-day schedule. This is shown in the familiar "Optimization" curve of Figure 2–10. If an allowable total cost feasibility was set by management at $1,790, it can be seen from Table 2–5 that schedules of 16 and 17 days would be acceptable. In summary, it can be said that CPM does indeed achieve an optimum minimum total cost schedule *assuming* the estimates are valid and assuming the basic times are *deterministic*. CPM has had its prime acceptance in the construction industry where it might be said that relatively little stochastic effect may be present on most jobs. Also, construction estimates are among the best available. A fallacy of CPM that will be corrected in Chapter 6 is the fact that resources are assumed unlimited. If they are not, then the schedule arrived at may not be feasible.

As an example, consider the optimum schedule of 16 days for the CPM problem just discussed, on a Gantt chart in Figure 2–11. It can be seen that jobs G, D, B, and F have to be worked on simultaneously at least for day 8. This is assuming jobs B and F are slipped to their latest possible schedule times. If each of these jobs requires a fork-lift truck full time during its schedule time, it is obvious that the minimum number of fork-lift trucks required is four, assuming no fork-lift truck requirement for the other jobs. If only three trucks are

ACTIVITY I	ACTIVITY J	STATUS		TIME	COST C+G	SCHEDULED START	SCHEDULED FINISH	EARLIEST START	EARLIEST FINISH	LATEST START	LATEST FINISH	FLOATS SCHED	FLOATS TOTAL	FLOATS FREE	WT. C/N	ACTIVITY M	ACTIVITY N
1	2	CRIT	ACTIVITY A	5	110	0	5	0	5	0	5	0			1C	0	1
1	3	CRIT	ACTIVITY C	5	95	0	5	0	5	0	5	0			1C	0	2
1	5	CRIT	ACTIVITY G	16	264	0	16	0	16	0	16	0			1C	0	4
2	3	CRIT	DUMMY	0	0	5	5	5	5	5	5	0			0C	1	2
2	4		ACTIVITY B	4	80	5	9	5	9	8	12	3	3	3	1C	1	3
3	4	CRIT	ACTIVITY D	7	115	5	12	5	12	5	12	0			1C	2	3
3	5		ACTIVITY E	8	75	5	13	5	13	8	16	3	3	3	1C	2	4
4	5	CRIT	ACTIVITY F	4	64	12	16	12	16	12	16	0			1C	3	4

DIRECT PROJECT COST   603
PROJECT DURATION IS   16

GE 225 CPM SCHEDULE SUMMARY
DURATION IS IN DAYS
BEDWORTH CPM TEST DDR TEXT

SCHEDULE NUMBER	PROJECT DURATION	DIRECT COST	INDIRECT COST	TOTAL COST
0	16	757		
1	17	775		
2	16	603		
3	14	861		
4	13	924		

Figure 2-9. Computer algorithm output for optimum CPM schedule.

Table 2-5

Calculation of Total Cost for CPM Example Problem

Time Schedule	Direct Cost	Indirect Cost	Total Cost
18	$757	$1,040	$1,797
17	775	1,010	1,785
16	803	980	1,783
15	842	950	1,792
14	881	920	1,801
13	924	890	1,814

available then the project cannot be met in 16 days. The easiest way out of this dilemma would be to start job *F* at time period 9. This would create a 17-day schedule. A more detailed discussion of limited-resource assignment will be presented in Chapter 6. The next topic in this chapter will be a discussion of PERT, an attempt to introduce stochastic effects in research and development project evaluation.

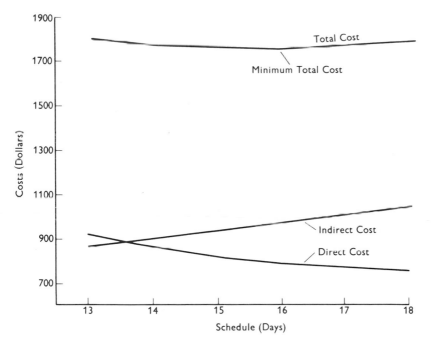

Figure 2–10. Graphical evaluation of minimum total cost schedule for CPM example.

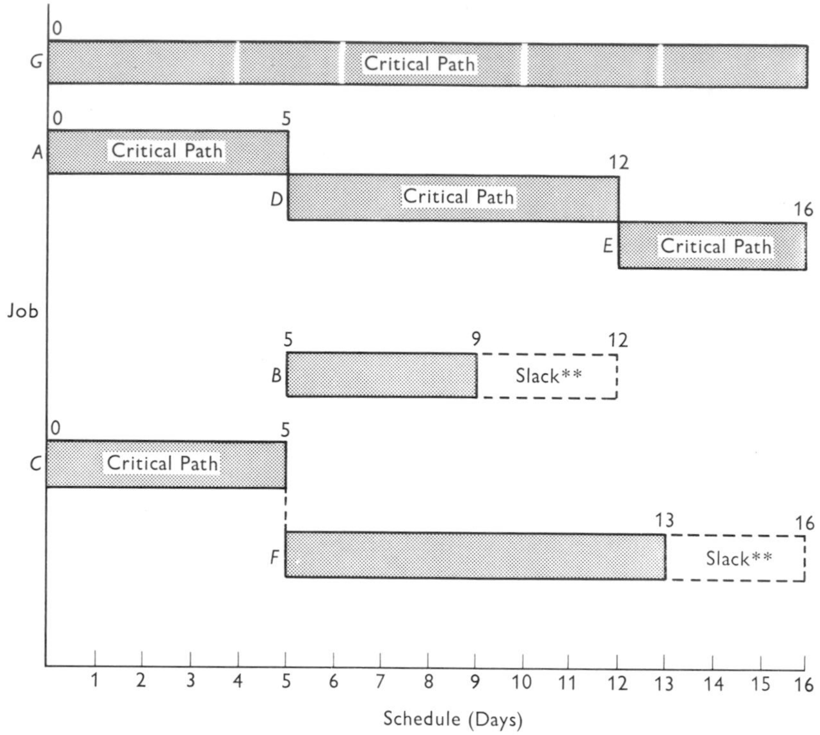

** Slack indicates freedom of scheduling for non-critical jobs. For example, Job B
could be scheduled from Period 8 to Period 12 without extending the schedule.

Figure 2–11. Gantt chart for optimum CPM schedule of 16 days.

2–7. PROJECT EVALUATION AND REVIEW TECHNIQUE (PERT)

One of the shortcomings of CPM has to be its deterministic characteristic. PERT, designed for the research and development type project, attempts to eliminate some of the possible CPM objections by assuming that each job time does come from some probability distribution, rather than having fixed time values. The objective of PERT is to obtain from mean and variance estimates for each job a probability distribution for the entire project. Actually, this overall distribution is obtained for the critical path, which is then assumed representative of the project completion characteristics. This latter assumption may or may not be valid, depending on the relative size and distributions of other paths through the network, as contrasted to the critical path.

Beta Approximations:

$$Mean = \mu = \frac{a + 4m + b}{6}$$

$$Standard\ Deviation = \sigma = \frac{b - a}{6}$$

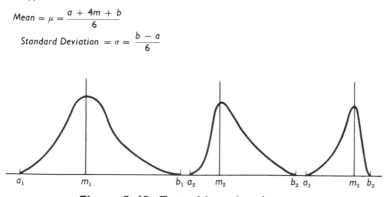

Figure 2–12. Typical beta distributions.

Once a project probability distribution is assumed, then the probability of attainment of certain schedules can be obtained. This then gives management planning information that can be used in evaluating the feasibility of the project.

The job probability distributions are assumed to follow a beta distribution. This has the characteristics of being unimodal with finite end points. Depending on the values of the parameters that describe the distribution, it may or may not be symmetrical. Possibly the main reason for adopting the beta distribution was the fact that the mean and variance can be *approximated* very simply by the equations given with typical beta distributions in Figure 2–12. Since the approximation of the mean is based on three parameters, it follows that these parameters, a, b, and m, have to be estimated. The PERT approach, therefore, utilizes *three* time estimates where CPM required two. One possible advantage for PERT is that it forces the planner to think a little more about the estimates for each job. The parameters of a, b, and m can be defined by:

1. a: The *minimum* time in which the job could reasonably be expected to be accomplished. This could be analogous to the *crash* time in CPM.

2. b: The *maximum* time in which the job would be expected to take, assuming "normal type" problems crop up. In the b time estimate, those activities classified as "Acts of God" are excluded. Since a and b define the finite boundaries of the beta distribution, it follows that the estimates of a and b should take these expected boundaries into consideration.

3. m: That value of time which is expected to occur the most often. This might be analogous to the *normal* time in CPM.

Once the values of a, m, and b have been estimated for all jobs, then their means and standard deviations are computed, using the beta approximations. From the job means, the critical path(s) are determined in the fashion of CPM. The familiar *central limit theorem* from statistics is interpreted in the determination of the critical path probability distribution. Basically, it is assumed that if one considers the sum of a group of independent variables, each with a mean μ_i and variance $\sigma_i{}^2$, then the sum of these variables will have a distribution that approaches normal, with mean μ equal to the sum of the μ_i's, and a variance σ^2 equal to the sum of the $\sigma_i{}^2$. A brief empirical discussion of the central limit theorem is given in Appendix D. From the PERT point of view, the jobs on the critical path are assumed independent. The distribution of the critical path times, assuming the central limit theorem is applicable, is assumed normal with the distribution mean equal to the sum of the means of those jobs on the critical path, and the variance equal to the sum of the variances of these same jobs. In the case where multiple critical paths exist, then the variance is assumed to be the larger of the path variances.

Once the project distribution parameters under the guise of the critical path distribution are obtained, then the completion probabilities of certain schedules can be obtained using standard normal distribution tables, as given in Appendix A.

As a *PERT example*, consider the same network evolved for the CPM example, with PERT estimates as given in Figure 2–13. The first step in the PERT procedure is to determine the mean for each job, i, by

$$\mu_i = \frac{a + 4m + b}{6}$$

Using these times, the critical path(s) is found in the normal CPM manner. The variances of those jobs on the critical path are then determined by

$$\sigma_i{}^2 = \left(\frac{b - a}{6}\right)^2$$

And the variances of the critical path(s) are determined by summing the individual job variances on the critical path(s). The maximum of these is then assumed to represent the project variance. The result of this initial analysis for the PERT data is summarized in Figure 2–14.

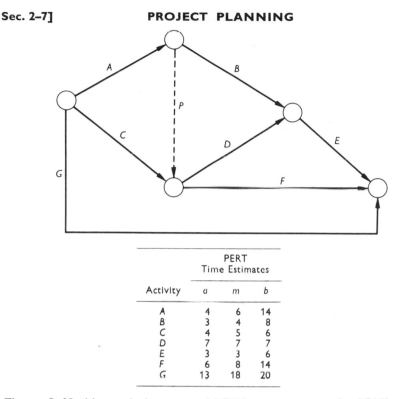

Activity	PERT Time Estimates		
	a	m	b
A	4	6	14
B	3	4	8
C	4	5	6
D	7	7	7
E	3	3	6
F	6	8	14
G	13	18	20

Figure 2–13. Network diagram and PERT time estimates for PERT example problem.

Since two critical paths accrue, the project variance is assumed to be the *maximum* of the two critical path variances. For path $APDE$ the variance would be

$$\sigma_A^2 + \sigma_P^2 + \sigma_D^2 + \sigma_E^2 = \frac{100 + 0 + 0 + 9}{36} = \frac{109}{36}$$

For path G the variance is

$$\sigma_G^2 = \frac{49}{36}$$

Path $APDE$ has the largest variance and so the project times are assumed to be normally distributed with mean, μ, equal to 17.50 and variance, σ^2, equal to 109/36.

Now, with the normal distribution data given in Appendix A, it is possible to determine the probabilities associated with certain schedules. Table A–1 gives the cumulative normal distribution corresponding to

I. Mean and Variance Calculations Give:

Activity	a	m	b	μ_i *	σ_i^2 **
A	4	6	14	7.00	100/36
B	3	4	8	4.50	25/36
C	4	5	6	5.00	4/36
D	7	7	7	7.00	0
E	3	3	6	3.50	9/36
F	6	8	14	8.67	64/36
G	13	18	20	17.50	49/36

$$* \; \mu_i = \frac{a + 4m + b}{6} \qquad ** \; \sigma_i^2 = \left[\frac{b - a}{6}\right]^2$$

II. Two Critical Paths of 17.50 Days Appear, G and *APDE*:

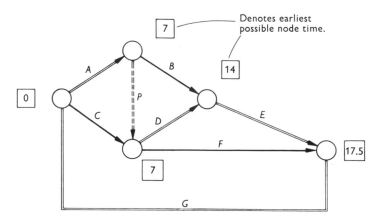

Figure 2–14. PERT calculations for example problem.

the area shown shaded in Figure 2–15(A). If the standard variable, Z, as given by the formula

$$Z = \frac{x - \mu}{\sigma} \tag{2-3}$$

is negative, the table value for positive Z (from Appendix A) is subtracted from 1. The result is the shaded area shown in Figure 2–15(B). Figure 2–16 gives a few example cases for clarification. For our PERT example, $\sigma^2 = 109/36$, and $\mu = 17.50$. The probability for completing a schedule *within* 17.5 days would simply be the area of the normal curve lying *below* 17.50. This is, of course, 50 percent—which might not be very good from a planning point of view if 17.50 is a desired time constraint. A more logical approach is to determine that schedule which satisfies a particular *probability constraint*. For example, for our PERT problem, if management wants that schedule which has a 95 percent probability of being completed on time, how do we find it?

A. Definition of μ and x

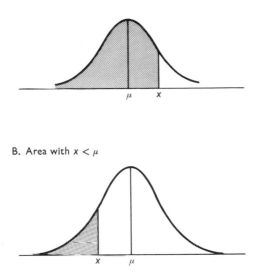

B. Area with $x < \mu$

Figure 2–15. Using Appendix Table A–1 for normal curve areas.

First of all we need to find the standard variable, Z, that corresponds to an area under the normal curve of 0.95. This turns out to be about 1.64. Solving Equation 2–3 in reverse, for the sample PERT data:

$$1.64 = \frac{x - 17.50}{\sqrt{\dfrac{109}{36}}}$$

and

$$x = \frac{(1.64)(10.45)}{6} + 17.50 = 20.35 \text{ days}$$

The interpretation would be that the probability of completing a 21-day schedule on time would be 95 percent.

2–8. PERT CONCLUSIONS AND FALLACIES

PERT attempts to account for some of the stochastic effects prevalent in large-scale projects due to various uncertainties that exist. Specifically, the technique was originally designed for research and development projects which certainly have a large degree of uncertainty, not only in completion times, but also in the particular branches which are taken in the network. The end result of the PERT analysis is a probability statement concerning project completion, that can be used in management decision making. For example, if a 95 percent confidence

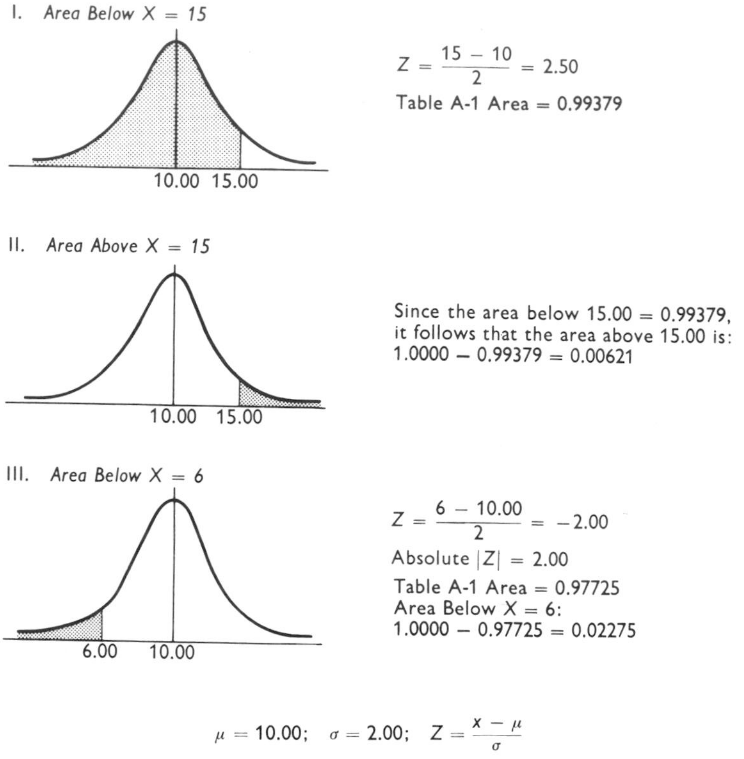

I. *Area Below X = 15*

$$Z = \frac{15 - 10}{2} = 2.50$$

Table A-1 Area = 0.99379

10.00 15.00

II. *Area Above X = 15*

Since the area below 15.00 = 0.99379,
it follows that the area above 15.00 is:
1.0000 − 0.99379 = 0.00621

10.00   15.00

III. *Area Below X = 6*

$$Z = \frac{6 - 10.00}{2} = -2.00$$

Absolute $|Z| = 2.00$
Table A-1 Area = 0.97725
Area Below $X = 6$:
1.0000 − 0.97725 = 0.02275

6.00   10.00

$$\mu = 10.00; \quad \sigma = 2.00; \quad Z = \frac{x - \mu}{\sigma}$$

Figure 2–16. Examples of the use of Appendix Table A–I in the determination of areas under the normal curve.

level is set as satisfactory for completion, then the schedule time that will meet that probability can be determined and then a decision has to be made regarding the reasonability of such a schedule in a project go–no go situation.

There is a definite contribution in the PERT technique. However, there are many assumptions which may prove somewhat untenable in certain situations. A few of these would be:

1. PERT requires that *all* jobs be traversed for project completion. This certainly is *not* the case in the research and development environment. For example, suppose your company is engaged in the development of machine-tool control by digital computer. A few of the initial jobs might be as shown in Figure 2–17. Once a decision has been made at node 3, only *one* job will be performed, of the two emanating from node 3. The same goes for nodes 6 and 7. The argument that the paths out of nodes 4 and 5 are the same holds no water either. The study, its

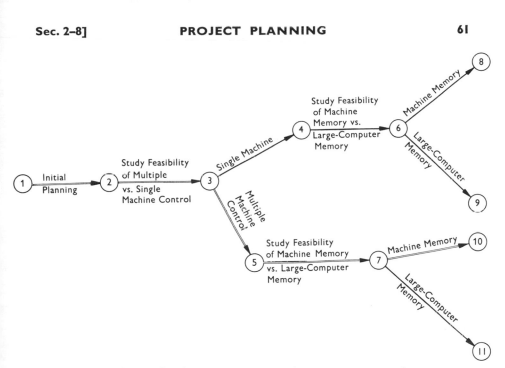

Figure 2–17. Initial jobs in machine-tool computer control project.

approach and results, would be different for the single-machine versus multiple-machine control situation. One typical final path might be the double-arrow path, with all single-arrow jobs not even being tackled.

2. One consideration in determining a critical path is that the jobs on that path should receive priority treatment so as to insure that the project will not slip. A fallacy of this argument can be seen in Figure 2–14. If G actually took 20 days and path ADE took 14 days, as they could with the given data, there would be no sense in pouring the main effort on path ADE as our original analysis concluded.

3. The assumption of the beta distribution for the jobs may not be valid. Even worse, the simple approximations used to calculate the mean and variance may not be correct, especially if the time distribution does not follow the beta.

4. The central limit theorem requires independence of jobs for the pure additive law to work for the mean and variance of the critical path. Conceptually, it is hard to conceive that the times for adjacent jobs would be independent.

5. In line with Item 4, the normal distribution assumption for the project may be untenable.

Even though this short list of possible PERT errors may seem traumatic, PERT does present an approach to the stochastic project problem. Subsequent techniques have had one major obstacle—complexity. The next section will introduce some ways that have been suggested to combat the PERT problems.

2–9. NETWORK STOCHASTIC CONSIDERATIONS

Probably the most significant evaluation of PERT assumptions was accomplished by MacCrimmon and Ryavec.[5] One concept they introduced is rather interesting. This relates to the fact that the concept of a *critical activity* may be more valid than that of the *critical path* in PERT analyses. As they say:

In a stochastic model, each path has a specific probability (in general, nonzero) of being the longest path at any particular time. However, if the network is large, the probability that any given path is the critical one may be very small . . . . Thus, the most probable critical path may occur only rarely, and an activity that has a high probability of being on a longest path may not be on this most probable critical path.

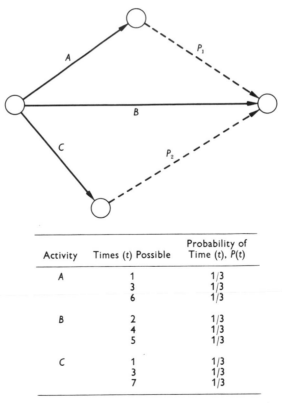

Activity	Times (t) Possible	Probability of Time (t), $P(t)$
A	1	1/3
	3	1/3
	6	1/3
B	2	1/3
	4	1/3
	5	1/3
C	1	1/3
	3	1/3
	7	1/3

Figure 2–18. Example data for critical activity consideration.

The objective of determining *critical activities* would be to determine those activities that you want to insure have no schedule slippage. The usual PERT approach is to calculate a critical path, based on activity means, and then to assume that the activities on that path should be the ones to watch closely. It may be that some activities having the highest probabilities of being on a critical path will not fall on the critical path defined by activity means. Unfortunately, the critical activity calculations can become extremely cumbersome, probably requiring a computer simulation analysis in the realistic case. However, be that as it may, the concept is certainly interesting.

As a critical activity example, consider the naive network given in Figure 2–18. Three times are given for each activity, with the exception of the two pseudo activities. Each of the times given has the same probability of occurrence for simplicity of calculation, and these are the *only* times possible. Since there are three parallel paths, each with three possible time values, it follows there are twenty-seven possible path combinations, each equally likely. Table 2–6 gives these possible time values, along with the activities in each combination that are critical. Adding up all times that activities A, B, and C are critical, we find:

1. Activity A: Critical 8 times.
2. Activity B: Critical 9 times.
3. Activity C: Critical 11 times.

Since there are 27 combinations, it follows that activity C has a probability of 11/27 of falling on a critical path. If the network was analyzed with activity arithmetic mean values, activities B and C would be most critical, with mean times of 11/3 versus 10/3 for activity A. By PERT, activity B would get the preferred attention as it would be on the critical path. If the three time estimates for each activity were assumed the PERT beta estimates, then the resultant activity means for A, B, and C would be 19/6, 23/6, and 20/6. Activity B would get the preferential treatment. If mathematically feasible, as far as computation is concerned, the *critical activity* approach still does assume that each activity will be traversed. It would be possible to re-evaluate the situation each time a node has been achieved in the actual project; however, this does not satisfy the desire to determine an *initial* expected duration of the project.

The problem of stochastic *entry* to activities was evaluated by Graham.[2] He considered that a known probability for entering each activity, once the activities' initial node had been attained, could be

Table 2-6

**Possible Path Combinations and Critical Activity(s)
for Each Combination**

Activity A Possible Times	Activity B Possible Times	Activity C Possible Times		
		1	3	7
	2	B*	C	C
1	4	B	B	C
	5	B	B	C
	2	A	A,C	C
3	4	B	B	C
	5	B	B	C
	2	A	A	C
6	4	A	A	C
	5	A	A	C

*For combination of times $A=1$, $C=1$, $B=2$; activity B is critical.

estimated. However, the activity *durations* were still assumed at some deterministic mean value. As an example, consider the network of Figure 2–19. Nodes 5 and 7 represent successful project attainment, while nodes 6 and 8 indicate the opposite result. The probability of attaining these nodes is as follows:

1. Node 5: $(0.3)(0.7) = 0.21$
2. Node 6: $(0.3)(0.3) = 0.09$
3. Node 7: $(0.7)(0.5) = 0.35$
4. Node 8: $(0.7)(0.5) = 0.35$

The probability of success, node 5 or node 7, would have a probability of 0.56. The expected duration of the project could be obtained by

$$E(\text{Project Length}) = \sum_{\text{all paths}} (\text{Path Lengths})(\text{Probability of Path})$$

If the paths to nodes 5, 6, 7, and 8 have time values of 16, 15, 18, and 17 respectively, then the expected duration would be

$$(16)(0.21) + (15)(0.09) + (18)(0.35) + (17)(0.35) = 17 \text{ days}$$

Similar calculations could be performed for cost and profit expectations.

Now, how about the combination of activity *length* stochastic effects as well as stochastic *entry* conditions?

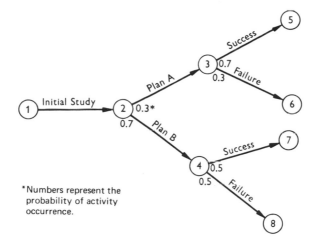

Figure 2–19. Network example for probability analysis.

2–10. GRAPHICAL EVALUATION AND REVIEW TECHNIQUE (GERT)

In a general introduction to current network research, it is not fair to discuss the Graphical Evaluation and Review Technique (GERT) in just a few paragraphs. Unfortunately, the prerequisite technical knowledge required for GERT is more than intended as a requirement for this text. A knowledge of flow-graph theory, probability moment generating functions (MGF), and transmittance calculations are required. An example will be given in this brief section to at least *demonstrate* GERT, but the reader interested in further investigation of the application of GERT is advised to utilize those references at the end of the chapter pertinent to flow-graph theory and GERT itself.

Those steps employed in applying GERT are as follows[5]:

1. Convert a qualitative description of a system or problem to a model in network form.

2. Collect necessary data to describe the branches of the network.

3. Apply the topology equation to determine the equivalent function or functions of the network.

4. Convert the equivalent function into the following two performance measures of the network:
   a. The probability that a specific node is realized.
   b. The moment-generating function of the time associated with an equivalent network.

5. Make inferences concerning the system under study from the information in 4 above.

An example of GERT application will be taken from Whitehouse,[9] to a problem originally developed by Elmaghraby.[1] The problem is as follows:

Consider a shop which produces electro-mechanical equipment by the following sequence. There is a series of operations that terminates at an inspection station I. Inspected units are dispatched to one of two areas: a further testing area T, or an adjustment operation J. Units in the test area are either accepted and sent to J, or rejected and sent to the repair area R. From the repair area, material flows back to be tested. After the adjustment in J, the units are packed and delivered to stock.

A flow-graph, or network, of the problem is given in Figure 2–20. All parts have to take activity A-I. The branch from I directly to J is for those units not rejected at I. Those rejected at I go to further testing at T where they have the possibility of repair at R or being sent to J after adjustment. Finally, all units take the final packing and delivery to stock branch.

In determining the *expected time* to traverse the network from node A to node F, it is now necessary to determine the *transmittance* of the network. According to Whitehouse, each transmittance of the GERT network will have two parameters associated with it: (1) the probability that the path will be taken given that the node from which it originates is realized, (p), and (2) a function of the time required to complete the activity which the transmittance represents, $f(t)$. If $f(t)$ is represented by the moment-generating function (MGF) $M(s)$, then the transmittance for an activity, $W(s)$, is given by $(p)[W(s)]$. The transmittance through node F can be found by reduction of the network by Mason's rule.[3]

$$W_F(s) = \frac{[W_a(s)W_b(s)W_c(s)W_g(s)] + [W_a(s)W_f(s)W_g(s)][1 - W_d(s)W_e(s)]}{[1 - W_d(s)W_e(s)]}$$

$$(2-4)$$

The probability of attaining node F, P_f, is found by evaluating $W_F(s)$ at $s = 0$. The expected time to node F is found by

$$\frac{dM_F(s)}{ds}$$

evaluated at $s = 0$, where $M_F(s)$ is found by

$$\frac{W_F(s)}{P_f}.$$

Obviously, data have to be obtained to allow estimates to be made concerning each activity time. For our example, assume the data given

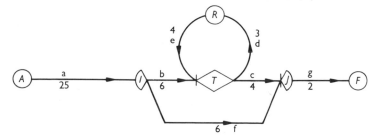

Figure 2–20. Flowgraph for example GERT problem.

in Table 2–7. By Equation 2–4, $W_F(s)$ is now

$$W_F(s) = \frac{(e^{25s})(0.7e^{6s})(0.7e^{4s+3s^2})(e^{2s}) + (e^{25s})(0.3e^{6s})(e^{2s})(1 - (0.3e^{3s})(e^{4s}))}{1 - (0.3e^{3s})(e^{4s})}$$

which reduces to

$$W_F(s) = \frac{0.49e^{37s+3s^2} + 0.3e^{33s}(1 - 0.3e^{7s})}{(1 - 0.3e^{7s})}$$

P_F can now be found by evaluating $W_F(s)$, at $s = 0$:

$$P_F = \frac{0.49 + (0.3)(0.7)}{1 - 0.3} = 1.0$$

This is a happy result; otherwise units would be lost in the inspection process. $M_F(s)$ can now be found by

$$M_F(s) = \frac{W_F(s)}{P_F} = W_F(s)$$

Table 2-7

Data for GERT Example Problem

Activity	(p)	E(Time) Distributions	M(s)*	W(s)
a	1	25, Constant	e^{25s}	e^{25s}
b	0.7	6, Constant	e^{6s}	$0.7e^{6s}$
c	0.7	4, Normal ($\sigma^2 = 6$)	e^{4s+3s^2}	$0.7e^{4s+3s^2}$
d	0.3	3, Constant	e^{3s}	$0.3e^{3s}$
e	1	4, Constant	e^{4s}	e^{4s}
f	0.3	6, Constant	e^{6s}	$0.3e^{6s}$
g	1	2, Constant	e^{2s}	e^{2s}

*For typical $M(s)$ formulas, see Ref 9, p. 30.

and the expected time to node $F = \dfrac{dM_F(s)}{ds}$, evaluated at $s = 0$; which evolves a result of 37.9 time units.

This short example has shown the relative complexity of GERT. However, the information gained is mathematically accurate, assuming the element data is correct. It is a further example of the adage, "you get what you pay for." The reader who is interested in pursuing network research is urged to delve into the pertinent references more fully.

2-11. CASE PROBLEM FOR CPM *

The erection of two-story prefabricated buildings in a tropical climate, such as Southeast Asia's, is being considered. These wood buildings are considered to be temporary structures and have no windows, bathrooms, or running water. Presently, the U.S. Army is using such buildings in Southeast Asia to billet combat troops. The Army Corps of Engineers is responsible for the prefabrication and limited erection of these buildings in designated areas. Organizations (units) of the various branches of service draw these buildings in prefabricated form and erect them with the technical assistance of the Army Engineers. Being unskilled in the arts of carpentry, most constructing units waste considerable time, money, and manpower trying to erect these buildings. Construction sequence, project duration, and project management problems vary widely between units.

Data are given that will allow a CPM analysis to be made. The end result of this CPM scheduling will be a standard operating procedure schedule for those units erecting the prefabricated buildings.

Preplanning work has been accomplished and is summarized in Figure 2–21 and Tables 2–8 through 2–10. The network for the project is given in Figure 2–21, with associated CPM data given in Table 2–8. The jobs are identified in terms of their starting (i) and ending (j) nodes for convenience. Tables 2–9 and 2–10 list resource information required for scheduling the project. This information is more pertinent to Chapter 6 and the project will be further discussed in case problem format in that chapter. However, CPM problems with limited resources will be pointed out briefly after the CPM analysis in this problem. Table 2–9 lists the resources available, while Table 2–10 gives the resource

---

* This problem was developed by Charles C. Washington, while a graduate student at Arizona State University and is used here with his kind permission.

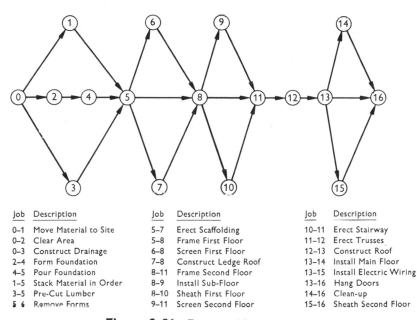

Job	Description	Job	Description	Job	Description
0–1	Move Material to Site	5–7	Erect Scaffolding	10–11	Erect Stairway
0–2	Clear Area	5–8	Frame First Floor	11–12	Erect Trusses
0–3	Construct Drainage	6–8	Screen First Floor	12–13	Construct Roof
2–4	Form Foundation	7–8	Construct Ledge Roof	13–14	Install Main Floor
4–5	Pour Foundation	8–11	Frame Second Floor	13–15	Install Electric Wiring
1–5	Stack Material in Order	8–9	Install Sub-Floor	13–16	Hang Doors
3–5	Pre-Cut Lumber	8–10	Sheath First Floor	14–16	Clean-up
5–6	Remove Forms	9–11	Screen Second Floor	15–16	Sheath Second Floor

Figure 2–21. Case problem network.

Table 2-8

Case Problem CPM Job Data

Job		Duration (days)		Cost Slope	Normal Cost
I	J	Normal	Crash	(dollars/day)	(dollars)
0	1	2	1	84	116
0	2	2	1	38	112
0	3	2	1	100	200
2	4	2	1	200	256
4	5	2	1	600	672
1	5	1	1	—	64
3	5	2	1	40	80
5	6	2	1	18	32
5	7	1	1	—	64
5	8	4	2	300	300
8	9	2	1	100	150
8	10	2	1	150	250
9	11	3	1	43	64
8	11	4	2	300	400
10	11	3	2	200	300
11	12	2	1	100	200
12	13	3	1	300	400
13	14	2	1	70	150
13	15	2	1	150	200
13	16	2	1	50	100
14	16	2	1	50	50
15	16	2	1	200	300
6	8	3	1	43	64
7	8	2	1	100	150

Table 2-9

Resource Availability Sheet for Case
Problem

Resource Identification		
Number	Description	Available
01	Flat bed truck	1
02	Concrete mixer	1
03	Truck-mounted crane	1
04	Portable scaffolding	3
05	Circular saw	2
06	Small hand tools	3
07	Pick-up truck	1
08	Dump truck	1
09	Front loader	1
10	Road grader	1
11	Electricians	2
12	Carpenters	2
13	Laborers	15

requirement per job. It is assumed that resources scheduled for a particular job will be assigned to that job for the entire job schedule period. In addition to the information just given, the *indirect costs* are quoted at $100 per day. The CPM approach first has the *normal* critical path(s) determined, and this is shown in Figure 2–22A. The schedule duration is 25 days. The direct cost, summing all the normal costs, turns out to be $4,674 and the indirect cost, at $100 per day, is $2,500, for a 25-day schedule total cost of $7,174. The critical path activities are denoted by a double arrow designation and a rather formidable initial number of critical paths, 4, appears, when all possible combinations are considered. However, it is readily seen that it is possible to reduce all these paths by reducing only *one* of several possible critical jobs. The minimum increase in direct cost is achieved by reducing job 5-6 when going to 24 days—Iteration 2, Figure 2–22B. This forces job 5-8 to be on a critical path, with a resultant combination now of 8 critical paths. On the next iteration, Figure 2–22C, it is seen that reducing job 0-2 by 1 day actually reduces all 8 critical paths by 1 day, with an increase of only $38 in direct costs over the previous schedule.

Only five iterations are given in Figure 2–22, even though further reduction is possible. It is seen that iterations 3 and 4 have the same total cost of $7,030, which is the minimum for the five iterations. Since iteration five gave a higher total cost, $7,123, and the indirect costs are

Table 2-10

Job Resource Requirements for Case Problem

Activity		Resource												
i	j	01 Qty	02 Qty	03 Qty	04 Qty	05 Qty	06 Qty	07 Qty	08 Qty	09 Qty	10 Qty	11 Qty	12 Qty	13 Qty
0	1	1	—	1	—	—	1	1	1	1	—	—	—	6
0	2	—	—	—	—	—	1	—	1	—	1	—	—	4
0	3	—	—	—	—	—	1	—	—	—	—	—	—	6
2	4	1	1	1	—	1	1	1	—	1	—	—	2	4
4	5	—	—	—	—	—	1	—	—	—	—	—	2	10
1	5	—	—	—	—	1	1	—	—	—	—	—	—	6
3	5	—	—	—	—	—	1	—	—	1	—	—	2	4
5	6	—	—	—	1	—	1	—	—	—	—	—	1	2
5	7	—	—	—	1	—	1	—	—	—	—	—	—	2
6	8	—	—	—	1	1	1	—	—	—	—	—	1	4
8	8	—	—	—	1	1	1	—	—	—	—	—	2	4
8	9	—	—	—	1	1	1	—	—	—	—	—	2	6
9	10	—	—	—	1	1	1	—	—	—	—	2	2	6
10	11	—	—	—	1	1	1	—	—	—	—	—	2	4
11	11	—	—	—	1	1	1	—	—	—	—	—	2	6
12	13	—	—	—	1	1	1	—	—	—	—	—	2	6
13	14	—	—	—	1	1	1	—	—	—	—	—	2	6
13	15	—	—	—	—	—	1	—	—	—	—	—	2	6
15	16	—	—	—	1	1	1	—	—	—	—	—	—	2
14	16	—	—	—	—	—	1	—	1	—	—	—	1	2
5	8	—	—	—	1	1	1	—	—	—	—	—	2	8
8	11	—	—	—	1	1	1	—	—	—	—	—	2	8

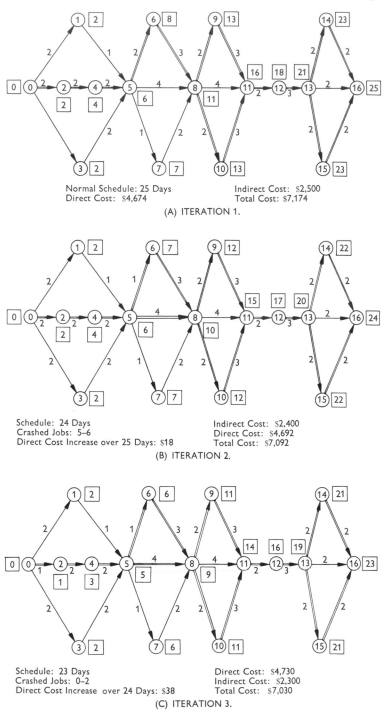

Normal Schedule: 25 Days
Direct Cost: $4,674

Indirect Cost: $2,500
Total Cost: $7,174

(A) ITERATION 1.

Schedule: 24 Days
Crashed Jobs: 5–6
Direct Cost Increase over 25 Days: $18

Indirect Cost: $2,400
Direct Cost: $4,692
Total Cost: $7,092

(B) ITERATION 2.

Schedule: 23 Days
Crashed Jobs: 0–2
Direct Cost Increase over 24 Days: $38

Direct Cost: $4,730
Indirect Cost: $2,300
Total Cost: $7,030

(C) ITERATION 3.

Figure 2–22. Case problem network solution.

linear, the *minimum total cost* has been reached. This is because the direct cost from iteration to iteration can *never* be *less* than the previous iteration, due to the process whereby the *minimum* increase is selected each time. The total set of possible schedules is given in Table 2–11, leading to a crash schedule of 21 days.

The optimum CPM schedules would be 22 and 23 days. The longer schedule will be more adaptable to limited resources so that is the one we will consider knowing resource requirements. A Gantt chart for the 23-day schedule is given in Figure 2-23. The dashed lines with *non-critical path jobs* indicate the amount of time within which these jobs can be scheduled. For example, jobs 0-1 and 1-5 can be scheduled

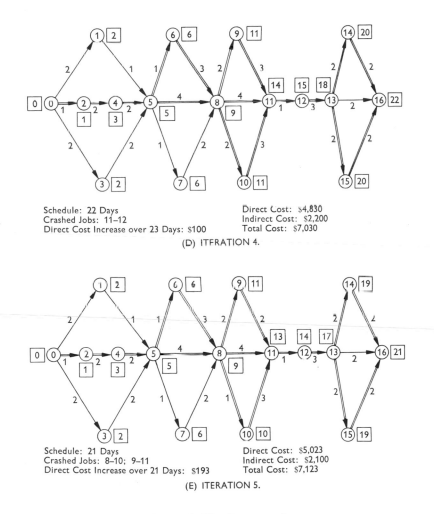

Schedule: 22 Days
Crashed Jobs: 11–12
Direct Cost Increase over 23 Days: $100

Direct Cost: $4,830
Indirect Cost: $2,200
Total Cost: $7,030

(D) ITERATION 4.

Schedule: 21 Days
Crashed Jobs: 8–10; 9–11
Direct Cost Increase over 21 Days: $193

Direct Cost: $5,023
Indirect Cost: $2,100
Total Cost: $7,123

(E) ITERATION 5.

Figure 2–22. Continued.

Table 2–11

Case Problem—Total Cost Plot

Schedule Time (days)	Minimum Direct Costs (dollars)	Indirect Costs (dollars)	Total Costs (dollars)
25	4,674	2,500	7,174
24	4,692	2,400	7,092
23	4,730	2,300	7,030
22	4,830	2,200	7,030
21	5,023	2,100	7,123
20	5,223	2,000	7,223
19	5,423	1,900	7,323
18	5,693	1,800	7,493
17	5,993	1,700	7,693
16	6,203	1,600	7,893
15	6,636	1,500	8,136
14	7,079	1,400	8,479
13	7,622	1,300	8,922
12	8,262	1,200	9,462

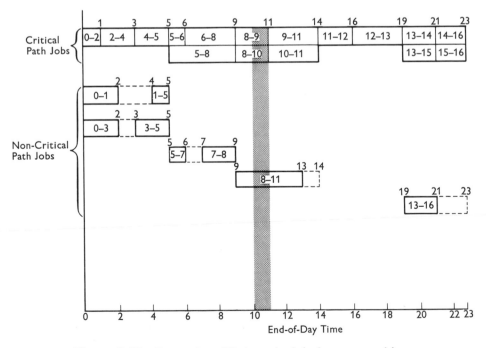

Figure 2–23. Gantt chart 23-day schedule for case problem.

between time 0 through time 5. Their combined times add to 3 days. One possible schedule would be to have job 0-1 scheduled for days 3 and 4, and job 1-5 for day 5. If we consider only day 11, shaded in Figure 2–23, we see that jobs 8-9, 8-10, and 8-11 *have* to be scheduled that day. If we look at the laborers and carpenters required for these jobs, from Table 2–10, it is seen that 20 laborers are required and 6 carpenters. Table 2–9 tells us that only 15 laborers and 2 carpenters are available, *maximum*. Also, three circular saws are required where only two are available. Obviously, this particular CPM schedule is invalid. This is not to say that CPM is useless in this case. The network alone is invaluable in determining resource limitations. Also, starting from the CPM schedule it is possible to adjust job times so that the *minimum increase* in time, above the CPM time, is obtained that satisfies a particular limited resource constraint. This topic will be further analyzed in Chapter 6.

REFERENCES CITED

1. ELMAGHRABY, S. E. "An Algebra for the Analysis of Generalized Activity Networks," *Management Science*, Vol. 10, No. 3, 1964.
2. GRAHAM, P. "Profit Probability Analysis of Research and Development Expenditures," *The Journal of Industrial Engineering*, Vol. XVI, No. 3, May–June, 1965.
3. HUGGINS, W. H. "Signal Flow Graphs," *Proceedings of the Institute of Radio Engineers*, Vol. 9, No. 9. 1957.
4. KELLEY, JAMES E., and WALKER, M. "Critical-Path Planning and Scheduling," *Proceedings Eastern Joint Computer Conference*, 1959.
5. MACCRIMMON, K. R., and RYAVEC, C. A. "An Analytical Study of the PERT Assumptions," *Operations Research*, Vol. 12, January–February, 1964.
6. MODER, J. J., and PHILLIPS, C. R. *Project Management with CPM and PERT*, Reinhold Publishing Corporation, New York, N.Y., 1964.
7. PRITSKER, A. A. B. GERT: *Graphical Evaluation and Review Technique*, Memorandum RM-4973-NASA, The Rand Corporation, Santa Monica, Calif., April, 1966.
8. PRITSKER, A. A. B., and HAPP, W. W., "GERT: Graphical Evaluation and Review Technique, Part I, Fundamentals," *Journal of Industrial Engineering*, Vol. XVII, No. 5, May, 1966.
9. WHITEHOUSE, G. E., *Extensions, New Developments and Applications of GERT*, Unpublished Ph.D. Dissertation, Arizona State University, August, 1965.

FURTHER READING

FRY, B. L. *Network-Type Management Control Systems Bibliography*, Memorandum RM-3074-PR, The Rand Corporation, Santa Monica, California, February, 1963. [This lists most of the available literature prior to 1963.]
FULKERSON, D. R. "Expected Critical Path Lengths in PERT Networks," *Operations Research*, Vol. 10, No. 6, 1962.

MALCOLM, D. G., ROSENBLOOM, J. H., CLARK, D. E., and FAZAR, W. H. "Application of a Technique for Research and Development Program Evaluation," *Operations Research*, Vol. 7, September–October, 1959.

MASON, S. J. "Feedback Theory—Some Properties of Signal Flowgraphs," *Proceedings of the Institute of Radio Engineers*, Vol. 41, No. 9, 1953.

RABORN, W. F. "Lesson in Management: Program Evaluation and Review Technique," *Aviation Week*, January 29, 1962.

WHITEHOUSE, G. E. "Model Systems on Paper With Flowgraph Analysis," *Industrial Engineering*, Vol. 1, No. 6, June, 1969.

PROBLEMS

1. This problem is recommended only if a CPM digital computer program is available.

Consider the following jobs developed by a CPM planner that have to be accomplished in getting a plant's new product on the market:

	Normal		Crash	
Job Description	Duration (weeks)	Cost (dollars)	Duration (weeks)	Cost (dollars)
Conduct market research	6	$ 30,000	2	$ 125,000
Develop price demand schedules	3	6,250	1	27,400
Develop product planning specs	6	28,120	4	48,500
Conduct engineering research	7	33,750	4	159,590
Conduct patent search	1	10,000	1	10,000
Prepare cost estimates	5	9,380	2	26,420
Develop lab model	9	51,250	5	158,760
Conduct product appraisal	4	15,650	2	51,950
Conduct profit and loss analysis	3	5,630	1	24,750
Design final product	8	40,620	5	151,870
Train sales force	1	5,000	1	5,000
Prepare advertising	6	18,750	3	47,500
Issue drawings and specs	2	3,120	1	7,100
Determine price	3	5,130	1	16,420
Establish distribution outlets	8	56,250	5	132,500
Release advertising	3	4,380	3	4,380
Determine manufacturing methods	2	5,630	1	14,200
Procure raw material	3	3,750	2	9,250
Procure buy items	8	11,880	5	28,880
Prepare service literature	2	5,000	1	12,000
Design and procure packaging	4	10,500	1	73,700
Train production personnel	1	9,370	1	9,370
Manufacture "make" items	4	68,750	1	237,380
Assemble	4	49,380	3	95,750
Train service organization	2	11,500	1	27,500
Test	2	12,500	2	12,500
Box, pack and ship	2	5,000	1	11,230
		$516,540		$1,528,900

A. Develop a CPM network, justifying the precedence relationships you utilize between jobs. It is realized that the job descriptions give leeway as regards their interpretation, so your interpretations should be given with your justification.

B. If indirect project costs are calculated as follows: $600,000 + 10,000 per week until project is completed, and anticipated market is as follows, find and justify a schedule for this project.

If Shipped by Week	Total Anticipated Market
30	$2,750,000
31	2,695,000
32	2,650,000
33	2,610,000
34	2,575,000
35	2,540,000
36	2,510,000
37	2,485,000
38	2,460,000
39	2,440,000
40	2,422,000
41	2,405,000
42	2,395,000
43	2,375,000
44	2,360,000
45	2,341,000
46	2,335,000
47	2,325,000
48	2,315,000
49	2,310,000
50	2,305,000
51	2,300,000
52	2,295,000

C. After twenty weeks everything is on the schedule that you set up for it. However, a Revised Market Forecast has been issued as follows:

Weeks After 20th Week	Sales Anticipated
10	$2,800,000
11	2,775,000
12	2,750,000
13	2,725,000
14	2,700,000
15	2,680,000
16	2,660,000
17	2,640,000
18	2,600,000
19	2,590,000
20	2,550,000
21	2,500,000
22	2,475,000
23	2,425,000
24	2,375,000
25	2,360,000
26	2,340,000
27	2,330,000
28	2,320,000
29	2,310,000
30	2,305,000
31	2,300,000
32	2,290,000

Indirect labor cost estimates have also changed. To date $800,000 (600,000 + 200,000) has been spent but it is estimated that additional indirect labor will be at the rate of $7,500/week. Would you continue under your previous schedule or would you change? If you would change, what would the new schedule be?

2. A group of jobs are given below, each with their immediate predecessor's jobs. Develop a network for these jobs, minimizing pseudo jobs:

Job	Immediate Predecessor(s)
A	None
B	None
C	None
D	A, B
E	B
F	C
G	B, F
H	D, E

3. For the jobs given in Problem 2, the following CPM data have been estimated; indirect costs are estimated at $25 per day. Determine the optimum total cost schedule for your network developed for Problem 2.

Job	Time (days)		Cost ($)	
	Normal	Crash	Normal	Crash
A	6	5	$100	$120
B	5	3	85	145
C	2	2	95	95
D	4	3	95	120
E	5	3	88	125
F	6	5	85	115
G	1	1	90	90
H	7	6	110	123

4. Consider Problem 3. Put your schedule in Gantt Chart format. The jobs require a scarce resource as follows:

Job	Resource Required per Day
A	2
B	1
C	3
D	2
E	1
F	3
G	4
H	2

If only 4 units of the resource are available, can the CPM optimum schedule be attained? If not, suggest a revised schedule.

5. Consider the PERT data given in Figure 2–13. What is the probability of meeting a 20-day schedule? 15-day schedule? 18-day schedule?

6. Consider the PERT data given in Figure 2–13. Job D is now found to be stochastic, and not deterministic as originally given. It is assumed to follow a beta distribution, with a, m, and b estimates of 6, 7, and 11. What schedule time will give a probability of 90% of being successfully met? 95%? 75%?

7. Normally, CPM and PERT are techniques oriented to a one-of-a-kind project. Discuss the pro's and con's regarding their application to repeating type projects, say in assembly-line operation.

8. This problem is recommended only for those familiar with GERT and its background material.

Consider the GERT network given in Figure 2–20, with associated data given in Table 2–7. Activity c time is now assumed constant rather than normal, with a time value of $4 : [M(s) = e^{4s}]$. If all other activity data stay the same, determine the expected duration of time to node F.

3
Forecasting: Regression Analysis

3–1. GENERAL CONSIDERATIONS

Shakespeare, without a doubt, was one of history's great playwrights. If the above quotation accurately represents his feelings regarding business forecasting, then he certainly had the correct vocation when he stayed with play writing. It certainly does not "sufficeth" that the forecast is known at the end of a forecasting period. However, comparing the forecasts with their respective true demand values will allow better forecasting procedures to be evolved through statistical analysis.

Forecasting is a true "systems" tool. The underlying concepts of time-series analysis come from automatic control theory and statistical analysis. Certain techniques for determining predominant frequencies in information theory can be just as applicable to finding cyclic relationships in sales data. Mathematical procedures for determining polynomial relationships can certainly be applied to determining growth trends in sales data. The major portion of this chapter and Chapter 4 will be devoted to the basics of time-series analysis. This is predicated on the theory that most forecasts, such as prediction of airplane position, are based on trends in past data. Forecast techniques not based on past data-trend analysis would be applied primarily to sales forecasting. Certain of these approaches would have to be custom-designed for the particular production facility.

The most logical general consideration to be covered first is the *benefit* of forecasting. After this, the three forecasting criteria of accuracy, simplicity of calculation, and ability to adjust the rate of response will be discussed. The requirements for the forecast will, to a large degree, dictate the emphasis placed on the three criteria in each individual forecasting case. Finally, the last general consideration will discuss briefly the concept of *lead time* within the forecasting system. It is realized that a whole book could be written on the topic of forecasting. Such considerations as share of the market, correlation with federal indices, and so on would be, and should be, discussed. However, those considerations deemed only beneficial for *sales forecasting* will not be discussed. Several excellent books and pamphlets* deal with this topic in detail. This chapter material, including the time-series information, is given as an *introduction* to the more general *systems* concept of forecasting.

A hypothetical example was given in Chapter 1 to demonstrate the interaction between forecasting and scheduling. This same example was also used to *justify* forecasting. It was shown for the specific example that a best profit situation was always achieved when forecasting was employed versus some non-forecasting approach. Even though this was a hypothetical problem, the same could *almost* certainly be said for the real-world problems. However, it should be realized that the total cost of a forecast includes the cost of forecast method development, cost of actually making the forecast, and the cost of forecast errors. The cost of method development may be minimal, but this may result in high error costs. Minimizing error costs possibly could result in a very complex forecasting procedure that would have high development costs and maybe high application costs. Not considering that forecasting costs are the sum of costs for interacting factors could easily result in a forecast procedure being more expensive overall than a non-forecast method. The most obvious *benefit* is that the system which is employing the forecast is not operating in a vacuum as regards real-world conditions. This is of course assuming that conditions of *uncertainty* exist for the particular system. A few sales

---

* One particularly excellent pamphlet is *Forecasting Sales, Studies in Business Policy, No. 106*, published by the National Industrial Conference Board, Inc.

demand cases exist where the demand for the product exceeds the capacity to produce. Demand is then limited to capacity. However, long-term conditions may not be so predictable. Therefore, in any system that has uncertain characteristics, such as customer whims, economic fluctuations, weather variations, flight landing conditions, etc., the ability to observe applicable conditions and from these observations make subsequent predictions allows a measure of knowledge to be inserted into the uncertain categories. If nothing else, the need for forecasting to be based on something tangible necessitates *thinking* about what affects the forecast and to what degree. This, in itself, has to be a benefit of forecasting.

The two primary, and obvious, considerations to be made in determining a *forecasting approach* are: What is the forecast to be used for, and why? The answers to these two questions will dictate, for the most part, the forecast approach. For example, if we wish to make a personal forecast of the weather for tomorrow because we are not sure whether to sprinkle the flowers tonight, we may forecast using the old adage:

> Red sky at night, shepherd's delight;
> Red sky in the morning, shepherd's warning.

In the long run this would probably be correct more often than not. It has the advantage of being simple, quick, and economical. It has the disadvantage of being somewhat inaccurate.

Conversely, if the weather prediction is made in preparation for a manned "Mars shot" then the requirements of the forecast will be much more complex. Wind trends, potential cloud build-ups, temperature, and so forth, will all be critical factors. The cost of failure of the operation would be enormous, thus justifying high expenditures for insuring success. Therefore, exotic equipment would be utilized to gather data on which the forecast is to be made. Weather balloons and weather planes will be used to gather up-to-the-minute data over a wide geographic area.

Brown suggests that the criteria for forecasting fall into the three categories of *accuracy, simplicity of computation*, and *flexibility to adjust the rate of response*.[1] Even though these three criteria are primarily geared to time-series analysis, they are just as applicable to any type of forecast model.

The meaning of the term *accuracy* in forecasting is self-evident. It is a measure of how well a forecasted condition matches the actual condition when it occurs. In general, high accuracy requirements will not allow *simplicity of computation*. Therefore, a trade-off between the two is usually required. If time is of the essence, as in the prediction of when to adjust tension rolls in a steel rolling process in order to maintain required steel thickness and yet avoid shear when the steel is moving at a speed of hundreds of feet a minute, a lot of time can not be spent in actually calculating the forecast if data have to be computer-scanned every hundredth of a second. In the earlier rocket shot example, a lot of time is available for weather prediction and so *simplicity of computation* is not a worrisome problem.

The *ability to adjust the rate of response* is a measure of the ability of a forecast to adapt to changing conditions. In the steel rolling example, if the thickness of steel has been decreasing at a very gradual slope and suddenly steepens due to equipment malfunction, predicting when corrective action will take place based on the earlier gradual slope would be fallacious. The forecast technique has to be able to adjust model parameters, such as the slope in a ramp data change, with respect to time. If operational procedures for the Mars moon shot were so rigid that they *had* to be based on weather prediction, say a week earlier, then such a shoot would in all probability never be successful. In actual practice real-time computers are undoubtedly utilized to constantly monitor weather conditions and accordingly adjust flight controllers until such time as the rocket is outside the Earth's atmosphere.

A further general consideration of forecasting has to be the lead time. Lead time is here defined as the elapsed time between making the forecast and implementing the result of the forecast. For example, in predicting schedule requirements for a job-shop, the lead time might be the elapsed time from making the forecast for a particular month, say May, through the actual production time of May. One problem with a long lead time is that forecast errors grow as the length of lead time increases.

In automatic control situations, the forecasting lead times could be smaller than a second in steel rolling control to maybe two or three minutes in cement kiln control. Such short lead times require very short computational time while requiring high accuracy and flexibility of response. Special computational procedures are necessitated which are oriented to digital computer application. Therefore, the exponential smoothing procedure will be developed as a curve-fitting technique (in the next chapter), which is beneficial for such critical problems.

How often to gather data is another good problem. In sales forecasting this is usually dictated by the requirements of the forecast.

Forecasting for job-shop monthly scheduling would logically be based on monthly historical demand values. In process control, data may need to be filtered to remove process or instrumentation noise and therefore, even though a prediction once a minute might be required by the process, data may be required at a much faster rate. However, it cannot be brought in at a slower rate than the maximum allowable lead time. Even though sales forecasting may be thought of in some cases as ruler prediction—placing a ruler through a series of demand data and drawing a line through the points to give an estimate of demand at some future time period—it is apparent that several complicated interacting factors are involved in general systems forecasting, many of which are applicable to sales forecasting. Accuracy required, simplicity of computation, flexibility of response, lead time, and rate of data input all interact. Only on some cost criterion can all be optimized, possibly only through computer simulation.

3–2. TYPES OF FORECAST

Before getting into the mathematics of basic time-series analysis applied to forecasting, some *general* comments should be made about it and *other* types of forecasting approaches. One disadvantage of time-series analysis when applied to forecasting might be that in certain cases the resulting *forecast model* used to predict future events may be of such mathematical complexity as to make it rejectable by confused management, even though it has the ability to forecast within the proverbial gnat's eyebrow. This would not be a problem in certain systems forecasting situations, such as a computer-actuated automatic control device, but it certainly could be detrimental in a sales forecasting environment where decisions have to be made based on the forecasts, and therefore, underlying reasons behind the forecasts have to be known. An obvious offshoot of this is that forecasting is frequently made from a somewhat intuitive approach. Logically, a *new* product's sales cannot be known by analyzing past sales. Correlating expected sales to similar products' past histories is one way out of this dilemma. Surveying the potential market is certainly another. The point to be made is that even though this chapter will be concerned with time-series forecasting due to its systems applicability, other simpler techniques might be available for certain conditions.

In order to clarify this a little further, four categories of forecasting, not all-encompassing, might be:

1. Committee agreement
2. Market survey
3. Time-series analysis
4. Correlation analysis

The first two might be examples of forecasting where little or no back data are available. The latter two would be examples where mathematical trends would be evaluated.

Committee Agreement.   In sales prediction, it certainly is reasonable to go to that source closest to the demand to determine sales expectations.   This would usually be the *marketing* group.   Sales personnel in the field make estimates of demand for products within their field of responsibility and within their geographical region. The individual estimates are then pooled by management at the home office and a forecast is made.   The advantages for this approach are clear-cut.   Those persons most knowledgeable about consumer needs make the forecast—at least the initial forecast.   It also has a relatively rapid evolvement.

The main disadvantage would seem to accrue as a result of the sales personnel being too close to the problem.   They would tend to overlook *environmental* conditions which could cloud overall sales. A competitor going out of business, impending strikes, general business economic trends, and utilization of existing facilities for an unrelated new product are all examples of conditions that affect *overall* sales, but may not be apparent to each and every salesman making his prediction.   Needless to say, it is management's responsibility to adjust the accumulated estimates in light of the environmental conditions. A further compounding of the problem may accrue from bias inherent in each of the estimators.   If regional sales quotas are set on the basis of the forecast, the estimates would tend to be low in order to insure meeting the quotas.   Maintaining past records of individual forecasts versus actual demand will allow a reasonable bias correction procedure to be developed.

Market Survey.   Before bringing a new product onto the market, the market survey method is frequently used to estimate potential demand for a product.   This procedure is also utilized to assist in developing design characteristics according to sampled customer

requirements. Two *reputed* automobile examples convey possible
patterns where customer whims are considered. Shortly after World
War II an automobile company surveyed design characteristics wanted
in an automobile by the American public. The response indicated
that a rocket-shaped car would be most acceptable. This was produced,
with a cone-shaped front and a similar trunk. The car, in styling,
was ahead of its time and the Studebaker hit rough times. A counter-
example is the automobile company that radically *assumed* customer
requisites without a survey. The Edsel had troubles similar to that of
the Studebaker. It is doubtful whether any major automobile will
ever be produced again with new design characteristics without a
market survey.

It should be mentioned that the market survey approach is also very
useful as a data-gathering technique for statistical analysis. One
should always go to the *ultimate* source of data in prediction. For
example, a wholesaler may carry significant inventories for long periods
of time, but the only way to know true seasonal or cyclic trends is to
determine actual sales movement at the consumer level. The average
length of time a product takes from manufacture to actual sale can be
evaluated, thus giving desired cycle production rates. This relationship
is depicted in Figure 3-1 with production preceding consumer requirements by two time periods, which represents the delay from production
to consumption.

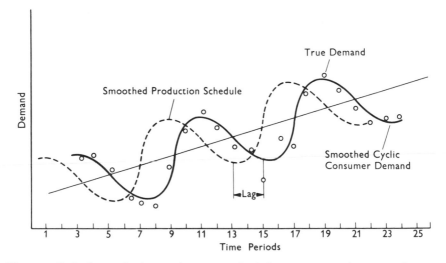

Figure 3–I. Smoothed production schedule corresponding to known
production/consumption lag of two time periods.

Time-Series Analysis. Mathematically analyzing back data to determine underlying data trends under the assumption that such trends will continue in the immediate future is a function of time-series analysis. A typical example would be in missile tracking. Future positions of a missile for possible destructive purposes can only be determined from its immediate past flight characteristics, unless of course a specific target for the missile has been determined. *Time-series analysis* forecasting will allow future positions of the missile to be ascertained even though anti-tracking maneuvers are undertaken. The objective of time-series analysis forecasting, as will be determined in the latter sections of this chapter, will be to respond to process changes such as anti-tracking or zig-zagging and yet damp out noise characteristics such as wind deflections or air pockets. If the zig-zagging has random characteristics, an objective would be to damp out these characteristics to determine the real underlying direction characteristics.

Correlation Analysis. In certain forecasting situations, it is found that future forecasts of a particular characteristic are not directly related to the historical values of that characteristic. An example is prediction of student enrollment in universities located in rapid-growth sections of the country; for instance, Arizona State University— whose approximate enrollment history is given in Table 3-1 and plotted in Figure 3-2. The enrollment plot from Figure 3-2 looks quite linear, possibly fit by the expression $[2000 + (1560)(t)]$ with t the number of years from 1953. If this had been used, the predicted enrollments for 1967, 1968, and 1969 would have been 21,840, 23,400, and 24,960 respectively. The errors would have been 1,839 for 1967; 1,960 for 1968; and 2,010 for 1969. The errors would have been less than 10 percent in each case, but in all cases they would have been *low*. From a university budgeting point or view, this would have been disastrous as appropriations are based on expected (and justified) enrollments. Another interesting point is: What would the expected enrollment be for 1975? Plugging in the linear equation pops out a figure of 36,320 students. There are many reasons why this could be unreasonable. As enrollment grows, the tendency increases to make entrance requirements tighter to curtail future enrollment. Out-of-state tuition seems to grow for the same reason. Also, constraints may be put on enrollment by the legislature of, say 30,000 students, as that may be considered the maximum number of students reasonable to manage in one facility. The moral of the story thus far is that the requirements for the forecast and the environment should be considered.

Table 3-1

Historical Enrollment
Figures at Arizona
State University

Year	Enrollment
1953-54	4,876
1954-55	5,258
1955-56	6,394
1956-57	7,745
1957-58	9,677
1958-59	11,702
1959-60	12,296
1960-61	12,913
1961-62	14,418
1962-63	16,024
1963-64	18,439
1964-65	20,090
1965-66	22,927
1966-67	23,679
1967-68	25,360
1968-69	26,970

*Source: Enrollment Summary
for the Academic Year 1968-69;*
Publication of the Registrar and
Director of Admissions, Arizona
State University, Tempe, Arizona.
August 1, 1969.

In the university forecasting case, accuracy is paramount and some means other than time-series prediction would be desirable.

Consider that a relationship with something other than historical data might be logical. In university enrollment growth, it would seem reasonable that population and economic growth of the state should be related to enrollment, perhaps with some lag in time. One possible sequence of data that might have correlation with enrollment is that of bank deposits. In an interesting study made by the American Can Company[2] to forecast beer consumption in the home for 1965, it was found that the amount spent on beer increased with income up to the $8000 level. Also, with respect to consumption in the home, growth is a function of home ownership trends. Combining these factors with estimates of population growth from the Bureau of Census projections forms the principal components of the company's forecast of home beer consumption. This is shown graphically in Figure 3-3.

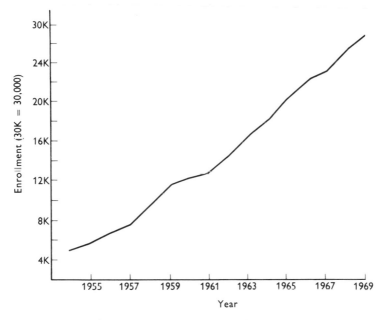

Figure 3–2. Plot of enrollment data given in Table 3–I.

The major problem with the correlation approach to forecasting is the determination of data that will correlate effectively with the data to be forecasted. In some cases this would be a common sense item. With university enrollment forecasting it is intuitive that enrollment should be correlated to regional growth and that a measure of regional growth would be bank deposit trends. Similarly it is logical that per capita home consumption of beer is correlated to the trends in home ownership and is also a function of the income characteristics of home owners. Another almost intuitive result of the beer consumption/income characteristic relationship was that beer consumption increased until an income level of $8,000 was reached and then declined. This trend could have been predicted (but *not* the dollar figure) on the theory that the more affluent the family, the stronger the tendency to prefer hard liquor to beer.

3–3. TIME-SERIES ANALYSIS—AN INTRODUCTION

The remainder of this chapter will be concerned with the specific topic of *time-series analysis* as it applies to forecasting future events based on historical data-trend evaluations. This will only be an

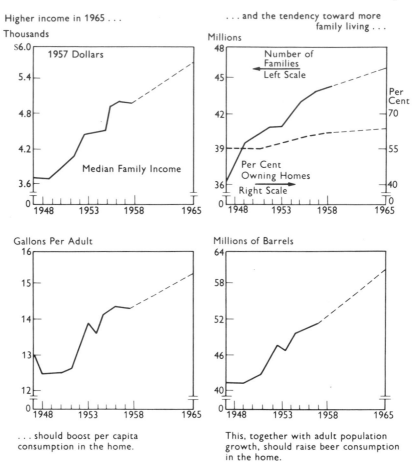

Higher income in 1965 . . .

. . . and the tendency toward more family living . . .

. . . should boost per capita consumption in the home.

This, together with adult population growth, should raise beer consumption in the home.

Figure 3–3. Components of beer consumption in the home forecast. (Courtesy of the Industrial Conference Board.)

introduction to time-series analysis, a fascinating subject which could fill one or more books.* If one is to find one forecasting approach that is truly *systems* oriented, it has to be that of *time-series* prediction. Process control, sales forecasting, population characteristics, flight control, quality control, and whole blood transfusion to combat massive hemorrhage are just a few of many cases where some facet of time-series prediction can be utilized beneficially.

Time-series analysis, with regard to prediction, can be classified as a curve-fitting technique. Assuming that characteristics of the

* For example, *Time Series Analysis Papers* by Emanuel Parzen, Holden-Day, Inc., San Francisco, California, 1967.

curve fit will continue, the curve is extended into the future for predictive purposes. For example, if past data indicates that the linear
equation $\hat{Y} = a + bt$ seems to be a reasonable fit, then a prediction of
Y for $t = 9$ would be $\hat{Y} = a + 9b$.

Unfortunately, life is not usually linear. This is probably lucky,
otherwise forecasting would be a rather dull, non-challenging task.
According to the National Industrial Conference Board, company
sales are usually affected by three basic factors: long-term growth
trends, cyclical business fluctuations, and seasonal variations.[2] Random
fluctuations about the composite of these factors clouds the pictorial
trend. In this text, these random fluctuations will be referred to as
noise or *noisy conditions*. The problem in time-series prediction, then,
is to determine all the additive trends that exist in a set of data even
though noise may be present. Such a condition is shown in Figure
3–4, which is plotted from data given in Table 3-2.

The *objectives* for time-series forecasting are to: (1) evaluate significant trends in historical data, (2) damp out noise in the data, (3)
dynamically respond to *true* changes in demand as they occur, (4)
project trends to the required future period for which forecasting is
required, and (5) perform these objectives with optimum forecast
parameters. The first two objectives define the curve-fitting function
required in time-series forecasting. The simplest forecast procedure
for time-series forecasting is the moving average where noise is damped

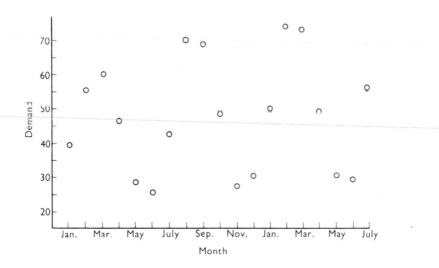

Figure 3–4. Additive trend pattern (plotted from Table 3–2 data.)

Table 3-2

Additive Trend Data

Month	Demand ($\times 10^2$)
January	39
February	55
March	60
April	46
May	28
June	25
July	42
August	70
September	69
October	48
November	27
December	30
January	50
February	74
March	73
April	49
May	30
June	29
July	56

by averaging several pieces of data. By updating the average sequentially with each new piece of data while dropping off the oldest value, it follows that true process changes can gradually be tracked. The average is then used as the forecast for future values. Holding a value of one piece of data in each average means that the average will respond 100 percent to noise as well as true demand changes with resultant wide fluctuations in forecast. Conversely, if ten pieces of data are held in the average only one-tenth of a noisy piece of data will be reflected in the forecast. Unfortunately, if a step change occurs in the data then 100 percent response to the change will not be reflected for ten periods, as shown in Figure 3–5.

The response to true changes in the demand data is attained by dynamically representing the process as new data are obtained. The *moving* average accomplishes this by the addition of the newest piece of the data to the average while at the same time dropping off the oldest

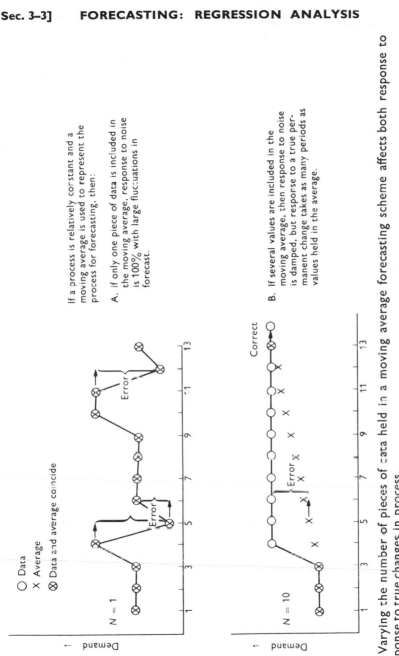

If a process is relatively constant and a moving average is used to represent the process for forecasting, then:

A. If only one piece of data is included in the moving average, response to noise is 100% with large fluctuations in forecast.

B. If several values are included in the moving average, then response to noise is damped, but response to a true permanent change takes as many periods as values held in the average.

Figure 3–5. Varying the number of pieces of data held in a moving average forecasting scheme affects both response to noise and response to true changes in process.

piece held in the previous average. The last two objectives, projecting trends and determining optimum forecast parameters, will be discussed in light of specific forecast techniques when these techniques are discussed.

3–4. TIME-SERIES FORECAST PROCEDURE

A logical sequence of steps should be followed when forecasting through time-series analysis.

1. Plot the data and visually determine any obvious time-series characteristics.

2. If a growth factor such as a polynomial or an exponential is apparent, remove it from the data.

3. Determine if a significant cyclic trend is present. This may be discernible from step 1; but, if not, then evaluate with a mathematical method—possibly autocorrelation or spectral analysis. An introduction to autocorrelation analysis is given in Chapter 4 for this purpose. If a cyclic pattern in obtained and fitted, remove it from the original data.

4. Now evaluate the growth factor from the original data from which any cyclic effects have been removed. Initially run a rough check as to the type of growth, such as order of polynomial or exponential. This will be discussed in the immediately subsequent sections.

5. After a rough determination of the order of the growth equation, fit the data by some acceptable method: least-squares regression or exponential smoothing, for example. These two topics will be discussed in Sections 3–8 and 4–1.

6. A forecast for the future will consist of the *addition* of cyclic and growth trends—both extended to the future time period. This will be covered in Chapter 4.

7. Continually update the equation of fit as new data are added, on the basis that new data will constitute a better representation of current demand trends than older data. It also allows a dynamic tracking of process changes to be achieved while damping out random fluctuations that exist around the underlying trends.

One paradoxical condition arises if cyclical and growth characteristics are both present in the data and a *dynamic* fit of the data is desired. In order to find the cyclic characteristics it is advisable to first remove growth effects. In order to accurately solve the growth equation, it is advantageous to first remove the cyclic effects. (Obviously, one has to be done before the other.) A rough estimation of a growth pattern could be made in step 1, and the results of this estimation are then removed from the data. Any cyclic effects are then fitted. These effects are then removed from the original or raw data. Also, if a cyclic trend is superimposed on a polynomial then the cycle will be treated like noise and the resultant fit will be a polynomial. Therefore, one way to find the growth trend in a mixed model is to attack all the data with a least-squares fit, assuming the growth trend is the only one present. Lastly, growth patterns are fitted as accurately as economically feasible. If a *static* or one-shot fit of the data is required, the least-squares approach could be used to fit a composite growth and trigonometric function. The problem with *fast* update is the time that would be taken in such a fit.

3–5. GROWTH CHARACTERISTICS

The most general growth equation used in forecasting is the polynomial of the basic form

$$\hat{Y}(t) = a + bt + ct^2 + \cdots + gt^{n-1} + ht^n \tag{3-1}$$

for an nth-order polynomial, where $\hat{Y}(t)$ is the estimated value of $Y(t)$ at time period t and $a, b \ldots, h$ are fitted coefficients of the polynomial.

Truncating later terms allows several familiar curve-fitting equations to be evolved:

1. $\hat{Y}(t) = a$: fit is simple *average* $\tag{3-2}$

2. $\hat{Y}(t) = a + bt$: *linear* fit with *slope b* $\tag{3-3}$

3. $\hat{Y}(t) = a + bt + ct^2$: *quadratic* fit with slope b and change of slope c $$\tag{3-4}$$

The growth characteristics that will be considered will be limited to Equations 3–2 through 3–4. The same approach could be utilized for higher-order polynomials, although the approach that will be utilized will be to fit the *highest expected-order* equation, in our case Equation 3–4, and show how the subsequent lower-order equations will evolve if the data are applicable.

The approach of fitting the *highest-order* polynomial negates the need to estimate the order of polynomial equation to be fit. If, however, only the *known correct* polynomial is to be fit, an estimate of that polynomial must be initially made. Since this is frequently desired, a procedure for roughly estimating the order will be given.

Considering a third-order polynomial, for example, and taking successive derivatives of $\hat{Y}(t)$ with respect to t, where $\hat{Y}^i(t)$ denotes the ith derivative, then the successive derivatives will be:

1. $\hat{Y}^0(t) = a + bt + ct^2 + dt^3$
2. $\hat{Y}^1(t) = b + 2ct + 3dt^2$
3. $\hat{Y}^2(t) = 1 \cdot 2c + 2 \cdot 3dt$
4. $\hat{Y}^3(t) = 1 \cdot 2 \cdot 3d$
5. $\hat{Y}^4(t) = 0$

It can inductively be seen that for an nth-order polynomial, the $(n + 1)$st derivative will equal zero. Also, it will be found that the nth derivative will give the coefficient of the nth-order polynomial, multiplied by $n!$. Knowing that the derivatives are changes with respect to time, it follows that if *successive differences* of the data are taken and if the data exactly fit an nth-order polynomial then the $(n + 1)$st difference (of the differences) will equal zero and the nth difference will equal the nth coefficient multiplied by $n!$. If this coefficient and its power of t, $a_n t^n$, are subtracted out of the data, then the resultant residual can again be analyzed by differences to get the next lower-order coefficient.

Example. Consider the noise-free data given in Table 3–3.

Of course, the t values can be chosen to facilitate the analysis, and choosing $t = 0$ to occur for the first piece of data forces the first coefficient in the polynomial, a, to be 12.0.* This is because Equation 3–1 evolves to $\hat{Y}(0) = a$, for $t = 0$. Knowing that a is 12 lets this *constant* value be pulled out from each $Y(t)$ value as that portion of the polynomial is now known. The residual will now be analyzed by successive differences Δ^i, where Δ^1 refers to the first difference, Δ^2 to the difference of the differences, and so on, as given in the table.

From the initial difference table it can be seen that a third-order polynomial term is significant. The third difference gives the third-order coefficient such that $d = \Delta^3/3! = 3/(3 \cdot 2 \cdot 1) = 0.5$. The third term of the polynomial is now known to be $0.5t^3$. This can now be subtracted from $[Y(t) - 12]$ in the initial difference table giving a second residual to be fit, with results as shown in Table 3–3.

---

* With noisy data never estimate the coefficient a with the value of Y at time zero. That value of Y might be very noisy and then the fit would be biased by that noise.

Table 3-3

Method-of-Differences Example

A. Original Data

t	Y(t)
0	12.0
1	14.5
2	20.0
3	31.5
4	52.0
5	84.5
6	132.0

B. First Residual Differences

t	Y(t)	Residual $[Y(t) - 12]$	Δ^1	Δ^2	Δ^3	Δ^4
0	12.0	0				
1	14.5	2.5	2.5			
2	20.0	8.0	5.5	3.0		
3	31.5	19.5	11.5	6.0	3.0	
4	52.0	40.0	20.5	9.0	3.0	0
5	84.5	72.5	32.5	12.0	3.0	0
6	132.0	120.0	47.5	15.0	3.0	0

C. Second Residual Differences

t	$[Y(t) - 12]$	Residual $[Y(t) - 12 - 0.5t^3]$	Δ^1	Δ^2
0	0	0		
1	2.5	2.0	2.0	
2	8.0	4.0	2.0	0
3	19.5	6.0	2.0	0
4	40.0	8.0	2.0	0
5	72.5	10.0	2.0	0
6	120.0	12.0	2.0	0

Table 3-4

Differences for Noisy Data

t	Y(t)	Δ^1	Δ^2
0	21.0		
1	27.0	6.0	
2	32.0	5.0	−1.0
3	38.0	6.0	1.0
4	43.0	5.0	−1.0
5	47.0	4.0	−1.0
6	52.0	5.0	1.0

The fact that the second difference is zero tells us that there is no ct^2 term in our fit. The first-order coefficient, b, is of course 2, and the complete polynomial fit is

$$\hat{Y}(t) = 12 + 2t + 0.5t^3$$

Using a test value of $t = 4$, it is found that

$$\hat{Y}(4) = 12 + (2)(4) + (0.5)(4)^3 = 52,$$

which corresponds to the original data at $t = 4$.

This procedure is highly satisfactory for noise-free polynomial data as the difference tables will give the *exact* polynomial fit. The rough determination of the order of polynomial is made, however, to evaluate prevalent trends in *noisy* data. For noisy data the $(n + 1)$st difference will *not* be zero for an nth-order polynomial. However, the $(n + 1)$st differences will *approach* an *average* value of zero, and the *average* of the nth differences will *approach* the nth coefficient when this average is divided by n-factorial. Therefore, in order to obtain a cut-off point in taking differences, an *allowable departure*, say ϵ^Δ, will have to be permitted from zero for the $(n + 1)$st difference. For example, consider the difference data given in Table 3–4.

The average of the Δ^2 values is $(-1)/5$, or -0.2. If, for example, a difference value between -0.5 and $+0.5$ is considered a reasonable departure from zero and yet can be considered zero, then a first-order polynomial could be assumed with b being an average of the Δ^1 values, which gives $31/6$ or 5.2. Subsequent difference values, such as Δ^3 or Δ^4, could be taken but the contribution of coefficients c and d would be negligible. However, if a more powerful fit of the data than the linear fit were required, then these terms would have to be considered. The complexity of adding more terms to the fitting equation has to be weighed against the benefit of added accuracy.

3–6. FALLACY IN METHOD-OF-DIFFERENCES FIT

A considerable problem arises when the method of differences is used to fit a polynomial. For example, Table 3–5 shows what happens with a first difference for the noisy data just considered in Section 3–5.

The sum of first differences is seen to be the last data value minus the initial piece of data. The slope estimate would be

$$\frac{Y_{(6)} - Y_{(0)}}{N - 1}$$

This is of course how we frequently *guestimate* slopes through data. It points out, though, that noisy initial or final data values would have a traumatic effect. However, for quadratic fits or less it has been found by Shweid* that the method-of-differences fit would realize the following for a quadratic fit, $Y_{(t)} = a + bt + ct^2$:

$$c = \frac{Y_{(T)} - Y_{(T-1)} - Y_{(T_0+1)} + Y_{(T_0)}}{2(T - 1 - T_0)} \tag{3–5}$$

$$b = \frac{Y_{(T)} - Y_{(T_0)} - c(T^2 - T_0^2)}{(T - T_0)} \tag{3–6}$$

$$a = \frac{\sum_{t=T_0}^{T} Y_{(t)} - b \sum_{t=T_0}^{T} t - c \sum_{t=T_0}^{T} t^2}{(T + 1 - T_0)} \tag{3–7}$$

Table 3-5

First-Difference Cumulative Sum

t	$Y(t)$	Δ^1	Cumulative Addition of Δ^1 Values
0	21.0		
1	27.0	27.0 – 21.0	
2	32.0	32.0 – 27.0	32.0 – 27.0 + 27.0 – 21.0
3	38.0	38.0 – 32.0	38.0 – 32.0 + 32.0 – 21.0
4	43.0	43.0 – 38.0	43.0 – 38.0 + 38.0 – 21.0
5	47.0	47.0 – 43.0	47.0 – 43.0 + 43.0 – 21.0
6	52.0	52.0 – 47.0	52.0 – 47.0 + 47.0 – 21.0
21.0	260.0		

* Shweid, G. B., "Simplified Formulas for Method of Differences Analysis." Senior Project in Development of Design, Faculty of Industrial Engineering, Arizona State University, Tempe, Arizona. 17 May 1971.

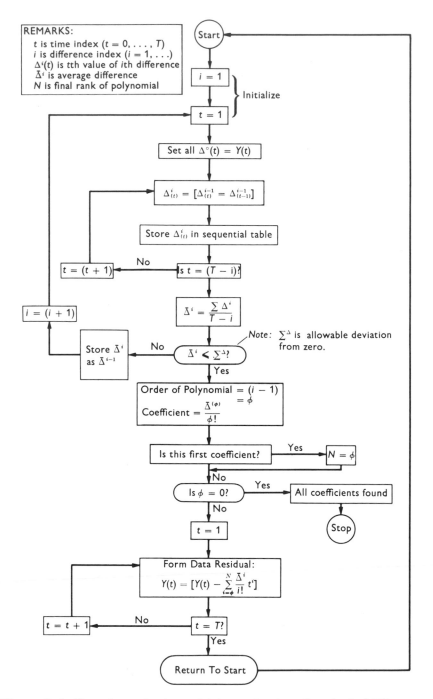

Figure 3–6. Flow chart of polynomial determination of method of differences.

where $Y_{(T)}$ = most recent value of data

$Y_{(T_0)}$ = initial value of dàta.

For N pieces of data

$$\sum_{t=1}^{N} t = \frac{(N)(N+1)}{2} \tag{3-8}$$

and

$$\sum_{t=1}^{N} t^2 = \left(\frac{N}{6}\right)(2N+1)(N+1) \tag{3-9}$$

Assuming a linear fit for the data in Table 3–5 we set c in Equations 3–5 through 3–7 to zero and find

$$b = \frac{Y_{(T)} - Y_{(T_0)}}{(T - T_0)} = \frac{52 - 21}{6 - 0} = \frac{31}{6} = 5.2$$

a, from Equation 3–7, realizes

$$a = \frac{260 - (b)(21)}{6 + 1 - 0} = \frac{260 - (5.2)(21)}{7}$$

$$a = \frac{260 - 109.2}{7} = \frac{150.8}{7} \doteq 21.5$$

And the methods-of-difference fit would be

$$Y_{(T)} = 21.5 + (5.2)(t)$$

For a fit higher than a second-order polynomial then the traditional differences process would have to be followed as shown in Figure 3–6. The fact that *not all the data* is utilized in the fit indicates that a technique such as *least-squares regression* would be more beneficial for quite noisy data.

3–7. EXPONENTIAL DATA

As an aside, since only polynomial data will be considered as growth data in this text, the difference table can be utilized for determining if an exponential fit may be more logical.

A simple exponential fit can be defined by the equation

$$\hat{Y}(t) = (C)(R)^t \tag{3-10}$$

where C denotes a constant coefficient and R indicates a constant *ratio* between successive data points, rather than differences, as in

Table 3-6

Difference and Ratio Table for Exponential Data

A. Exponential Differences

t	Y(t)	Δ^1	Δ^2	Δ^3	Δ^4	Δ^5
0	10					
1	20	10				
2	40	20	10			
3	80	40	20	10		
4	160	80	40	20	10	
5	320	160	80	40	20	10
6	640	320	160	80	40	20
7	1280	640	320	160	80	40

B. Exponential Ratios

t	Y(t)	Y(t)/Y(t-1)
0	10	
1	20	2
2	40	2
3	80	2
4	160	2
5	320	2
6	640	2
7	1280	2

the polynomial. If exponential data are analyzed in a difference table it is found that the *diagonal* differences will be a *multiple* of the previous difference values rather than moving to a subsequent decrease, as it is with polynomial differences. It will be found that this multiplication factor plus 1 equals the ratio R in Equation 3–10. In the Table 3–6 example this multiplication factor is 1 (40 to 40, etc.), so R is 2, as indicated in the later ratio check. Since $Y(t) = 10$ occurs at $t = 0$, it follows that the data can be fitted by the equation

$$\hat{Y}(t) = (10)(2)^t$$

from Equation 3–10, as predicted earlier from the difference table.

3–8. REGRESSION ANALYSIS

If it is possible to take derivatives of the fitting parameters of an equation then it is possible to fit data with that equation using the least-squares procedure of regression analysis. In this section, a quadratic polynomial equation will be analyzed by the least-squares procedure, and then all lower-order polynomial equations will be evaluated from this second-order fit. A third- or fourth-order polynomial could just as easily have been the starting point, but for academic use the quadratic will be the initial one considered. In some respects, in forecasting, it may not be desirable to utilize more than a second-order polynomial growth fit. As indicated in the method-of-differences discussion, each coefficient is a derivative function and successively higher-order coefficients will be smaller and smaller in a true polynomial fit. If this statement is not obvious, think about the fact that the nth coefficient was found by dividing the nth difference by $n!$. A fourth difference would be divided by 24 and a fifth difference by 120, resulting in coefficients that may well not contribute very much to the end prediction. A balance, therefore, as mentioned several times, has to be set between the accuracy possible and the computational complexity required to get that accuracy.

The second-order polynomial that will be analyzed is

$$\hat{Y}(t) = a + bt + ct^2 \tag{3–11}$$

$\hat{Y}(t)$ is used rather than the true value $Y(t)$ as the fitted equation gives an *estimate* of demand values at a point in time, t. If the data are plotted and Equation 3–11 is assumed to be the equation of fit, then it is apparent that an error term, $\epsilon(t)$, appears as the difference between the fitted line $\hat{Y}(t)$ and the data $Y(t)$ This is shown for Equation 3–11 in Figure 3–7.

The plan of attack is to minimize some function, $f[\epsilon(t)]$, of the $\epsilon(t)$ value. The first logical approach might be to force the sum of $\epsilon(t)$ for all demand values to zero:

$$f[\epsilon(t)] = \sum_{t=1}^{N} [Y(t) - \hat{Y}(t)] = 0 \tag{3–12}$$

The problem with this is that the value of $\hat{Y}(t)$ that accomplishes this expression is as follows:

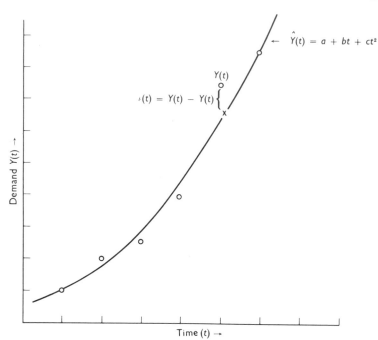

Figure 3–7. Development of error term, $\epsilon(t)$, in least-squares regression.

Expanding Equation 3–12 gives

$$f[\epsilon(t)] = \sum_{t=1}^{N}[Y(t)] - \sum_{t=1}^{N}\hat{Y}(t) = 0$$

and

$$\hat{Y}(t) = \sum_{t=1}^{N}\frac{[Y(t)]}{N} = \bar{Y}(t)$$

The value of $\hat{Y}(t)$ that zeroes $f[\epsilon(t)]$ is $\bar{Y}(t)$ and many lines fitting $\hat{Y}(t)$ would qualify as the "best" fit.

A way out of this dilemma would be to take the sum of the *absolute* values of $\epsilon(t)$, but this would be mathematically cumbersome. The usual approach is to square the $\epsilon(t)$ terms, such that

$$f[\epsilon(t)] = \sum_{t=1}^{N}[Y(t) - \hat{Y}(t)]^2 \qquad (3\text{--}13)$$

with the objective being to find the line $\hat{Y}(t)$ that minimizes $f[\varepsilon(t)]$. For a polynomial, this is accomplished by taking the partial derivatives of the coefficients in $\hat{Y}(t)$, setting each partial derivative solution to zero and solving the resultant equations simultaneously for the coefficients.* It seems a little unusual at first glance to take derivatives of *constants* but it should be remembered that a whole family of possible coefficients exists, and until the optimum $Y(t)$ is obtained, the coefficients may be thought of as *variables*.

Taking the partials of Equation 3–13 with respect to a, b, and c reveals

$$f[\epsilon(t)] = \sum_{t=1}^{N} [Y(t) - a - bt - ct^2]^2$$

$$\frac{\partial f[\epsilon(t)]}{\partial a} = -2 \sum_{t=1}^{N} [Y(t) - a - bt - ct^2]$$

$$\frac{\partial f[\epsilon(t)]}{\partial b} = -2 \sum_{t=1}^{N} t[Y(t) - a - bt - ct^2]$$

$$\frac{\partial f[\epsilon(t)]}{\partial c} = -2 \sum_{t=1}^{N} t^2[Y(t) - a - bt - ct^2]$$

When setting each equation to zero, it is possible to remove the 2 in each case. Also, for convenience, the minus sign will be removed by interchanging the $Y(t)$ and the coefficient terms:

$$\sum_{t=1}^{N} [a + bt + ct^2 - Y(t)] = 0 \qquad (3\text{–}14)$$

$$\sum_{t=1}^{N} t[a + bt + ct^2 - Y(t)] = 0 \qquad (3\text{–}15)$$

$$\sum_{t=1}^{N} t^2[a + bt + ct^2 - Y(t)] = 0 \qquad (3\text{–}16)$$

Knowing that the sum of a series of sums equals the sum of the individual components, Equations 3–14 through 3–16 may be rewritten:

$$aN + b \sum_{t=1}^{N} t + c \sum_{t=1}^{N} t^2 - \sum_{t=1}^{N} Y(t) = 0 \qquad (3\text{–}17)$$

$$a \sum_{t=1}^{N} t + b \sum_{t=1}^{N} t^2 + c \sum_{t=1}^{N} t^3 - \sum_{t=1}^{N} tY(t) = 0 \qquad (3\text{–}18)$$

$$a \sum_{t=1}^{N} t^2 + b \sum_{t=1}^{N} t^3 + c \sum_{t=1}^{N} t^4 - \sum_{t=1}^{N} t^2 Y(t) = 0 \qquad (3\text{–}19)$$

---

* This multi-variable optimization (minimization) approach is discussed briefly in Chapter 5.

If we consider the first three terms of Equations 3–17 through 3–19 as a 3 × 3 matrix, an obvious symmetrical pattern arises:

$$
\begin{bmatrix}
aN & b \sum_{t=1}^{N} t & c \sum_{t=1}^{N} t^2 \\
a \sum_{t=1}^{N} t & b \sum_{t=1}^{N} t^2 & c \sum_{t=1}^{N} t^3 \\
a \sum_{t=1}^{N} t^2 & b \sum_{t=1}^{N} t^3 & c \sum_{t=1}^{N} t^4
\end{bmatrix}
$$

If only the top-left term, aN, is considered as a 1×1 matrix and recombined with $-\sum_{t=1}^{N} Y(t)$, it forms

$$
aN - \sum_{t=1}^{N} Y(t)
$$

and if set to zero,

$$
a = \sum_{t=1}^{N} \frac{Y(t)}{N} \tag{3–20}
$$

Equation 3–20 is the solution to a 0-order polynomial with the result that the best fit is an average of the Y values.

Similarly, if the top-left 2×2 matrix only is considered and recombined with $- Y(t)\, t^i$, where i is 0 or 1 as in Equations 3–17 and 3–18, then the following results:

$$
aN + b \sum_{t=1}^{N} t - \sum_{t=1}^{N} Y(t) = 0
$$

$$
a \sum_{t=1}^{N} t + b \sum_{t=1}^{N} t^2 - \sum_{t=1}^{N} t Y(t) = 0
$$

and solving for a and b gives

$$
a = \bar{Y} - b\bar{t} \tag{3–21}
$$

$$
b = \frac{N \sum_{t=1}^{N} t Y(t) - \sum_{t=1}^{N} Y(t) \sum_{t=1}^{N} t}{N \sum_{t=1}^{N} (t)^2 - \left[\sum_{t=1}^{N} (t) \right]^2} \tag{3–22}
$$

These are two common *linear* regression equations for a first-order polynomial.

Conversely, if Equations 3–17 through 3–19 are expanded to include a d coefficient such that the d in each case is multiplied by a $\sum_{t=1}^{N} t^i$

term, such that i is one order higher than the highest i now existing in each equation, then the equations for a third-order polynomial are derived. Of course, one extra equation with a, b, c, and d is needed. This process can be continued to as high a polynomial fit as required.

Simultaneous equation solution of Equations 3–17 through 3–19 is algebraically messy but has a result as follows: If:

1. $\alpha = \sum\limits_{t=1}^{N} t \sum\limits_{t=1}^{N} t^2 - N \sum\limits_{t=1}^{N} t^3$

2. $\beta = \left(\sum\limits_{t=1}^{N} t\right)^2 - N \sum\limits_{t=1}^{N} t^2$

3. $\gamma = \left(\sum\limits_{t=1}^{N} t^2\right)^2 - N \sum\limits_{t=1}^{N} t^4$

4. $\delta = \sum\limits_{t=1}^{N} t \sum\limits_{t=1}^{N} Y(t) - N \sum\limits_{t=1}^{N} t\, Y(t)$

5. $\theta = \sum\limits_{t=1}^{N} t^2 \sum\limits_{t=1}^{N} Y(t) - N \sum\limits_{t=1}^{N} t^2 Y(t)$

Then it will be found that

$$b = \frac{\gamma \delta - \theta \alpha}{\gamma \beta - \alpha^2} \tag{3–23}$$

$$c = \frac{\theta - (b)(\alpha)}{\gamma} \tag{3–24}$$

$$a = \bar{Y} - (b)(\bar{t}) - \frac{(c) \sum\limits_{t=1}^{N} t^2}{N} \tag{3–25}$$

Solving for the coefficients in the sequence given in Equations 3–23 through 3–25 will result in the quadratic equation least-squares fit.

3–9. REGRESSION EXAMPLE

Consider the data vector [10 16 24 34 46] for t values of 0 through 4. The tabular values needed for coefficient solution are given in Table 3–7. Solving for α, β, γ, δ, and θ gives

$\alpha = (10)(30) - (5)(100) = -200$

$\beta = (10)^2 - (5)(30) = -50$

$\gamma = (30)^2 - (5)(354) = -870$

$\delta = (10)(130) - (5)(350) = -450$

$\theta = (30)(130) - (5)(1154) = -1870$

Table 3-7

Tabular Values for Quadratic Fit

t	t^2	t^3	t^4	$Y(t)$	$tY(t)$	$t^2 Y(t)$
0	0	0	0	10	0	0
1	1	1	1	16	16	16
2	4	8	16	24	48	96
3	9	27	81	34	102	306
4	16	64	256	46	184	736
$\sum\limits_{t=0}^{4}:$ 10	30	100	354	130	350	1154

And solving Equations 3–23 through 3–25 sequentially gives

1. $b = \dfrac{(-870)(-450) - (-1870)(-200)}{(-870)(-50) - (-200)^2} = 5$

2. $c = \dfrac{(-1870) - (5)(-200)}{-870} = 1$

3. $a = \dfrac{130}{5} - \dfrac{(5)(10)}{5} - \dfrac{30}{5} = 10$

And the polynomial fit is

$$\hat{Y}(t) = 10 + 5t + t^2 \qquad (3\text{--}26)$$

Time period 4 in the original data had $Y(4) = 46$. Checking Equation 3–26 for $t = 4$, we get $\hat{Y}(4) = 10 + (5)(4) + (4)^2 = 46$, which checks exactly. It should as the given data were noise-free.

Suppose the data had been linear, rather than quadratic. Would the fit eliminate quadratic effects? Take the quadratic data just

Table 3-8

Tabular Data for Quadratic Linear Data

t	t^2	t^3	t^4	$Y(t)$	$tY(t)$	$t^2 Y(t)$
0	0	0	0	10	0	0
1	1	1	1	15	15	15
2	4	8	16	20	40	80
3	9	27	81	25	75	225
4	16	64	256	30	120	480
10	30	100	354	100	250	800

analyzed and eliminate the t^2 term with the following residual vector, [10 15 20 25 30]. The tabular values for solution are given in Table 3–8.

Solving for α, β, γ, δ, and θ gives

1. Since α, β, and γ are not affected by $Y(t)$, they will be the same as for the quadratic fit
2. $\delta = (10)(100) - (5)(250) = -250$
3. $\theta = (30)(100) - (5)(800) = -1000$

Solving Equations 3–23 through 3–25 to get a, b, and c gives

$$b = \frac{(-870)(-250) - (-1000)(-200)}{(-870)(-50) - (-200)^2} = 5$$

$$c = \frac{(-1000) - (5)(-200)}{-870} = 0$$

$$a = \frac{100}{5} - \frac{(5)(10)}{5} - \frac{(0)(30)}{5} = 10$$

This gives a fit of $\hat{Y}(t) = 10 + 5t$ which *is* the linear fit of the given data. Similarly, if the data were constant then it would be found that the coefficients b and c would be zero. Therefore, if a computer automated system were being designed, a logical approach would be to design the curve fit for the largest polynomial growth pattern feasible, and the solution will take care of itself when lower-order fits are really the solution.

If hand fits are to be made, the partial solutions for Equations 3–17 through 3–19 would be used. If the data are relatively constant with random fluctuation, then a moving average is in order to represent the data as given in Equation 3–20 and also to project future values. The actual projection will be discussed in Chapter 4. Similarly, if the data seem to have a relatively linear growth pattern with superimposed random fluctuations, then Equations 3–21 and 3–22 would be in order.

One simplification that can be made for the linear fit that cannot be considered for the quadratic fit is coding the time data so that

$$\sum_{t=1}^{N} (t_c) = 0$$

where $t_c = [t - (N + 1)/2]$ if t runs from 1 to N. The intercept value will change but since the interval t_c to $(t + 1)_c$ is held the same as t to $(t + 1)$, it follows that the slope will remain the same. This can be shown with the linear data just considered. The values of a_c and b_c with coded data from Equations 3–21 and 3–22 would be

$$a_c = \bar{Y} \tag{3-27}$$

$$b_c = \frac{\displaystyle\sum_{t_c=\frac{1-N}{2}}^{\frac{N-1}{2}} t_c Y(t)}{\sum t_c^2}$$

The tabular values for fitting the data [10 15 20 25 30] would be as given in Table 3–9. Solving for a_c and b_c gives

$$a_c = \frac{100}{5} = 20$$

$$b_c = \frac{50}{10} = 5$$

The values calculated earlier for a and b were 10 and 5 respectively. Therefore, $b_c = b$, but $a_c \neq a$. The intercept could be corrected to the original intercept by the formula

$$a = a_c - \left[\frac{N+1}{2}\right] b \tag{3-29}$$

for original data correlated to $t = 1$ through $t = N$. Therefore, a would be

$$a = a_c - \left[\frac{N+1}{2}\right] b = 20 - (3)(5) = 5$$

Table 3-9

**Tabular Values for Fitting Linear Data
Using Coded Time Values**

t	t_c	t_c^2	$Y(t)$	$t_c Y(t)$
1	-2	4	10	-20
2	-1	1	15	-15
3	0	0	20	0
4	1	1	25	25
5	2	4	30	60
Σ	0	10	100	50

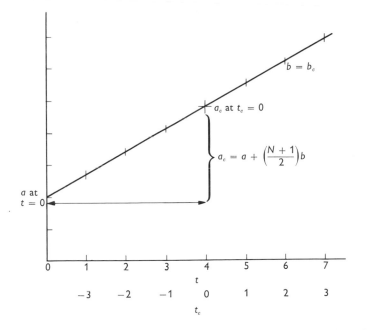

Figure 3–8. Relationship between intercept a and a_c with non-coded t linear regression and coded t linear regression.

The relationship between coded time values and non-coded is shown in Figure 3–8. The only difference is a shifting of the time axis, which can easily be corrected by Equation 3–29.

The main problem with regression analysis is the large amount of back data that might have to be maintained. The method of *exponential smoothing* will be one approach to minimize this problem, as discussed in the next chapter.

REFERENCES CITED

1. BROWN, ROBERT G. *Smoothing, Forecasting, and Prediction of Discrete Time Series.* Prentice-Hall, Inc., Englewood Cliffs, N.J., 1963.
2. *Forecasting Sales—Studies in Business Policy Number 106*, A Publication of the National Conference Board, Inc., New York, N.Y., 1964.
3. SHWEID, G. B., "Simplified Formulas for Method of Differences Analysis." Senior project in development of design, Faculty of Industrial Engineering, Arizona State University, May 17, 1971.

FURTHER READING

BROWN, Robert G. *Statistical Forecasting for Inventory Control.* McGraw-Hill Book Company, Inc., New York, N.Y., 1959.

Box, George E., and Jenkins, Gwilyn M., *Time-Series Analysis: Forecasting and Control*, Holden-Day, San Francisco, Calif., 1970.

Battersby, Albert, *Sales Forecasting*, Cassell, London, 1968.

Parzen, E. *Time Series Analysis Papers*. San Francisco: Holden-Day, Inc., 1967.

PROBLEMS

Note: Four data sets are given in the table below to be used in conjunction with certain of the time-series problems given as exercises. The data sets will be

Sample Data Sets for Problems

Month	A Constant Data Set	B Linear Data Set	C Quadratic Data Set	D Cyclic Data Set
January	996	910	905	910
February	970	982	993	820
March	1005	1075	1120	860
April	985	1140	1235	970
May	965	1210	1362	1020
June	1015	1288	1538	1030
July	991	1358	1720	890
August	998	1440	1993	780
September	973	1503	2155	770
October	1006	1580	2380	850
November	1003	1642	2610	940
December	978	1710	2905	960
January	988	1798	3290	890
February	1028	1900	3616	850
March	1011	1992	3630	870
April	1018	2003	3655	970
May	999	2098	3690	1060
June	1008	2203	3735	1000
July	1020	2299	3795	890
August	1025	2405	4175	780
September	1016	2506	4815	750
October	991	2589	4015	850
November	1010	2701	4110	930
December	1018	2805	4215	960

referred to in the specific problems as Data Set A, Data Set B, etc., with A, B, C, or D referring to the particular column headed by A, B, etc. The data are slightly noisy in each case. Data Sets A, B, and C have definite parameter shifts following the second January. Data Set D has no such process change.

1. Discuss the benefits of forecasting in a job-shop scheduling system. Conceptually, how would you design the lead-time for such a forecasting system?

2. Discuss an approach for determining how often to sample data to allow forecasting for the system in Problem 1.

3. Discuss the three "criteria for forecasting" as they affect the design of a forecast scheme for the system in Problem 1.

4. Analyze Data Set A by the "average" approach, for forecasting purposes, using the *first* 12 pieces of data only. Predict the process demand for the *third* January.

5. Do the same as in Problem 4, except base your forecast on the *last* 12 pieces of data only. In which forecast, Problem 4 or 5, would you have the most faith?

6. Analyze Data Set B with linear regression, for forecasting purposes, using the *first* 11 pieces of data. Predict the process demand for the *third* January.

7. Do the same as in Problem 6, except base your forecast on the *last* 11 pieces of data only. In which forecast would you have the most faith?

8. Analyze Data Set C for forecasting purposes with a second-order polynomial regression fit, using the first 9 pieces of data. Predict the demand for the *third* January.

9. Do the same as in Problem 8, except base your forecast on the *last* 9 pieces of data only. In which forecast would you have the most faith?

4

Forecasting: Exponential Smoothing and Cyclic Analysis

Order and simplification are the first steps toward the mastery of a subject—the actual energy is the unknown.

THOMAS MANN

4–1. GROWTH CHARACTERISTICS—EXPONENTIAL SMOOTHING*

Exponential smoothing is one of the more interesting mathematical techniques that has direct applicability to systems forecasting. The procedure has all the attributes of a moving average and yet *no demand* back data have to be held. Undoubtedly, the most significant work with exponential smoothing was accomplished by R. G. Brown.[1] Exponential smoothing will be applied to the same orders of polynomial as were considered with regression in the previous chapter, namely

* This section is based in part on original work by Robert G. Brown.[1]

quadratic through zero-order.   It is interesting to note that the same approach could be made in this section of starting with the highest order and showing that lower-order polynomial fits could be evolved. The derivation is rather complex and, therefore, an inductive approach will be utilized, starting this time with the 0-order polynomial and working up to the second-order situation. The reader who wants a further treatment should study Chapter 9 in Brown's book or study his proof of the Fundamental Theorem as it originally appeared in the *Operations Research Journal*.[2]

The equation that is the heart of exponential smoothing can be written

$$\hat{Y}(t), 1 = \alpha Y(t) + (1 - \alpha)\hat{Y}(t - 1), 1 \qquad (4-1)$$

where $\hat{Y}(t)$, 1 denotes the tth value of first-order exponential smoothing or average, $Y(t)$ is the tth demand value, and α is a smoothing constant such that $0 \leq \alpha \leq 1$.

From Equation 4-1 it can be seen that if α is 1, then $\hat{Y}(t)$, 1 = $Y(t)$. The average would be the most recent piece of data. Conversely, if α is 0, it follows that $\hat{Y}(t)$, 1 = $\hat{Y}(t - 1)$, 1. This means that the average would be the same as the previous average, with no response whatsoever to the most recent piece of data. An analogous situation exists in the conventional moving average, where all N pieces of data held in the average are weighted by $1/N$. If N is 1, then the new average would correspond exactly to the latest piece of data. If N is large, the effect of the most recent piece of data on the current average would be negligible. A moving average N of 1 then is relatable to an exponential smoothing α of 1, and one that is extremely large corresponds to an α of 0. If indeed exponential smoothing and the moving average are equivalent, it then follows that an α value between 0 and 1, tending toward 0 rather than 1, would be desirable to damp noise and yet respond to demand changes.

An interesting aspect of $\hat{Y}(t)$, 1 is that it contains some portion of all data that has been smoothed even though no back data are specifically held. This can be seen by expanding the previous values of $\hat{Y}(t)$, 1 as follows, from Equation 4-1, using $\beta = (1 - \alpha)$:

$$\hat{Y}(t), 1 = \alpha Y(t) + \beta \hat{Y}(t - 1), 1$$
$$\downarrow$$
$$\alpha\beta Y(t - 1) + \beta^2 \hat{Y}(t - 2), 1$$
$$\downarrow$$
$$\alpha\beta^2 Y(t - 2) + \beta^3 Y(t - 3), 1 + \cdots$$

which reduces to

$$\hat{Y}(t), 1 = \alpha Y(t) + \alpha\beta Y(t-1) + \alpha\beta^2 Y(t-2) + \cdots$$

and so

$$\hat{Y}(t), 1 = \alpha \sum_{i=0}^{t-1} \beta^i Y(t-i) + \beta^t \hat{Y}(0), 1 \qquad (4\text{--}2)$$

It can be seen that all past data are held in the average and that since α and β are both fractional values the data are most heavily weighted for recent values, with weights decreasing monotonically as data get older. This gives the advantage of the most recent data, which supposedly are the best data, contributing most heavily to the average. Also, the contribution of the initial smoothing estimate, $\beta^t \hat{Y}(0), 1$, will approach zero as t gets large. This means that initial inaccuracies will eventually be damped out.

If the coefficients α, $\alpha\beta$, $\alpha\beta^2$, etc., of $Y(t)$ from Equation 4–2 are summed, it is found that

$$\alpha \sum_{i=0}^{\infty} \beta^i$$

reduces to

$$\frac{\alpha}{1-\beta} = 1$$

assuming that the number of coefficients approaches infinity. This, of course, is not the case, but the sum will certainly approach 1. A fundamental criterion of a weighted average is that the weights sum to one, and so $\hat{Y}(t), 1$ has this attribute. The question to be answered, though, is: What α would be used to give an equivalent fit to that of a moving average?

It is known that when ramp data are averaged, the averages will lag the ramp by a constant amount. For example, if N values of data, $Y(T)$ through $Y(T-N+1)$, are averaged, and if the data constitute a noise-free ramp with slope b, then

$$\bar{Y}(T) = Y(T-N+1) + \frac{(b)(N-1)}{2}$$

and

$$Y(T) = Y(T-N+1) + (b)(N-1)$$

The lag is

$$Y(T) - \bar{Y}(T) = Y(T-N+1) + (b)(N-1)$$
$$- Y(T-N+1) - \left(\frac{N-1}{2}\right)(b) = \left(\frac{N-1}{2}\right)(b)$$

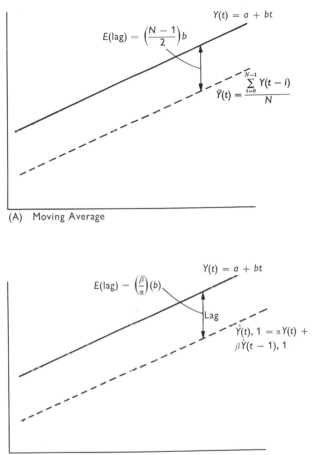

(A)   Moving Average

(B)   Exponential Smoothing

Figure 4-1. Expected lags to noise-free ramp data by a moving average and by exponential smoothing.

This lag is shown for the moving average in Figure 4-1. If a constant lag is the case for a moving average, then it would also be expected for single exponential smoothing. The fact that a *constant* lag will exist is easily shown:

From Equation 4-2:

$$\hat{Y}(t), 1 = \alpha Y(t) + \alpha\beta Y(t-1) + \alpha\beta^2 Y(t-2) + \cdots$$

Similarly:

$$\hat{Y}(t-1), 1 = \alpha Y(t-1) + \alpha\beta Y(t-2) + \alpha\beta^2 Y(t-3) + \cdots$$

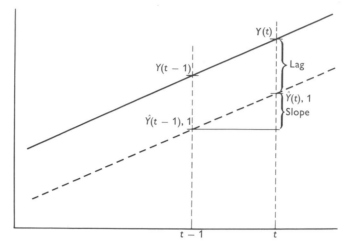

Figure 4–2. Ramp lag determination with averaging by exponential smoothing.

The *smoothing* lag characteristics can be described by

$$[\hat{Y}(t), 1 - \hat{Y}(t-1), 1] = \alpha[Y(t) - Y(t-1)] + \alpha\beta[Y(t-1)$$
$$- Y(t-2)] + \alpha\beta^2[Y(t-2)$$
$$- Y(t-3)] + \cdots$$

But all adjacent differences of data, $Y(t) - Y(t-1)$, will have the same value due to the noise-free slope, so

$$[\hat{Y}(t), 1 - \hat{Y}(t-1), 1] = (b)(\alpha + \alpha\beta + \alpha\beta^2 + \cdots) = b$$

Therefore, the adjacent smoothed values will have the same slope as the original data and subsequent smoothed values will parallel the original data, as shown in Figure 4–1B. What will this lag be? Looking at Figure 4–2, it can be seen that

$$\text{Lag} = [Y(t) - \hat{Y}(t), 1]$$

but

$$\hat{Y}(t), 1 = \alpha Y(t) + \beta\hat{Y}(t-1), 1$$

so

$$\text{Lag} = Y(t) - \alpha Y(t) - \beta\hat{Y}(t-1), 1 = \beta[Y(t) - \hat{Y}(t-1), 1] \quad (4\text{--}3)$$

From Figure 4–2, it is seen that

$$[Y(t) - \hat{Y}(t-1), 1] = [\text{Lag} + \text{Slope}].$$

So, from Equation 4–3:

$$\text{Lag} = \beta[\text{Lag} + \text{Slope}]$$

and

$$(1 - \beta)\text{Lag} = \beta(\text{Slope})$$

so:

$$\text{Lag} = \left(\frac{\beta}{\alpha}\right)(b) \tag{4–4}$$

Equating the moving average and exponential smoothing noise-free ramp lags we get

$$\frac{\beta}{\alpha} = \frac{(N - 1)}{2} \quad \text{and} \quad \alpha = \frac{2}{N + 1} \tag{4–5}$$

Conceptually, the effect of 0-order polynomial fitting by a moving average is easier to predict than by exponential smoothing. If an N-value of 9 is assumed reasonable, then an exponential smoothing α-value of 0.2 would *basically* have the same result. This cannot be 100 percent correct as exponential smoothing applies a *varying* weight to *all* the data whereas the moving average only averages the last N values with an *equal* weight being applied to those N data values.

Consider the following data vector which is assumed to have a 0-order polynomial fit: $\hat{Y}(t) = a$; [10 12 9 13 8 8 11 12 10]. The moving average fit of the polynomial, using all 9 values, would be

$$a = \frac{\sum\limits_{t=1}^{N} Y(t)}{N} = \frac{93}{9} = 10.33$$

Assuming $\hat{Y}(1)$, 1 equals $Y(1)$, to allow us to get started, and using $\alpha = 0.2$ as being equivalent to $N = 9$, the exponential smoothing fit of the same data would be as given in Table 4–1. The smoothed average is $\hat{Y}(9)$, 1 = 10.30. This compares quite favorably with the moving average value of 10.33.

With the exponential smoothing, it looks as though a lot of work was expended to calculate $\hat{Y}(9)$, 1. In actual fact, it should be recognized that eight individual averages, $\hat{Y}(2)$, 1 through $\hat{Y}(9)$, 1, were calculated and that in each case only the *previous* value of the *average* had to be maintained, as contrasted to only one average while holding eight pieces of old data with the moving average.

Table 4-1

Exponential Smoothing of Constant Data with Noise

t	Y(t)	(A) $\alpha Y(t)$	(B) $\beta \hat{Y}$ (t-1),1	$\hat{Y}(t)$, 1 = (A+B)
1	10	0	0	10.00
2	12	2.4	8.00	10.40
3	9	1.8	8.32	10.12
4	13	2.6	8.10	10.70
5	8	1.6	8.56	10.16
6	8	1.6	8.13	9.73
7	11	2.2	7.78	9.98
8	12	2.4	7.98	10.38
9	10	2.0	8.30	10.30

4-2. FIRST-ORDER POLYNOMIAL

Fitting a first-order polynomial can be accomplished with exponential smoothing almost as simply as for the linear case. Knowing that the expected value of $[Y(t) - \hat{Y}(t), 1]$ is $(\beta/\alpha)(b)$ from Eq. 4-4, it follows that noise-free data will be paralleled by successive values of $\hat{Y}(t)$, 1, in the fashion of Figure 4-2. If these values of $\hat{Y}(t)$, 1 are averaged by exponential smoothing, then it would be expected that the averages, $\hat{Y}(t)$, 2, will themselves parallel the $\hat{Y}(t)$, 1 values, and also have a consistent lag of $(\beta/\alpha)(b)$, as in Figure 4-3. The following relationships can now be written:

$$[Y(t) - \hat{Y}(t), 1] = \hat{Y}(t), 1 - \hat{Y}(t), 2.$$

So, in terms of the smoothed statistics:

$$Y(t) = 2\hat{Y}(t), 1 - \hat{Y}(t), 2. \tag{4-6}$$

Also,

$$[\hat{Y}(t), 1 - \hat{Y}(t), 2] = (b)\left(\frac{\beta}{\alpha}\right).$$

So,

$$b = \frac{\alpha}{\beta}[\hat{Y}(t), 1 - \hat{Y}(t), 2] \tag{4-7}$$

Equations 4-6 and 4-7 are predicated on the basis of perfect ramp data. However, with noisy data they will calculate *estimates* of a fitted

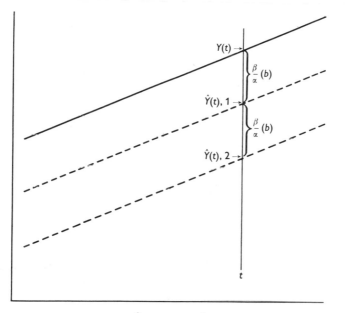

Figure 4–3. Relationship of $\hat{Y}(t)$, 1 and $\hat{Y}(t)$, 2 to noise-free ramp data.

line through the data. Therefore, these equations will be restated as

$$\hat{a}(t) = 2\hat{Y}(t),\ 1 - \hat{Y}(t),\ 2 \qquad\qquad (4\text{–}8)$$

and

$$\hat{b}(t) = \left(\frac{\alpha}{\beta}\right)[\hat{Y}(t),\ 1 - \hat{Y}(t),\ 2] \qquad\qquad (4\text{–}9)$$

The intercept, $\hat{a}(t)$, will occur at the *end*, or more recent, point of the regression line.

Because the $\hat{Y}(t)$, 1 and $\hat{Y}(t)$, 2 values are expected to lag the data, it follows that initial conditions for the smoothed statistics should be calculated. From Figure 4–3, it is seen that logical initial conditions would be

$$\hat{Y}(0),\ 1 = Y(0) - \hat{b}(0)\frac{(\beta)}{(\alpha)} \qquad\qquad (4\text{–}10)$$

$$\hat{Y}(0),\ 2 = Y(0) - 2\hat{b}(0)\frac{(\beta)}{(\alpha)} \qquad\qquad (4\text{–}11)$$

where $\hat{b}(0)$ is an initial estimate of the slope at $t = 0$.

Example.   Consider the following data which we will fit by both linear regression (coded t) and exponential smoothing:

$$Y(t) = [4\quad 6\quad 9\quad 12\quad 14\quad 16\quad 19].$$

Table 4-2

Regression and Exponential Smoothing Linear Fit for Example Problem

A. Regression Fit

t	$Y(t)$	t_c	t_c^2	$Y(t)t_c$	Regression Calculations
1	4	-3	9	-12	
2	6	-2	4	-12	$\hat{a}(7) = \sum\limits_{t=1}^{7} \dfrac{Y(t)}{7} = \dfrac{80}{7} = 11.4$
3	9	-1	1	-9	
4	12	0	0	0	
5	14	1	1	14	$\hat{b}(7) = \dfrac{\sum\limits_{t=1}^{7} Y(t)/t_c}{\sum t_c^2} = \dfrac{70}{28} = 2.5$
6	16	2	4	32	
7	19	3	9	57	
	80		28	70	$t_c = (t-4)$

B. Exponential Smoothing Fit

t	$Y(t)$	$\alpha Y(t)$ $(0.25)[Y(t)]$	$+$	$\beta\hat{Y}(t-1),1$ $(0.75)\hat{Y}(t-1),1$	$= \hat{Y}(t),1$	$\alpha\hat{Y}(t),1$ $(0.25)\hat{Y}(t),1$	$+$	$\beta\hat{Y}(t-1),2$ $(0.75)\hat{Y}(t-1),2$	$= \hat{Y}(t),2$
					-(2)				-(8)
1	4	-		-	-	-		-	-
2	6	1.50		-1.50	0.00	0.00		-6	-6.00
3	9	2.25		0.00	2.25	0.56		-4.50	-3.94
4	12	3.00		1.69	4.69	1.17		-2.96	-1.79
5	14	3.50		3.52	7.02	1.76		-1.34	0.42
6	16	4.00		5.27	9.27	2.32		0.31	2.63
7	19	4.75		6.95	11.70	2.93		1.97	4.90

$\hat{a}(7) = 2\hat{Y}(7),1 - \hat{Y}(7),2 = (2)(11.70) - 4.90 = 18.5$ $\qquad$ $\hat{b}(7) = \dfrac{\alpha}{\beta}[\hat{Y}(7),1 - \hat{Y}(7),2] = (\tfrac{1}{3})[11.70 - 4.90] = 2.3$

The tabular values needed for regression and exponential smoothing linear fits are given in Table 4–2. An alpha value of 0.25 was used, as this corresponds to an N value of 7 by Equation 4–5. Initial conditions for $\hat{Y}(1), 1$ and $\hat{Y}(1), 2$ were calculated with Equations 4–10 and 4–11, using a value for $\hat{b}(1)$ of 2. These values would then be

$$\hat{Y}(1), 1 = 4 - (2)\left(\frac{0.75}{0.25}\right) = -2$$

$$\hat{Y}(1), 2 = 4 - (2)(2)\left(\frac{0.75}{0.25}\right) = -8$$

It might seem that the exponential smoothing is a rather complicated procedure for calculating the fit at time period 7. It should be realized again that six regression lines were really calculated, one at each time period, except for the simple conversion of $\hat{Y}(t), 1$ and $\hat{Y}(t), 2$ into $\hat{a}(t)$ and $\hat{b}(t)$. Also, the iterative approach to calculating the various orders of smoothing certainly lends itself to very efficient digital computer solution, as is shown later in Figure 4–4.

The results of the exponential smoothing and regression fits are as follows:

1. Regression:

$$\hat{Y}(t) = \hat{a}(7) + \hat{b}(7)t_c = \hat{a}(7) + \hat{b}(7)\left(t - \frac{N+1}{2}\right) = 11.4 + (2.5)(t - 4)$$

2. Exponential smoothing:

$$\hat{Y}(t) = \hat{a}(7) + \hat{b}(7)(t - T') = 18.5 + (2.3)(t - 7)$$

where T is the latest data-value time period used in the analysis.

The $(t - 4)$ multiplication factor for $\hat{b}(7)$ with regression analysis comes about due to the fact that $\hat{a}(7)$ occurs at the mid-value of the t-values. Also, it should be stressed that $\hat{a}(7)$ means the intercept value *calculated* at time period 7, not *occurring* at time period 7. Similarly, the exponential smoothing multiplication factor $(t - 7)$ arises as the intercept, in this case, actually occurs at the end of the fitted line, or at $T = 7$.

Comparing the results of regression and exponential smoothing, it can be seen that the slopes are quite similar. At *no unique point in time* should these values be expected to be the same value. However, in the *long run*, the *prediction* and *fitting* effect should be the *same*. If the intercepts are to be equated, then [$\hat{a}$ (exponential smoothing)] = [$\hat{a}$ (regression analysis)] + $\left(\frac{N-1}{2}\right)(\hat{b})$. Again, at no unique point in time should these be expected to be the same. However, in the long run this effect should be the same. Equating the two intercepts in our case, we get

1. 18.5 for exponential smoothing
2. $(11.4) + (2.5)(3) = 18.9$ for regression

Table 4–3

**Prediction Values Using Exponential Smoothing
and Regression**

t	Exponential Smoothing $\hat{Y}(t)$	Regression $\hat{Y}(t)$
1	4.7	3.9
2	7.0	6.4
3	9.3	8.9
4	11.6	11.4
5	13.9	13.9
6	16.2	16.4
7	18.5	18.9

The predictive effect for time periods 1 through 7 only would be as given in Table 4–3.

4–3. SECOND-ORDER POLYNOMIAL

Finally, in this brief introduction to exponential smoothing and its application to polynomial fitting, the use of exponential smoothing as applied to quadratic fits will be considered. The mathematics of the quadratic fit can be rather cumbersome. For the interested reader, the derivation of the fit, using $\hat{Y}(t)$, 3, or third-order smoothing, is given in Appendix C. The equation to be fitted, as with regression analysis, is

$$\hat{Y}(t) = a + bt + ct^2$$

The values of the coefficients can be estimated by the use of exponentially smoothed statistics, in the following manner:

$$\hat{a}(t) = 3\hat{Y}(t), 1 - 3\hat{Y}(t), 2 + \hat{Y}(t), 3 \qquad (4-12)$$

$$\hat{b}(t) = \frac{\alpha}{2\beta^2}[(1 + 5\beta)(\hat{Y}(t), 1) - (2 + 8\beta)(\hat{Y}(t), 2) + (1 + 3\beta)(\hat{Y}(t), 3)] \qquad (4-13)$$

$$\hat{c}(t) = \frac{\alpha^2}{2\beta^2}[(\hat{Y}(t), 1) - 2(\hat{Y}(t), 2) + (\hat{Y}(t), 3)] \qquad (4-14)$$

with initial conditions:

$$\hat{Y}(0), 1 = \hat{a}(0) - \frac{\beta}{\alpha} \hat{b}(0) + \frac{\beta(1 + \beta)}{\alpha^2} \hat{c}(0) \qquad (4\text{–}15)$$

$$\hat{Y}(0), 2 = \hat{a}(0) - \frac{2\beta}{\alpha} \hat{b}(0) + \frac{2\beta(1 + 2\beta)}{\alpha^2} \hat{c}(0) \qquad (4\text{–}16)$$

$$\hat{Y}(0), 3 = \hat{a}(0) - \frac{3\beta}{\alpha} \hat{b}(0) + \frac{3\beta(1 + 3\beta)}{\alpha^2} \hat{c}(0) \qquad (4\text{–}17)$$

where

$$\hat{Y}(t), 3 = \alpha \hat{Y}(t), 2 + \beta \hat{Y}(t - 1), 3$$

As already mentioned, derivation of these equations is given in Appendix C, so only an example of the equation utilization will be presented at this time, to allow comparison with the regression fit.

Example. The following data will be analyzed by both regression and third-order exponential smoothing:

$$Y(t) = [2 \quad 3 \quad 6 \quad 10 \quad 15 \quad 20 \quad 26], \text{ for } t = 0 \text{ through } 6.$$

The *regression fit*, using equations 3–23 through 3–25, gives

$$\hat{a}(6) = 1.90$$
$$\hat{b}(6) = 1.10$$
$$\hat{c}(6) = 0.50$$

so

$$\hat{Y}(t) = 1.90 + 1.10t + 0.50t^2. \qquad (4\text{–}18)$$

Intermediate calculations are given in Table 4–4. Similarly, the calculations for a second-order smoothing fit are given in Table 4–5, with the resulting fit of:

$$\hat{Y}(t) = 26.37 + (7.04)(t - 6) + (0.5)(t - 6)^2 \qquad (4\text{–}19)$$

Initial conditions for $\hat{Y}(0), 1$; $\hat{Y}(0), 2$; and $\hat{Y}(0), 3$ were found as follows. An alpha value of 0.25 was used to allow an equivalence to the regression N of 7 to be maintained.

Initial Conditions Calculation:

1. $\hat{a}(0)$; $\hat{b}(0)$; $\hat{c}(0)$; estimated by method of differences:

$$\hat{a}(0) = 2; \qquad \hat{b}(0) = 1; \qquad \hat{c}(0) = 0.5$$

2. $\hat{Y}(0), 1 = 2 - \left(\frac{0.75}{0.25}\right)(1) + \frac{(0.75)(1.75)(0.5)}{(0.25)^2} = 9.50 \text{ (from Eq. 4–15)}$

Table 4–4

Intermediate Regression Calculations for Example Problem

t	t^2	t^3	t^4	$Y(t)$	$tY(t)$	$t^2Y(t)$
0	0	0	0	2	0	0
1	1	1	1	3	3	3
2	4	8	16	6	12	24
3	9	27	81	10	30	90
4	16	64	256	15	60	240
5	25	125	625	20	100	500
6	36	216	1296	26	156	936
21	91	441	2275	82	361	1793

$$\alpha = (21)(91) - (7)(441) = -1,176$$
$$\beta = (21)^2 - (7)(91) = -196$$
$$\gamma = (91)^2 - (7)(2275) = -7,644$$
$$\delta = (21)(82) - (7)(361) = -805$$
$$\theta = (91)(82) - (7)(1793) = -5,089$$

I. $\hat{b} = \dfrac{\gamma\delta - \theta\alpha}{\gamma\beta - \alpha^2} = \dfrac{(-7644)(-805) - (-5089)(-1176)}{(-7644)(-196) - (1176)^2} = 1.10$

II. $\hat{c} = \dfrac{\theta - (b)(\alpha)}{\gamma} = \dfrac{-5089 - (1.10)(-1176)}{-7644} = 0.50$

III. $\hat{a} = \bar{Y} - (b)(\bar{t}) - (c)(\bar{t}^2) = 11.7 - (1.10)(3) - (0.50)(13) = 1.90$

3. $\hat{Y}(0), 2 = 2 - (2)\left(\dfrac{0.75}{0.25}\right)(1) + \dfrac{(1.75)(2.75)(0.5)}{(0.25)^2} = 26.0$

from Equation 4–16

4. $\hat{Y}(0), 3 = 2 - (3)\left(\dfrac{0.75}{0.25}\right)(1) + \dfrac{(2.25)(3.25)(0.5)}{(0.25)^2} = 51.5$

from Equation 4–17

It should be remembered that the intercept value of 26.37 for Equation 4–19 occurs at $t = 6$. In trying to relate the regression results with exponential smoothing, the following relations should hold in the long run (t_0 is time at

Table 4-5

Exponential Smoothing Calculations for Example Problem

t	$Y(t)$	$\alpha Y(t)$	$\beta \hat{Y}(t-1),1$	$\hat{Y}(t),1$	$\alpha \hat{Y}(t),1$	$\beta \hat{Y}(t-1),2$	$\hat{Y}(t),2$	$\alpha \hat{Y}(t),2$	$\beta \hat{Y}(t-1),3$	$\hat{Y}(t),3$
0	2	–	–	9.5	–	–	26.0	–	–	51.5
1	3	0.75	7.13	7.88	1.97	19.50	21.47	5.37	38.63	44.00
2	6	1.50	5.91	7.41	1.85	16.10	17.95	4.49	33.00	37.49
3	10	2.50	5.56	8.06	2.02	13.46	15.48	3.87	28.12	31.99
4	15	3.75	6.05	9.80	2.43	11.61	14.04	3.51	23.99	27.50
5	20	5.00	7.35	12.35	3.09	10.53	13.62	3.41	20.63	24.04
6	26	6.50	9.26	15.76 $\hat{Y}(6),1$	3.94	10.22	14.16 $\hat{Y}(6),2$	3.54	18.03	21.57 $\hat{Y}(6),3$

$$\hat{a}(6) = 3[\hat{Y}(6),1] - 3[\hat{Y}(6),2] + [\hat{Y}(6),3] = 26.37$$

$$\hat{b}(6) = \frac{\alpha}{2\beta^2} \left[(1+5\beta)(\hat{Y}(6),1) - (2+8\beta)(\hat{Y}(6),2) + (1+3\beta)(\hat{Y}(6),3) \right] = 7.04$$

$$\hat{c}(6) = \frac{\alpha^2}{2\beta^2} \left[\hat{Y}(6),1 - 2\hat{Y}(6),2 + \hat{Y}(6),3 \right] = 0.50$$

which $\hat{a}_{(\text{regression})}$ occurs and t is time when smoothing is calculated):

1. $[\hat{a}_{(\text{regression})}] + [\hat{b}_{(\text{regression})}(t - t_0)] + [\hat{c}_{(\text{regression})}(t - t_0)^2]$
$$= \hat{a}_{(\text{exponential smoothing})}$$

2. $[\hat{b}_{(\text{regression})}] + 2[\hat{c}_{(\text{regression})}(t - t_0)] = \hat{b}_{(\text{exponential smoothing})}$

3. $[\hat{c}_{(\text{regression})}] = \hat{c}_{(\text{exponential smoothing})}$

It will be left as an exercise to the reader to show this is correct, and in fact this is one of the problems suggested at the end of this chapter.

If the three relationships are checked, it is found that

1. Adjusted $\hat{a}_{(\text{regression})} = 1.90 + (6)(1.10) + (36)(0.50) = 26.50$ as contrasted to $\hat{a}_{(\text{exponential smoothing})} = 26.37$

2. Adjusted $\hat{b}_{(\text{regression})} = 1.10 + (2)(6)(0.5) = 7.10$ as contrasted to $\hat{b}_{(\text{exponential smoothing})} = 7.04$

3. $\hat{c}_{(\text{regression})} = 0.50$ as contrasted to $\hat{c}_{(\text{exponential smoothing})} = 0.50$

No attempt to contrast the two schemes further will be made at this time.

Suffice it to say that the minor difference might be due to the fact that exponential smoothing has responded a little better to changes later in the data. The long-term results will be equivalent, though it is apparent that the two immediate results are almost equal.

One final comment regarding exponential smoothing. It is highly amenable to digital computer evaluation due to the iterative aspects employed. A very short and simple digital computer program will allow several orders of smoothing to be calculated through the efficient use of indexing. A flow chart of such a procedure is given in Figure 4–4 for k-orders of smoothing.

4–4. FORECASTING AND TIME-SERIES ANALYSIS

Forecasting using time-series data fits is very simple. Just project the data-fit equation to the time period for which the forecast is required. For example, if a second-order polynomial equation is fit to the data through regression with the resultant equation

$$\hat{Y}(t) = a + bt + ct^2$$

then the forecast for $t = 10$ is obtained by

$$\hat{Y}(10) = a + 10(b) + 100(c)$$

The actual manner of projection is dependent, of course, on the way the fitted equation was obtained. A summary of projection equations is

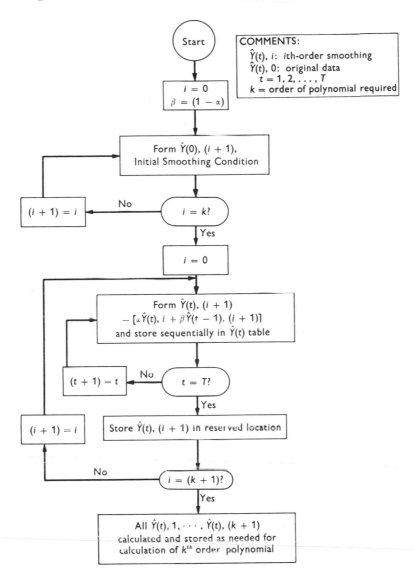

Figure 4-4. Flow chart for multiple smoothing calculation.

given at this time to tie together the techniques just discussed for growth determination. In each of these procedures, the following symbolic relationships are assumed:

1. N = Number of pieces of data held in a regression fit
2. α = Exponential smoothing constant
3. $\beta = (1 - \alpha)$
4. T = Time period to which prediction is required

Constant Model

With data relatively constant, either a moving average or single exponential smoothing is used as the predictor for any future time period.

a. Moving average: $\hat{Y}(T) = \dfrac{\sum\limits_{t=1}^{N} Y(t)}{N}$, for last N pieces of data.

b. Exponential smoothing: $\hat{Y}(T) = \hat{Y}(t), 1$ where t represents the current time period.

Linear Model

With data following a relatively smooth linear growth pattern, either linear regression or double exponential smoothing is applicable as a predictor for the future time period required.

a. Linear regression (time values $1, 2, \ldots, N$ *not* coded to sum to zero): $\hat{Y}(T) = a + (b)(T)$ where a and b are calculated with the last N pieces of data and time zero is referenced at the current time period minus N.
b. Linear regression (time values $1, 2, \ldots, N$ coded to sum to zero): $Y(T) = a + (b)\left[T - \left(\dfrac{N+1}{2} \right) \right]$ under the same assumptions as those listed for linear regression, non-coded data.
c. Double exponential smoothing: $\hat{Y}(T) = a + (b)(T - N)$ where N represents the current time period and a and b are determined from $\hat{Y}(N), 1$ and $\hat{Y}(N), 2$.

Quadratic Model

With quadratic data, either second-order regression or triple exponential smoothing is applicable.

a. Second-order regression: $\hat{Y}(T) = a + (b)(T) + (c)(T)^2$ where b and c are calculated with the last N pieces of data and time zero is referenced at the current time period minus N.
b. Triple exponential smoothing: $\hat{Y}(T) = a + (b)(T - N) + (c)(T - N)^2$ where N represents the current time period and a, b, and c are determined from $\hat{Y}(N), 1$, $\hat{Y}(N), 2$; and $\hat{Y}(N), 3$.

Control Limits for Forecasting

No one should ever commit himself to an exact unique forecast value when management judgment is required. A range of forecast values is required to allow an expectation of worst and best prediction conditions. A *standard error of estimate* is frequently calculated for this purpose by

$$S_{\hat{Y}}{}^2 = \sum_{t=1}^{N} \frac{[Y(t) - \hat{Y}(t)]^2}{N}$$

which is actually the average of the sum of the squares of the difference between the actual data and the forecasted value. A common range to put on the predicted value would be $\hat{Y}(t) \pm 2S_{\hat{Y}}$.

While talking about limitations on sales data prediction by time-series analysis, it should be realized that the resultant forecast is a guide to management decision-making. The external environment (or real-world conditions) has to be analyzed in conjunction with the forecast. For example, an impending steel strike would certainly affect buying strategies for steel—rather than relying on forecasted sales alone.

4–5. OPTIMUM N AND α

The question always arises in forecasting as to what value of N or α to use. A good value of α is usually assumed to be 0.1 if the data are as expected by the model. However, under very noisy conditions a lower value may be in order, and for a rapidly changing process, a larger value would be desired. We will look at a method for determining a starting value of α in exponential smoothing, while Chapter 11 will discuss possible *adaptive smoothing* procedures that would allow this value of α to be adjusted in changing conditions. The same comments could be made concerning an optimum value of N to use in regression analysis.

Assuming back data are available, one iterative approach to take is to cycle through historical data with a minimum α value, forecasting each time according to the required lead time. The absolute values of the errors between the forecasted values and their respective time values are then averaged. Now α is increased some incremental amount and the process is repeated until a maximum α value is reached. That α value which achieves the *minimum mean absolute deviation* is the one utilized. An example of this process is shown in Table 4–6. This process is amenable to computer solution and is summarized in Figure 4–5. A logical minimum α would be 0.01, with a possible incremental value for iteration also set at 0.01. A maximum value of α is logically about 0.3 or 0.4. If the optimum α approaches the maximum, it

Table

Iterative Determination of "Optimum" α for Single Exponential Smoothing

	$\alpha = 0.1$				$\alpha = 0.2$			
$Y(t)$	$\alpha Y(t)$	$\beta \hat{Y}(t-1),1$	$\hat{Y}(t),1$	$[Y(t) - \hat{Y}(t-1),1]$	$\alpha Y(t)$	$\beta \hat{Y}(t-1),1$	$\hat{Y}(t),1$	$[Y(t) - \hat{Y}(t-1),1]$
5			5				5	
3	0.3	4.50	4.80	2.00	0.6	4.00	4.60	2.00
4	0.4	4.32	4.72	0.80	0.8	3.68	4.48	0.60
2	0.2	4.24	4.44	2.72	0.4	3.58	3.98	2.48
6	0.6	4.00	4.60	1.56	1.2	3.18	4.38	2.02
4	0.4	4.14	4.54	0.60	0.8	3.50	4.30	0.38
5	0.5	4.09	4.59	0.46	1.0	3.44	4.44	0.70
3	0.3	4.13	4.43	1.59	0.6	3.55	4.15	1.44
4	0.1	3.99	4.39	0.43	0.8	3.32	4.17	0.15
				10.16				9.77

Note: In forecasting the value for period t as $\hat{Y}(t-1),1$, the error for t is $Y(t) - \hat{Y}(t-1),1$.

means that the wrong forecasting model is probably being used for the data set being analyzed. The same iterative approach would be used in finding the optimum N in regression analysis.

4–6. EVALUATION OF CYCLIC EFFECTS

In Chapter 3 it was stipulated that the three major components of a historical data set to be evaluated by time-series analysis for predictive purposes are

1. Long-term growth trends.
2. Cyclical fluctuations in business conditions.
3. Seasonal effects.

So far we have really only tackled the first of these—the long-term

4-6

Given a Set of Data and Feasible α Values of 0.1, 0.2, 0.3, and 0.4

	α = 0.3				α = 0.4		
$\alpha Y(t)$	$\beta \hat{Y}(t-1),1$	$\hat{Y}(t),1$	$[Y(t) - \hat{Y}(t-1),1]$	$\alpha Y(t)$	$\beta Y(t-1),1$	$\hat{Y}(t),1$	$[Y(t) - \hat{Y}(t-1),1]$
		5				5	
0.9	3.50	4.40	2.00	1.2	2.00	4.20	2.00
1.2	3.08	4.28	0.40	1.6	2.52	4.12	0.20
0.6	3.00	3.60	2.28	0.8	2.47	2.55	2.12
1.8	2.52	4.32	2.40	2.4	1.53	3.93	3.45
1.2	3.02	4.22	0.32	1.6	2.36	3.96	0.07
1.5	2.95	4.45	0.78	2.0	2.38	5.38	1.04
0.9	3.12	4.02	1.45	1.2	3.23	4.43	2.38
1.2	2.81	4.01	0.02	1.6	2.66	4.26	0.43
			9.65				11.69

Summary of Mean Absolute Deviation:

α	Deviation
0.1	10.16/8
0.2	9.77/8
0.3*	9.65/8
0.4	11.69/8

*Optimum α = 0.3

growth trends. This section will give a brief introduction to the determination of possible cyclical effects in a set of noisy data. Autocorrelation analysis will be utilized to determine significant periodic effects and the possible use of trigonometric relationships in conjunction with these significant periods will be discussed. Mainly, this section's value will be the brief introduction to autocorrelation analysis

What is the difference between a *cyclic* and *seasonal* effect? A cyclic relationship may be said to occur if there is a relationship existing between items of data from one source that are separated by a specific time value. This might be every eighteen months, or ten seasons, for example. The seasonal situation indicates that a relationship exists between data separated by specific time values that are seasonally oriented. For example, domestic airline passenger usage has a marked seasonal peak in December and January, around the Christmas–New Year holiday period.

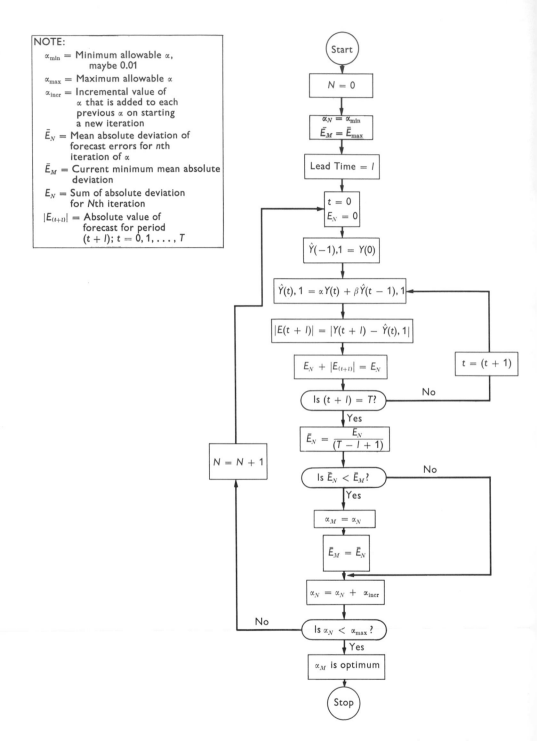

Figure 4–5. Flow chart of procedure to find optimum α for single smoothing using historical data.

Exponential Smoothing and Cyclic Data

Cyclic data are not amenable to exponential smoothing analysis due to inherent characteristic lags, as shown in Figure 4–6. It is seen that lag characteristics are minimized as α increases. However, a high α is dangerous with noisy data due to the high response to the noise characteristics. Therefore, if exponential smoothing is to be used in an iterative forecasting system, the cyclic component(s) should *not* be updated with exponential smoothing. Growth characteristics would be evaluated separately from the cyclic conditions, and the two projections would be added to make a composite forecast.

Autocorrelation Analysis

One of the more readily understandable approaches for determining periodic effects in time-series data is that of autocorrelation analysis. It should be strongly repeated that this will *not fit* the cyclic effect, only give a series of clues as to the way to fit the data. This latter might be a simple trigonometric fit or could necessitate a combination of trigonometric terms such as is encountered in Fourier analysis, or it might simply indicate a growth trend in cyclic values. It is possible under certain highly unusual circumstances that the analysis may pinpoint *exactly* how to forecast.

Conventional correlation analysis may analyze the relationship existing between two variables. If such a relationship between two

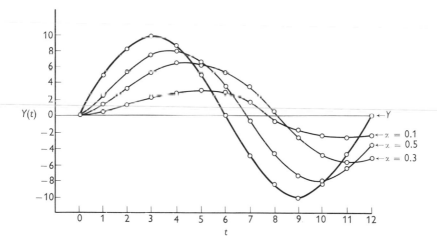

Figure 4–6. Single exponential smoothing applied to noise-free data.

variables, X and Y, is assumed to be linear, a measure of the linear relationship is given by the correlation coefficient:

$$P = \frac{\sum\limits_{i=1}^{N} \dfrac{(X_i - \bar{X})(Y_i - \bar{Y})}{N}}{\sqrt{\left[\dfrac{\sum\limits_{i=1}^{N}(X_i - \bar{X})^2}{N}\right]\left[\dfrac{\sum\limits_{i=1}^{N}(Y_i - \bar{Y})^2}{N}\right]}} \tag{4-20}$$

It can be seen that the numerator is the *covariance* of X and Y and the denominator is the square root of the product of the variances of X and Y.

Now P gives a measure of the linear relationship between X and Y, with $-1 \le P \le 1$. If P has a value of plus or minus one, a perfect correlation exists between the two sets of data, either negative or positive, of course. What if a similar calculation is made on *one* set of data, Y, to check the relationship between values in the same data set that are separated in time? It would seem that if a perfect correlation can be found for some specific time separation, then that information could certainly be used to advantage in cyclic evaluation as the time separation would define a periodic effect. The similarity in the comparison procedure is shown in Figure 4-7. Since the data Y and the lagged data $Y(l)$ can be considered as two variables, Equation 4-20 can be rewritten for autocorrelation purposes as

$$P = \frac{\sum\limits_{i=1}^{N-l} \dfrac{(Y_i - \bar{Y})(Y_i(l) - \bar{Y})}{(N - l)}}{\sqrt{\left[\dfrac{\sum\limits_{i=1}^{N}(Y_i - \bar{Y})^2}{N}\right]\left[\dfrac{\sum\limits_{i=1}^{N}(Y_i(l) - \bar{Y})^2}{N}\right]}} \tag{4-21}$$

The $(N - l)$ found in Equation 4-21 comes about because there are that many cross-products when the data is lagged, as can be seen in Figure 4-7. Also, since there are as many $Y_i(l)$ as Yi, it follows that the denominator reduces to the variance of the data Y.

To simplify the equation writing, Equation 4-21 will be rewritten as

$$P(l) = \frac{\overline{\prod\limits_{l}}}{\prod\limits_{0}} \tag{4-22}$$

$$
\begin{array}{l}
X = [1 \quad 5 \quad 7 \quad 6 \quad 4 \quad 3 \quad 2 \quad 9 \quad 4 \quad 8] \\
\quad\; \updownarrow \;\; \updownarrow \;\; \updownarrow \;\; \updownarrow \;\; \updownarrow \;\; \updownarrow \;\; \updownarrow \;\; \updownarrow \;\; \updownarrow \;\; \updownarrow \\
Y = [4 \quad 6 \quad 3 \quad 8 \quad 4 \quad 6 \quad 3 \quad 8 \quad 4 \quad 6] \\
i = [1 \quad 2 \quad 3 \quad 4 \quad 5 \quad 6 \quad 7 \quad 8 \quad 9 \quad (10 = N)]
\end{array}
$$

A.   Schematic of Correlation Study Between the Variables X and Y

$$
\begin{array}{l}
Y = [4 \quad 6 \quad 3 \quad 8 \quad 4 \quad 6 \quad 3 \quad 8 \quad 4 \quad 6] \\
\qquad\qquad\quad \updownarrow \;\; \updownarrow \;\; \updownarrow \;\; \updownarrow \;\; \updownarrow \;\; \updownarrow \\
Y\,(l = 4) = \qquad\quad [4 \quad 6 \quad 3 \quad 8 \quad 4 \quad 6 \quad 3 \quad 8 \quad 4 \quad 6]
\end{array}
$$

B.   Schematic of Autocorrelation Study Between the Variable Y
and the Variable $Y(l)$ Lagged 4 Time Units

Figure 4–7. Comparison between correlation and autocorrelation.

where $\overline{\overline{\prod}}_{l}$ is the average of the lagged cross-products of Y, mean corrected, with a lag of l, and will be called the autocovariance of Y, with a lag l, and $\overline{\overline{\prod}}_{0}$ is the variance of Y which is the average of the lagged cross-products of Y, mean corrected, with a lag of zero.

The autocorrelation analysis procedure will be to determine the P vector of all feasible $P(l)$ values. Each $P(l)$ will lie between $0 \leq |P(l)| \leq 1$. For good statistical results the number of cross products should be quite large. Brown[1] suggests that there should be a minimum of $(20)(l)$ pieces of data for a $P(l)$ calculation. For monthly sales data, at least 240 pieces of data would be needed to determine yearly lag effects. This would probably be prohibitively large. At least a relative indication of periodic effects will be obtained with much less data.

As an example of autocorrelation analysis, before looking at simple trigonometric fits, consider the following data:

$$
\underset{\sim}{Y} = [10 \quad 3 \quad 15 \quad 9 \quad 4 \quad 16 \quad 11 \quad 3 \quad 14 \quad 10 \quad 4]
$$

which runs from $t = 1, 2, \ldots, 11$. Autocorrelation coefficients for lags of 1, 2, and 3 will be calculated. Before calculating the cross-products it is necessary to mean correct the data, or subtract the mean from each

individual value. The mean of the data is 9. Subtracting this value*
from the individual data gives

$$(Y - \bar{Y}) = [1 \quad -6 \quad 6 \quad 0 \quad -5 \quad 7 \quad 2 \quad -6 \quad 5 \quad 1 \quad -5].$$

The denominator of each $P(l)$ will be the variance of the data, or $\overline{\overline{\Pi}}$,
which is

$$\overline{\overline{\Pi}}_0 = \frac{(1)^2 + (-6)^2 + (6)^2 + \cdots + (-5)^2}{11} = 21.6$$

The value $\overline{\overline{\Pi}}_1$ will be formed as the average of the following cross-
products:

$$1 \quad -6 \quad 6 \quad 0 \quad -5 \quad 7 \quad 2 \quad -6 \quad 5 \quad 1 \quad -5$$

and so,

$$\overline{\overline{\Pi}}_1 = \frac{(1)(-6) + (-6)(6) + (6)(0) + \cdots + (1)(-5)}{10} = -10.5$$

Similarly,

$$\overline{\overline{\Pi}}_2 = \frac{(1)(6) + (-6)(0) + (6)(-5) + \cdots + (5)(-5)}{9} = -10.9$$

$$\overline{\overline{\Pi}}_3 = \frac{(1)(0) + (-6)(-5) + (6)(7) + \cdots + (-6)(-5)}{8} = 21.1$$

The autocorrelation coefficients are now found by Equation 4–22:

$$P(1) = \frac{\overline{\overline{\Pi}}_1}{\overline{\overline{\Pi}}_0} = \frac{-10.5}{21.6} = -0.49$$

$$P(2) = \frac{\overline{\overline{\Pi}}_2}{\overline{\overline{\Pi}}_0} = \frac{-1.09}{21.6} = -0.51$$

$$P(3) = \frac{\overline{\overline{\Pi}}_3}{\overline{\overline{\Pi}}_0} = \frac{21.1}{21.6} = +0.98$$

It is seen that $P(3)$ indicates an almost perfect correlation between data
lagged 3 time units apart. If all possible combinations of the data

---

* Mean correction really means *model* correction. If a cycle were superimposed on a
quadratic growth pattern then the quadratic effect would have to be subtracted out
rather than the mean.

lagged in time by 3 units are considered, we see

   a. 10   9 11 10

   b. 3   4   3   4

   c. 15 16 14

A prediction for time period $t = 12$ could logically be made by averaging those earlier demand values which would have $Y(12)$ in their series, lagged by 3 time units. In this case it would be the average of set c data, above. This would be 15. Similarly, a prediction for $\hat{Y}(13)$ would be 10 and for $\hat{Y}(14)$ would have a value of 3.5.

As an aside, what does the $P(2)$ value of -0.51 convey to us? The negative sign indicates that in most cases the cross-products of data lagged two time periods will in general be a product of a positive number and a negative number. The only way this can occur is for the data to alternate in an increasing/decreasing fashion, somewhat in a sinusoidal fashion. This might indicate a trigonometric fit would be possible.

4-7. TRIGONOMETRIC RELATIONSHIPS

The determination of a significant periodic relationship is only the first step in fitting cyclic data. Trends in the data with the particular periodic lag should now be investigated. For a monthly period of 12, for example, it might be found that data 12 months apart are increasing at a constant rate. A prediction equation for $\hat{Y}(t)$ could well be

$$\hat{Y}(t) = Y(t - 12) + b$$

where $Y(t - 12)$ would be the piece of data lagged 12 time periods before t, and b is the yearly increase between the data.

Sometimes it is found that a trigonometric relationship may be applicable. Typical might be,[3] with t defined from 0 to P:

1. $\hat{Y}(t) = \sum_{n=1}^{\infty} \left[A_n \cos 2\frac{n\pi t}{P} + b_n \sin 2\frac{n\pi t}{P} \right]$ (4-23)

2. $\hat{Y}(t) = \sum_{n=1}^{\infty} b_n \sin 2\frac{n\pi t}{P}$ (4-24)

3. $\hat{Y}(t) = \sum_{n=1}^{\infty} A_n \cos 2\frac{n\pi t}{P}$ (4-25)

4. $\hat{Y}(t) = \sum_{n=1}^{\infty} \left[A_n \cos 2\frac{n\pi t}{P} + b_n \sin 2\frac{n\pi t}{P} \right]$ (4-26)

As many terms, n, are taken as required for accuracy and, of course, the problem is determining the coefficients A_n and b_n to fit the data. Considering only Equation 4–26, and only taking $n = 1, 2$:

$$\hat{Y}(t) = A_1 \cos \frac{2\pi t}{P} + b_1 \sin \frac{2\pi t}{P} + A_2 \cos \frac{4\pi t}{P} + b_2 \sin \frac{4\pi t}{P} \quad (4\text{–}27)$$

Assuming a significant P is determined through autocorrelation analysis, it is possible to solve for the four coefficients through least-squares analysis, or through a series of simultaneous equations. If an offset value is required, an A_0 term could be added to $\hat{Y}(t)$.

Example. Assume the following mean-corrected data is to be fit by a trigonometric series:

$$\underset{\sim}{Y} =$$

$$[12 \quad 7.5 \quad -2 \quad -8 \quad -6 \quad -0.54 \quad 4 \quad 0.54 \quad -6 \quad -8 \quad -2 \quad 7.5 \quad 12]$$

Also assume that prior analysis has indicated a period of 12 is significant. Also, assume only the cosine terms, a half-wave condition, from Equation 4–27 are significant, so that

$$\hat{Y}(t) = A_1 \cos \frac{2\pi t}{12} + A_2 \cos \frac{4\pi t}{12} \quad (4\text{–}28)$$

The regression fit is accomplished exactly as discussed earlier in Section 3–8. The objective is to minimize

$$\sum_{t=1}^{N} [Y(t) - \hat{Y}(t)]^2 \quad (4\text{–}29)$$

If this is done for Equation 4–28, partial derivatives are taken of Equation 4–29 with respect to A_1 and A_2, and the resulting equations set equal to zero. These equations are then solved simultaneously for the desired coefficients A_1 and A_2. For Equation 4–28, it would be found that

$$A_2 = \frac{\sum\limits_{t=1}^{N} A(t)^2 \sum\limits_{t=1}^{N} B(t)\,Y(t) - \sum\limits_{t=1}^{N} B(t)A(t) \sum\limits_{t=1}^{N} A(t)\,Y(t)}{\sum\limits_{t=1}^{N} B(t)^2 \sum\limits_{t=1}^{N} A(t)^2 - \left(\sum\limits_{t=1}^{N} A(t)B(t)\right)^2}$$

where $A(t) = \cos \dfrac{2\pi t}{12}$, $B(t) = \cos \dfrac{4\pi t}{12}$, and

$$A_1 = \frac{\sum\limits_{t=1}^{N} A(t)\,Y(t) - A_2 \sum\limits_{t=1}^{N} A(t)B(t)}{\sum\limits_{t=1}^{N} A(t)^2}$$

The solution for the simple data is given in Table 4–7. A_2 is found to be 7.9 and A_1 has a fitted value of 4.2. It is left to the reader to check the fit, which is quite excellent since the original data were determined by the author. For any value, $\hat{Y}(t)$ is found by $A_1A(t) + A_2B(t)$. For example,

$$\hat{Y}(11) = (4.2)(0.866) + (7.9)(0.5) = 7.59$$

as contrasted to $Y(11) = 7.50$.

4–8. SEASONAL INDICES

Seasonal effects are frequently a specific *percentage* of a long-term trend. For example, a greeting card company might find that its November sales average 40 percent of annual sales. Similarly, April sales might average 30 percent of the yearly situation.

Consider the quarterly sales figures given in Table 4–8 for four years of data. A percentage seasonal index for each quarter is found by taking for each quarter, the ratio of the true demand divided by the quarterly average for the year in which the quarter occurs. For example, for quarter 1 in 1968, this ratio would be 19/25, or 76 percent. The seasonal indices are calculated in Table 4–9 in this same fashion. *De-seasonalization* of data is accomplished by dividing the *original* data by its average quarterly seasonal index. In Table 4–10, quarter 1 for 1968 is de-seasonalized by dividing the original quarter data, 19, by the *fractional* average seasonal index, 0.79. The de-seasonalized data could now be evaluated for growth effects. Forecasting for some future quarter would be a prediction for that quarter from the de-seasonalized data, multiplied by its respective average seasonal index. If the seasonal effect is thought to be *constant* then a *base series* might be developed corresponding to the constant seasonal values for each period. The base series value is then subtracted from each data value and conventional growth evaluation is made. The respective base series value is then added to the growth prediction to give a forecast value.

4–9. COMPLEX MODEL OR COMMON SENSE: PROBLEM IN ECONOMICS

One of the problems incurred when getting involved in time-series analysis is the fact that, once attacked, it forces the attacker to stay with the problem until the most accurate solution has been attained. In forecasting this may not be either necessary or even feasible. If a *common-sense* fit of the data works, then that certainly should be

Table 4-7

Fitting Values for Equation 4–28 and the Given Data, $Y(t)$

t	$Y(t)$	$A(t)$*	$A(t)Y(t)$	$A(t)^2$	$B(t)$†	$B(t)Y(t)$	$B(t)^2$	$A(t)B(t)$
0	12.00	1.000	12.00	1.00	1.0	12.00	1.00	1.000
1	7.50	0.866	6.50	0.75	0.5	3.75	0.25	0.433
2	-2.00	0.500	-1.00	0.25	-0.5	1.00	0.25	-0.250
3	-8.00	0	0	0	-1.0	8.00	1.00	0
4	-6.00	-0.500	3.00	0.25	-0.5	3.00	0.25	0.250
5	-0.54	-0.866	0.47	0.75	0.5	-0.27	0.25	-0.433
6	4.00	-1.000	-4.00	1	1.0	4.00	1.00	-1.000
7	0.54	-0.866	-0.47	0.75	0.5	0.27	0.25	-0.433
8	-6.00	-0.500	3.00	0.25	-0.5	3.00	0.25	+0.250
9	-8.00	0	0	0	-1.0	8.00	1.00	0
↑0	-2.00	0.500	-1.00	0.25	-0.5	1.00	0.25	-0.250
11	7.50	0.866	6.50	0.75	0.5	3.75	0.25	0.433
12	12.00	1.000	12.00	1	1.0	12.00	1.00	1.000
Σ		1.000	37.00	7.00	1.0	59.50	7.00	1.000

*$A(t) = \cos 2\frac{\pi t}{12}$

†$B(t) = \cos 4\frac{\pi t}{12}$

$$A_2 = \frac{(7.000)(59.56) - (1.000)(37.00)}{(7.00)(7.00) - (1.000)^2} = \frac{379.50}{48.00} = 7.9$$

$$A_1 = \frac{37.00 - (7.9)(1.000)}{7.00} = \frac{29.10}{7.00} = 4.2$$

Table 4–8

Quarterly Data for Seasonal Evaluation

	Quarter				Total	Quarterly Average
	1	2	3	4		
1968	19	39	31	11	100	25
1969	22	50	36	12	120	30
1970	29	57	40	14	140	35
1971	34	62	49	15	160	40

Table 4–9

Seasonal Index Values

	Quarter				Total*
	1	2	3	4	
1968	76%	156%	124%	44%	400%
1969	73%	167%	120%	40%	400%
1970	83%	163%	114%	40%	400%
1971	85%	154%	125%	38%	402%
Total	317%	640%	483%	162%	
Average Index	79%	160%	121%	40%	400%

*Note: The sum of all seasonal index values should equal (100) (number of data values per year). If it does not, then a corrective multiplication factor should be applied to each data value affected. The one value, 402%, is sufficiently close to 400 to be considered 400.

Table 4–10

De-Seasonalized Data

	Quarter			
	1	2	3	4
1968	24.1	24.4	24.8	27.5
1969	28.0	31.3	29.8	30.0
1970	36.7	35.6	33.1	35.0
1971	43.0	38.8	40.5	37.5

used—especially if it is simple—which it should be if common sense is employed.

A case in point is the data given in Table 4–11, plotted in Figure 4–8. The plot reveals that the data have a definite increasing growth pattern which is indicative of an *exponential* growth problem. A basic exponential growth pattern appears when each piece of data is related to the previous value by some constant multiplier. For example, the following pieces of data represent an exponential growth:

$$4 = 4$$
$$(4)(3) = 12$$
$$(4)(3)^2 = 36$$
$$(4)(3)^3 = 108$$

If each piece of data is separated from the previous piece by some constant unit of time, t, then in general the predicted value for $\hat{Y}(t)$ would be $(4)(3)^t$, assuming the first value occurs at $t = 0$. Further generalizing, since the 4 is a constant, say C, and the 3 is a constant *ratio*, say R, then the exponential growth pattern could be represented by

$$\hat{Y}(t) = (C)(R)^t \qquad (4\text{–}30)$$

Since each piece of data, in the long run, is related to its immediate predecessor by the multiplier, R, it follows that this can be estimated

Table 4–11

Exponential Growth Data

Month	Exponential Data
January	100
February	200
March	390
April	741
May	1,371
June	2,468
July	4,319
August	7,342
September	12,114
October	19,382
November	30,042
December	45,063

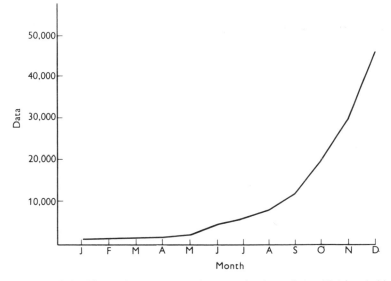

Figure 4–8. Plot of exponential growth data from Table 4–11.

by averaging ratios of consecutive data. For example, with the four values evolved by $\hat{Y}(t) = (4)(3)^t$ earlier, these ratios would be as given in Table 4–12. And of course, the average of the ratios given is 3.

An aspect of an exponential growth pattern is that if a difference table is evolved, as was developed in initial polynomial determination, the differences tend to grow as first, second differences, etc., are taken. Therefore the procedure for determining an expected order of polynomial can also be used to determine if a polynomial or exponential growth exists. As an exercise, the reader might like to observe the difference pattern for the data [4, 12, 36, 108, 324, . . .].

Now, will the procedure of averaging successive ratios to approximate R in Equation 4–30 work for the data given in Table 4–11? Taking

Table 4–12

**Exponential Data with Constant
Adjacent Data Ratios**

t	$Y(t)$	$R(t) = Y(t)/Y(t-1)$
0	4	
1	12	12/4 = 3
2	36	36/12 = 3
3	108	108/36 = 3

adjacent ratios of the first five pieces of data results as shown in Table 4–13. It is seen that the $R(t)$ values are decreasing, and in this example are decreasing at a constant rate. Therefore, to forecast for time t in the future would require

$$\hat{Y}(t) = (100)(2.00)(1.95) \cdots [2.00 - (0.05)(t - 1)]$$

Generalizing this forecast in the fashion of Equation 4–30, we get, for the data given in Table 4–11,

$$\hat{Y}(t) = (K)(a)(a - b)(a - 2b)(a - 3b) \cdots [a - (t - 1)(b)]$$

$$= K \prod_{i=1}^{t} [a - b(i - 1)] \tag{4-31}$$

where $K = 100$

$a = 2.00$

$b = 0.05$

Expansion of the first four terms which include a yields the following results:

$$t = 1: \ \hat{Y}(1) = (K)(a)$$
$$t = 2: \ \hat{Y}(2) = (K)(a^2 - ab)$$
$$t = 3: \ \hat{Y}(3) = (K)(a^3 - 3a^2b + 2ab^2)$$
$$t = 4: \ \hat{Y}(4) = (K)(a^4 - 6a^3b + 11a^2b^2 - 6ab^3) \tag{4-32}$$

It can be seen by inspection that each forecast has as many terms in it as the time value being predicted and these terms include the values of a raised to all powers of time from 1 to t, and all values of b raised to powers of time from 1 to $(t - 1)$. Equation 4–32 can therefore be written as

$$\hat{Y}(t) = (K)(a^t - 6a^{t-1}b + 11a^{t-2}b^2 - 6a^{t-3}b^3) \tag{4-33}$$

for $t = 4$.

Trying to develop a general time-series equation for any $\hat{Y}(t)$ is not quite so easy. The first two terms by inspection always are

$$\hat{Y}(t) = (K)\left(a^t - \frac{(t - 1)(t)}{2} a^{t-1}b + \cdots\right) \tag{4-34}$$

but the other terms are complex for general development. The question is, should we? If accuracy is required to the nth degree then no stone should be left unturned. In most cases a *reasonable* accuracy is all that is required. One way in the current example to achieve reasonable accuracy would be to truncate terms on the supposition that powers of

Table 4–13

**Exponential Data with Decreasing
Adjacent Data Ratios**

t	$Y(t)$	$R(t) = Y(t)/Y(t-1)$
0	100	
1	200	2.00
2	390	1.95
3	741	1.90
4	1371	1.85

b^t for large t will approach zero for a fractional b. For $t = 4$, Equation 4–34 yields:

$$\hat{Y}(4) = (100)[(2.0)^4 - (6)(2.0)^3(0.05)]$$

$$= (100)(16 - 2.4) = 1,306 \qquad (4\text{–}35)$$

This is not too bad when it is seen that the correct value (May in Table 4–11) is 1,371. The prediction for December, which has a true value of 45,063, turns out to be approximately 201,730, a ghastly approximation. Obviously, later terms in Equation 4–34 will have quite an effect on the solution.

One possible *common sense* fit would be to look at what happens if $(K)(a)^t$ is used as a fitting equation, and then to attempt to reduce errors by some logical manipulation. If $(100)(2.0)^t$ were used to estimate the data in Table 4–11, then the errors given in Table 4–14 would result.

It turns out, quite logically, that the errors themselves are growing in an exponential manner. Trying to subtract from $(100)(2)^t$ an amount estimating the error will just result in the same problem being attacked. What is the solution? The mathematician would want to find the general equation that would resolve Equation 4–31 into a closed-form solution in terms of *any* t value. This might take days and be very complex to calculate. Justifying an *approximation* should be from an economic point of view. What will errors cost versus the cost of determining an exotic mathematical model? This really falls into what Brown calls the "rubber stamp of Operations Research" problem.[1] This is depicted in Figure 4–9. With some foresight, the *common sense* solution will achieve a total forecast cost somewhere in the vicinity that minimizes these total costs. The *mathematical-nicety* forecast will

Table 4–14

Errors Generated if $\hat{Y}(t) = (100)(2)^t$ Is Used to Predict Data
Given in Table 4–11

Month	t	$Y(t)$	$\hat{Y}(t) = (100)(2.0)$	Error $= \hat{Y}(t) - Y(t)$
January	0	100	100	0
February	1	200	200	0
March	2	390	400	10
April	3	741	800	59
May	4	1,371	1,600	229
June	5	2,468	3,200	532
July	6	4,319	6,400	2,081
August	7	7,342	12,800	5,458
September	8	12,114	25,600	13,486
October	9	19,382	51,200	31,818
November	10	30,042	102,400	72,358
December	11	45,063	204,800	159,737

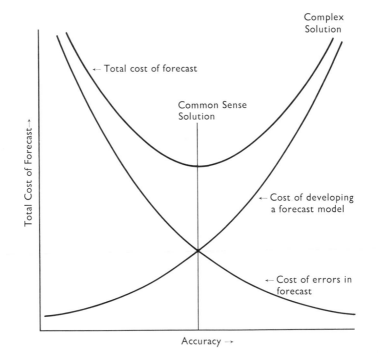

Figure 4–9. Total cost of developing forecast model.

probably lie to the right of this value and so have large associated total costs. The *common sense* solution would, in this example, have low error costs and also low development costs. The computation cost, not shown in Figure 4–9, might be higher than that for a closed-form solution, if one exists at all. The approach would be to develop predictions using the *immediate* predecessor prediction. This would be the obvious iterative way to go, if predictions are to be made from each time period for the next. Equation 4–31, which gives

$$\hat{Y}(t) = K \prod_{i=1}^{t} [a - b(i - 1)]$$

indicates that

$$\hat{Y}(t) = \hat{Y}(t - 1)[a - b(t - 1)] \qquad (4\text{–}36)$$

Start

Initialize:
$t = 0$
$Y(t) = Y(t)$
$C = R(t) = Y(t + 1)/Y(t)$

REMARKS: t is time index where $t = 0, 1, \ldots, T$.
$\hat{Y}(t)$ is estimated data value at t.
C is starting constant.
$R(t)$ is exponential ratio at time t.
b is average change from $R(t)$ to $R(t + 1)$. This could be computed by exponential smoothing average.

Increment t such that
$t = (t + 1)$

Calculate
$\hat{Y}(t) = \hat{Y}(t - 1)[C - b(t - 1)]$

Is $t = T$?   No

Yes

$Y(T)$ has been evolved.

Stop

Figure 4–10. Flow-chart for iteratively determining $\hat{Y}(T)$ from exponentially growing data with a declining R value.

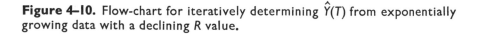

for any time period. For example, from Table 4–14, suppose $\hat{Y}(6)$ equals $Y(6)$, or 4,319. $\hat{Y}(7)$ would be calculated, from Equation 4–36, as

$$\hat{Y}(7) = \hat{Y}(6)[2.0 - (0.05)(6)] = \hat{Y}(6)[1.7] = (4,319)(1.7) = 7,342.$$

The iterative approach is very simple, but does require all intermediate terms to be computed. The flow-chart procedure is given in Figure 4–10 and indicates that an electronic calculator program would probably be satisfactory for a large T value. The *moral* of this story is that mathematical niceties have their place, but for a time-series forecasting point-of-view, the development cost for the forecasting model, the application cost, and the cost of forecasting errors when using an approximation to the exact model, should all be considered from an *economic* basis. Earlier, forecasting criteria were discussed. One of the criteria was *accuracy* of forecast. Certain cases, such as prediction of enemy missile position for interception, have to be as accurate as is humanly possible. Economics would not come into play. The larger group of prediction problems would fall into that situation where accuracy can be dispensed with to some degree in favor of simplicity and ease of application.

REFERENCES CITED

1. BROWN, ROBERT G. *Smoothing, Forecasting and Prediction of Discrete Time Series.* Prentice-Hall, Inc., Englewood Cliffs, N.J., 1963.
2. BROWN, ROBERT G., and MEYER, R. F. "The Fundamental Theorem of Exponential Smoothing," *Operations Research*, IX (September–October, 1961), 673–87.
3. SNEDDON, I. N., *Fourier Series*, The Free Press, Glencoe, Illinois, 1961.

PROBLEMS

Note: Data Sets A, B, C, and D refer to the data sets given in the Problems of Chapter 3, on page 112.

1. Assuming N values of 8, 10, or 12 are deemed feasible for predicting Data Set A with a moving average, determine the "optimum" N by the iterative procedure. Use a lead time of one month when forecasting.

2. Assuming N values of 9 or 11 are feasible for predicting Data Set B with linear regression, determine the optimum N value by the iterative process. Use a lead time of one month when forecasting.

3. Analyze Data Set A using single exponential smoothing, for forecasting purposes, using an α value that corresponds to your N value obtained in Problem 1. Are the results compatible?

4. Analyze Data Set B with second-order exponential smoothing, using an alpha value that corresponds to the optimum N from Problem 2. Do the results seem compatible with Problem 2's forecast for the third January?

5. Analyze Data Set C for forecasting purposes with third-order exponential smoothing. Predict the demand for the *third* January. Do the results seem compatible with Chapter 3's Problem 9's forecast? Use the last 10 pieces of data only.

6. In Section 4–7 we analyzed by regression a model that conformed to $\hat{Y}(t) = a_1 \cos \dfrac{2\pi t}{p} + a_2 \cos \dfrac{4\pi t}{p}$. Derive the formulas for a_1 and a_2 that allow the fit: $\hat{Y}(t) = a_1 \sin \dfrac{2\pi t}{p} + a_2 \sin \dfrac{4\pi t}{p}$. Set $p = 12$.

7. Data Set D conforms to the model analyzed in Problem 6. Fit this data and predict for the third January demand.

8. Would a "method of differences" fit of the last 12 pieces of Data Set C give you about the same predictive results as with third-order exponential smoothing?

9. In relating exponential smoothing parameters to regression parameters in the text it was stipulated that, for a second-order polynomial, the following should hold in the long run:

a. $[\hat{a}_{(\text{regression})}] + [\hat{b}_{(\text{regression})}(t - t_0)] + [\hat{c}_{(\text{regression})}(t - t_0)] =$

$$\hat{a}_{(\text{exponential smoothing})}$$

b. $[\hat{b}_{(\text{regression})}] + 2[\hat{c}_{(\text{regression})}(t - t_0)] = \hat{b}_{(\text{exponential smoothing})}.$

c. $[\hat{c}_{(\text{regression})}] = \hat{c}_{(\text{exponential smoothing})}.$

Do they?

II

ANALYSIS

5
Concepts of Optimization

The best is the cheapest.

BENJAMIN FRANKLIN

Quality, not quantity, is my measure.

DOUGLAS JERROLD

5-1. ANALYSIS

The first of the three parts that constitute this text has now been completed. Up to this point we have been concerned with the *planning* function. As soon as planning is concluded and accepted, then implementation of the plans in the best manner possible is desirable. *Forecasting* might indicate that a specified production rate should be maintained in a particular industrial facility. Actually obtaining this production value with limited resources might be a formidable task. Analysis, the topic of this second part, will be defined as the process involved in the determination of means for accomplishing plans with given or obtainable resources and in accordance with some desired *criterion of optimization*. Granted, we attempted to optimize a forecasting technique by analyzing accumulated results from a variety of forecasting methods, and with varying parameters. That technique/parameter combination which minimized some *error* criterion was then assumed to be optimum. This looks like an intermix of planning and analysis, at least by the analysis definition just given. As mentioned in an earlier chapter, there certainly exists a hazy gray area between planning and analysis. In the forecasting case, though, we are optimizing *planning* and not *implementation*.

Part III, covering systems *control*, will be concerned with *dynamically maintaining conditions* specified by *analysis* in order to conform to some criterion of optimization. This immediate chapter will introduce *only topics pertinent for later material* in the analysis and control sections. Several operations research texts are available that give a comprehensive coverage of the optimization topic. We will be concerned only with an introduction to a few of the more simple techniques to give the reader a foundation for the later material and also a foundation for possible later more-advanced study. For the impatient reader, one particularly excellent text covering optimization is by Wilde and Beightler.[6]

The topic of *linear programming* will be introduced through the simplex and transportation algorithms. However, there are large classes of problems that are not amenable to solution by these algorithms. The general field of *mathematical programming* would consider also non-linear programming, quadratic programming, geometric programming, zero-one integer programming, and so on. These latter topics, which will not be considered in this volume, will not be utilized in later material and so should not constitute a problem to the current reader. It should be remembered that this book is designed to be *introductory* and survey-oriented in nature, although geared for the university senior/beginning graduate student.

We have all heard the benefits extolled by local politicians that will supposedly accrue upon their election. Minimally, these will include lowering taxes, raising tax-aided benefits, and increasing law and order. Needless to say, these are not items that can *all* be optimized as a whole system. Minimizing taxes inevitably results in lowered benefits. Increasing law and order either requires raising taxes or cutting down on other benefits. The two introductory quotes point out this same problem. Franklin felt that the cheapest item was the one for him, while Jerrold implied that since quality was his measure, price was not paramount. Needless to say, optimizing the criterion that is finally decided on as being most important will certainly affect the overall results of the optimization. Primarily, we will be concerned in this text with four criteria, each of which could usually fall into a maximization/minimization category.

In the forecasting material presented in Chapters 3 and 4 one method for finding the best parameters for a *given* forecasting model was through the *minimization* of accumulated forecast versus actual value errors. This was an example of accuracy optimization, the first of our four criteria. In this same forecasting problem, we found that when using a least-squares analysis for polynomial curve fitting this accuracy could be improved in certain "noisy" data cases by taking higher and higher order polynomials. However, the *cost* of improving the curve fit increases dramatically as the polynomial order increases due to the forced mathematical complexity. It does not take too long before the cost of obtaining the fit outweighs the benefits achieved with the added cost, or effort. This might be classified as the *diminishing returns syndrome.*

So, even though accuracy is deemed best for the criterion on which optimization is to be based, some *bound* on the degree of accuracy has to be set. For the sales forecasting situation this might average to about a 5- or even 10-percent error requirement. For earth re-entry trajectory for a Mars exploration team this is approximately a zero error requirement. The point that is being made is that once an optimization criterion is set then the degree of optimization should be defined, based on the system to be optimized and the particular characteristics within which the system lies, namely its environment.

The second criterion which follows logically from the accuracy discussion is that of *cost*. Whereas *accuracy* is to be *maximized, cost* is normally *minimized*. Only in extremely remote situations might minimization of cost lead to maximization of accuracy. (Can you think of one?)

Cost is usually measured in monetary units of course, such as dollars, pounds, rubles, and dinars. In system problems this cost might conceptually be very different. We hit one when we discussed the accuracy of forecasting. This concerned the *cost* of improving accuracy which might be measured in dollars. Frequently, though, it is quite difficult to put such items as *effort* into monetary terms. Cost also in this case might be *time* in which the system being developed is actually implemented, though time minimization certainly might create a traditional cost maximization. This at least should lead to the conclusion that *careful* evaluation of optimization criteria is mandatory.

Profit can be handled in exactly the same manner as cost and by definition is more clearly defined. The objective for optimizing profit would be maximization of profit. It might seem at first glance that this should be the prime goal of any capitalistic venture. Unfortunately, profit maximization might tax existing production facilities, or even glut a particular market. When we discuss inventory control we will see that if items are produced in batches then one method of optimization would be to maximize the batch profit. It will be shown that this will not necessarily maximize overall profit, though this latter goal can be attained by maximizing *unit* profit. It might seem a roundabout picture, but it should show that careful *planning for the optimization* is required before optimization is actually attempted.

The last of the four criteria to be later utilized is that of *time*, usually an item to be *minimized*. In scheduling this will become a prime criterion. Usually one thinks that if something is to be scheduled, say an operation in the local hospital's number three operating room, then the *time* criterion would preferably be to minimize the time for the operation, subject of course to patient safety and satisfaction of the operation requirements. This is probably not so. While satisfying patient needs, the optimization criterion for operating room scheduling would be more beneficially *maximizing* utilization. This might be attained through minimization of the overall time required for a *series* of operations where each unique operation might not itself be performed in the minimum possible time. This particular vagary will be examined a little further when the *scheduling* aspect of planning, analysis, and control is presented.

Finally, a few definitions would be apropos to give a common foundation for later discussion, even though we certainly will have used some of these terms earlier and even though most terms will be quite clear-cut as far as meaning is concerned to most readers.

1. *Optimization:* The process whereby a particular function, mathematical or otherwise, is maximized or minimized according to some predetermined criterion of optimality, such as accuracy, time, cost, or profit.
2. *Algorithm:* A procedure or series of iterative steps that might or might not lead to optimization of the desired criterion.
3. *Optimum Algorithm:* An algorithmic procedure that will result in the end with a result that is optimum.
4. *Heuristic Algorithm:* An algorithmic procedure that is *not* guaranteed to result in an optimum condition. Frequently, the optimum characteristic may be achieved, but all that can be guaranteed is a *good* solution.

5–2. CLASSICAL OPTIMIZATION

Classical optimization will be defined as optimization procedures that can be accomplished by *conventional* mathematical approaches, such as maximization or minimization of certain functions through the use of differential calculus. This is in contrast to some of the newer optimization approaches using *linear programming, dynamic programming, nonlinear programming, zero-one programming,* and so on. The latter are examples of *algorithmic* procedures which can evolve optimized conditions for problems not previously amenable to solution by classical techniques.

It is realized that a large group of this text's readership will be familiar with the brief material to be presented in this section, and will be familiar with even a wider spread of classical optimization including possibly Lagrangian multipliers, multi-variable maxima and minima procedures, and so on. As mentioned several times in this text though, the text philosophy is for a *general, self-contained overview of the industrial planning, analysis, and control field.* In line with this, then, an introduction will be made to the application of mathematical derivatives in the determining of maximum or minimum conditions of certain well-defined functions. This material will be particularly beneficial to the neophyte when inventory analysis is presented. Also, when the least-squares procedure for curve fitting was discussed as a forecasting aid earlier we cheated a little and actually used a classical calculus approach for multi-variable optimization. What is the place of the derivative in classical optimization? Consider the polynomial depicted in Figure 5–1 for which we have the equation

$$Y = 5t - 2t^2 \tag{5–1}$$

We might feel that the maximum value of Y can be found by taking a sequence of integer (t) values and calculating the Y values according to this t:

$$t = 0; \quad Y = (5)(0) - (2)(0)^2 = 0$$
$$t = 1; \quad Y = (5)(1) - (2)(1)^2 = 3$$
$$t = 2; \quad Y = (5)(2) - (2)(2)^2 = 2$$
$$t = 3; \quad Y = (5)(3) - (2)(3)^2 = -3$$
$$t = 4; \quad Y = (5)(4) - (2)(4)^2 = -12$$

and so on. Aha, the maximum (optimum?) is a Y value of 3, found at $t = 1$. This may or may not be so. Equation 5–1 is a continuous function for which *all* values of t, both fractional and integer, are allowable as contrasted to a *discrete* function of t for which only integer values of t would be allowed. So all we can say with certainty is that the maximum Y lies between $t = 0$ and $t = 2$.

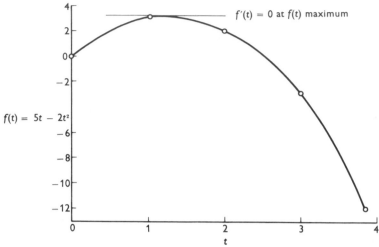

Figure 5–I. Polynomial defined by $f(t) = 5t - 2t^2$.

If we look at the polynomial plot in Figure 5–1, what can we say about the derivative at the maximum $f(t)$ value? The slope is of course zero. Also, the slope immediately following the maximum value is negative. The first point, that of the slope being zero, can be utilized to good advantage. By finding the derivative of Equation 5–1 and setting it to zero, we can solve for the t value at which the slope is zero:

$$\frac{dy}{dt} = 5 - 4t = 0$$

$$4t = 5 \qquad t = 1.25$$

Therefore, the maximum Y did not occur at $t = 1$, but at $t = 1.25$. The optimum Y would be

$$Y_{max} = (5)(1.25) - (2)(1.25)^2 = 3.125$$

which is slightly higher than the presupposed maximum of 3.0.

Now, how can we be sure this is a maximum value? Since the change in slope has to be *negative* from a *maximum* value, it follows that by taking the derivative of the derivative (finding the slope of the slopes) and evaluating it at the optimum $f(t)$ abscissa value, a negative result indicates a maximum has been found. For our $f(t) = 5t - 2t^2$ we found

$$f'(t) = 5 - 4t*$$

---

* $f'(t)$ refers to the first derivative of the equation with respect to t.

If we take the derivative of $f'(t)$, which we will call $f''(t)$, we get:

$$f''(t) = -4$$

which of course is not dependent on t. This is negative so the change in slope is negative and at $t = 1.25$ we have a *true maximum*.

In summary then, a *maximum* value is realized if the value of the first derivative equation is evaluated at $f'(t) = 0$, and if the second derivative, $f''(t)$, is *negative* when evaluated at this same point.

As a further example, consider

$$f(t) = \tfrac{8}{3} + 10t - 10t^2 + \tfrac{10}{3}t^3$$

Taking the first derivative, $f'(t)$, we get

$$f'(t) = 10 - 20t + 10t^2$$

Setting this to zero and solving for t we find the solution is $t = 1$, which gives a value for $f(t)$ of 6. Is this maximum or minimum? Taking the second derivative, $f''(t)$:

$$f''(t) = -20 + 20t,$$

which evaluated at $t = 1$ gives a zero change in slope. A *maximum* has not been found. Obviously a minimum has not been found, for at $t = 0$ we get

$$f(0) = \tfrac{8}{3}$$

A plot of $f(t)$ in Figure 5–2 reveals the picture. Such a point as found at $t = 1$ is called an *inflection* point and of course is neither a maximum nor a minimum condition.

Finally, in this discussion of *one-variable* classical optimization, how do we know if a *minimum* is found? If such is the case then logically the change in slope evaluated at the minimum should be positive—the reverse of the situation at the maximum. Such is the case for

$$f(t) = 15 - 10t + t^2,$$

which is depicted in Figure 5–3. The first derivative being set to zero reveals

$$f'(t) = -10 + 2t = 0$$

and

$$t = 5$$

The second derivative is found to be *positive*:

$$f''(t) = 2$$

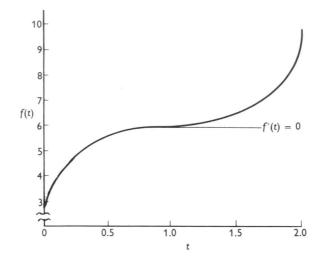

Figure 5–2. Plot of polynomial $f(t) = \frac{8}{3} + 10t - 10t^2 + \frac{10}{3}t^3$.

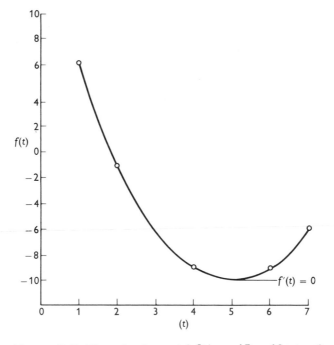

Figure 5–3. Plot of polynomial $f(t) = 15 - 10t + t^2$.

So, a minimum is found at $t = 5$ which has a value

$$f(5) = 15 - 50 + 25 = -10$$

In summary, then, we may find through the use of derivatives:

A. *Maximum:* $f''(t)$ *negative* evaluated at that value of t found by setting $f'(t) = 0$. Substituting this t in $f(t)$ gives *maximum* $f(t)$ value.

B. *Minimum:* $f''(t)$ *positive* evaluated at that value of t found by setting $f'(t) = 0$. Substituting this t in $f(t)$ gives *minimum* $f(t)$ value.

C. *Inflection Point:* slopes *positive* on both sides of point t being checked; or both *negative*. Also, $f''(t) = 0$.

5–3. TWO-VARIABLE CLASSICAL OPTIMIZATION

In the least-squares curve fit material in Chapter 3 we wished to find the straight line $\hat{Y} = a + bt$ that best fit a set of noisy data Y_t. The optimization criterion was to find a and b such that

$$\sum_{t=1}^{n} (Y_t - a - bt)^2$$

was minimized. This is a problem in two-variable optimization, being a function of both a and b:

$$f(a, b) = \sum_{t=1}^{n} (Y_t - a - bt)^2$$

This is solved by taking the *partial derivatives* of $f(a, b)$, first with respect to a and then with respect to b. The resultant equations then are set to zero and solved simultaneously to get the values a and b which define the line that minimizes the sum of the squared deviations of the line from the actual data Y_t. A partial derivative is taken in exactly the same fashion as a normal derivative, with *all other variables being assumed constant*. The partial derivative with respect to a is made assuming b is a constant and the partial derivative with respect to b is made assuming a is a constant.

Shapiro[5] defines the conditions that decide whether a maximum or minimum has been found. If the two-variable situation has variables x and y, define

$fx(x, y)$ to be the partial derivative of $f(x, y)$ with respect to x

$fy(x, y)$ to be the partial derivative of $f(x, y)$ with respect to y

$fxx(x, y)$ to be the partial derivative of $fx(x, y)$ with respect to x

$fxy(x, y)$ to be the partial derivative of $fx(x, y)$ with respect to y

Also, if a, b is a solution whereby $fx(a, b) = fy(a, b) = 0$ then:

A. If $[fxy(a, b)]^2 - fxx(a, b)fyy(a, b) < 0$, and if $fxx(a, b) > 0$, then $f(x, y)$ has a relative minimum value at (a, b).

B. If $[fxy(a, b)]^2 - fxx(a, b)fyy(a, b) < 0$, and if $fxx(a, b) < 0$, then $f(x, y)$ has a relative maximum value at (a, b).

C. If $[fxy(a, b)]^2 - fxx(a, b)fyy(a, b) > 0$, then $f(x, y)$ does not have a relative maximum or minimum value at (a, b)

It can be shown that the least-squares problem satisfies this criterion. As a two-variable example, consider the equation

$$f(x, y) = 3 - 2x^2 - y^2$$

For any value of x or y this *has* to have a *maximum* value of 3. Let us verify with the Shapiro checklist. The various partial derivatives and second partial derivatives are as follows:

$$fx(x, y) = -4x$$

$$fy(x, y) = -2y$$

Setting each partial to zero we get $x = 0$ and $y = 0$ as a solution. Since the *maximum* of $f(x, y)$ is 3 then this has to be correct. However, verification requires:

$fxy(x, y) = 0$; [the partial derivative of $4x$ with respect to y]

$fxx(x, y) = -4$; [the partial derivative of $-4x$ with respect to x]

$fyy(x, y) = -2$; [the partial derivative of $-2y$ with respect to y]

So $fxy(a, b) = 0$; $fxx(a, b) = -4$; $fyy(a, b) = -2$ and $[fxy(a, b)]^2 - fxx(a, b)fyy(a, b) = 0^2 - (-4)(-2) = -8$ which is < 0 so a maximum or minimum is achieved.

But $fxx(a, b) = -4 < 0$.

So we have the *maximum* by the Shapiro test.

This concludes the classical optimization material that will be applicable to this text. Now we can look at a few algorithmic approaches to optimization, of fairly recent vintage.

5–4. LINEAR PROGRAMMING

At the conclusion of the classical optimization material, dual-variable problems were considered, primarily as background for the least-squares curve fitting procedure. An example of this kind of problem might have been

$$f(x, y) = 15 - 40x^3 + 32y^2$$

for which we might wish to determine the values of x and y that maximize $f(x, y)$, probably with some bound on x and y values.

Now we will consider a class of problems that is an extension of the dual-variable classical optimization problem and embodies the following characteristics:

A. A *linear* equation of the form $f(x, y, z, \ldots)$ is required to be optimized (either maximized or minimized). This will be classified in the future as the *objective function*.

B. Restrictions, or *constraint* equations, are available putting boundary conditions on the values feasible for the variables or combinations of the variables. As with the objective function, we will deal only with a *linear* set of constraint equations.

Examples of this type of problem are varied. We will limit application in Chapter 6 to *limited capacity scheduling problems*. Typical is a problem where several products have to be manufactured through a limited number of processes in a particular industrial facility. Each process has a certain number of hours available for which it can be utilized. Similarly, storage capacity is limited and yet the products produced within a month, for example, have to be stored during that month. Knowing a profit per unit value for each product produced, it is possible to set up an objective function which is to maximize the sum of the product profits. But each product has an individual storage requirement and a certain length of time required to be produced through each process. Also, demand might be limited for certain of the products. Therefore, a series of *constraint* equations can be evolved from these latter conditions.

The material requiring linear programming solutions in Chapter 6 is quite self-contained, except for a discussion of the *simplex algorithm* technique. Simplex *solutions* are given but it is left to the reader to verify that these solutions are correct. Therefore, in this section we will be mainly concerned with detailing the steps that lead to such a simplex solution. First we will solve a given problem graphically, and then verify by the simplex process. This problem is:

Objective Function

$$f(x, y, z) = 10x + 20y + 14z$$

Maximize, subject to constraints:

$$x \leq 300$$

$$2x + 2y \leq 700$$

$$2x + y + z \leq 700$$

$$x, y, z \geq 0$$

The constraint equations were limited to three only to simplify the explanation of the graphical process.

Up to three-variable problems can be handled quite nicely by graphical techniques, though the three-variable case is frequently hard to visualize as we will see. The graphical solution requires that the constraints be plotted on a diagram that has as many axes as variables. Therefore, a two-variable problem will have a two-dimensional representation and a three-variable one will be three-dimensional, giving possible isometric visualization problems. Be that as it may, the plot of the constraint equations will define the boundary conditions for a feasible solution.

Figure 5–4 portrays the individual constraints. The first conforms to the constraint $x = 300$. Pictorially, this is a plane parallel to, and with a value of 300 above, the y–z plane. As far as x is concerned in this constraint, it can have a value from 0 to 300 so any point below the constraint plane and above the y–z plane represents a *feasible* value of x.

The second constraint representation is for $2x + 2y = 700$. If y is zero then x is 350, and vice versa if x is zero. Therefore, $2x + 2y = 700$ is the equation of a straight line between $x = 350$ and $y = 350$. This also evolves as a plane in Figure 5–4 as this line forms an x/y boundary along the entire allowable z range. For this constraint only, x and y can have any value that lies *on* or *below* the constraint plane.

Note that these constraints are discussed as *equalities*. This allows the constraint *boundary* to be defined.

The third constraint, $2x + y + z = 700$, also appears as a plane. z has a maximum value, if x and y are zero, of 700; similarly for y. x has a maximum value of 350. Unfortunately, *all three* constraints have to be considered as a whole, so the overall feasible boundary for x, y, and z is formed by the composite of the three, with *inner* constraint representations forming boundaries. This is shown in Figure 5–5. For each of the three planes defined by variables x/y, x/z, and y/z, the boundary surface is formed by tracing the *inner*

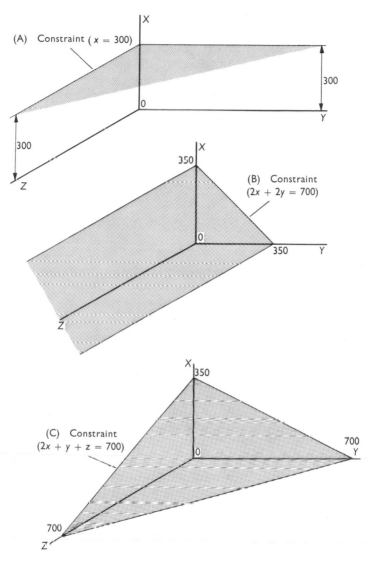

Figure 5–4. Linear programming problem individual constraints graphed.

constraint lines until a closed path has been formed. Any combination x, y, and z *on or below* the boundary surface so formed is a feasible set of x, y, and z. The question now is, what is the *maximum* set within these bounds?

For simplicity, suppose we only had the constraint, $2x + y + z = 700$, pictured in Figure 5–4C. Remembering the objective function

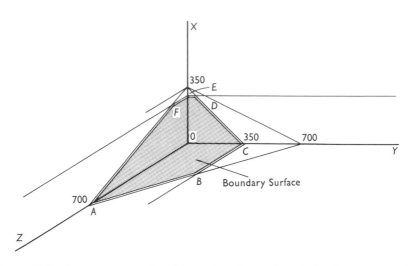

Figure 5–5. Composite graphical boundary formed with the three constraints from Figure 5–4.

$f(x,\ y,\ z) = 10x + 20y + 14z$, the value of $f(x,\ y,\ z)$ when z is 700 (x and y are 0) is $(700)(14) = 9{,}800$. Similarly, $f(x,\ y,\ z)$ is $(700)(20)$ or 14,000 if y is 700. Because of the linear objective function, $f(x,\ y,\ z)$ is linear between $z = 700$ and $y = 700$. Therefore, with regard to y and z only, $f(x,\ y,\ z)$ is a *maximum* at an *endpoint* of the constraining line connecting z and y. The same argument can be made regarding the composite *boundary surface* developed in Figure 5–5. The maximum $f(x,\ y,\ z)$ lies at a *breakpoint on the surface.* Six of these exist, so it is a relatively simple matter to check the six values of $f(x,\ y,\ z)$ to see which is largest. Corresponding to the alphabetic designations for these breakpoints, $A,\ B,\ C,\ldots$ given in Figure 5–5, the values of $f(x,\ y,\ z)$ are:

A. $z = 700;\quad x = 0;\quad y = 0$

   $f(x, y, z) = (700)(14) = 9{,}800$

B. $x = 0;\quad y,\ z$ defined by the intersection of the two constraints: $y = 350$ and $y + x = 700$. Actually, $y = 350$ comes from the constraint $2x + 2y = 700$ but x is zero at point B. Similarly for $y + z = 700$ coming from the constraint $2x + y + z = 700$. Since y is 350 and $y + z$ is 700, z has to be 350. So at point B, $f(x, y, z) = (350)(20) + (350)(14) = 11{,}900$

C. $y = 350;\quad x = 0;\quad x = 0$

   $f(x, y, z) = (350)(20) = 7{,}000$

D. $x = 300$; $x + y = 350$ so $y = 50$

$$f(x, y, z) = (300)(10) + (50)(20) = 4,000$$

E. At point E, $x = 300$; $y = 0$; $z = 0$

$$f(x, y, z) = (300)(10) = 3,000$$

F. Finally point F has $x = 300$ and $(2x + z) = 700$, so $z = 100$; $y = 0$

$$f(x, y, z) = (300)(10) + (100)(14) = 4,400$$

Thus, $f(x, y, z)$ has a *maximum* value of 11,900 when $x = 0$; $y = 350$; $z = 350$.

Another graphical way to find the point on the boundary surface at which $f(x, y, z)$ is maximum is to plot planes for $f(x, y, z)$ on each of which all values of $f(x, y, z)$ are equal. These can be classified as iso-value planes. For example, suppose we pick an iso-value of 14,000. Since $f(x, y, z)$ equals $10x + 20y + 14z = 14,000$, the x-axis intercept for the iso-value plane would be 1,400. Similarly, for the y-axis this would be 700 and for the z-axis a value of 1,000 would be realized. This particular iso-value plane is plotted against the constraint boundary surface in Figure 5–6. If several iso-value planes were plotted, say for $f(x, y, z) = 11,900, 20,000$, etc., it would be found that the planes are *parallel*, and that they would decrease in value of $f(x, y, z)$ as they move in towards the origin. Therefore, if one can visualize what happens as the iso-value plane in Figure 5–6 is moved in toward the constraint boundary surface, it follows that the first point on the boundary surface to be touched by an iso-value plane would represent the *maximum feasible* value of $f(x, y, z)$. Isometrically, this is harder for some to see than others. The problem represented in Figure 5–6 is about as easy to see as any, and the point B would be the first part of the surface to be hit as the iso-value plane is moved slowly inward.

Now we are ready to get away from the graphical approach to the more general simplex analytical procedure. However, a grounding in the graphical fundamentals can give the reader a better understanding of the simplex approach. If the graphical material still seems a little fuzzy, the reader is recommended to jump ahead to Chapter 6, where further two- and three-variable problems are attacked. In addition, proofs are given in that section showing the iso-value planes to be parallel and also showing the optimum $f(x, y, z)$ to fall on a boundary surface breakpoint.

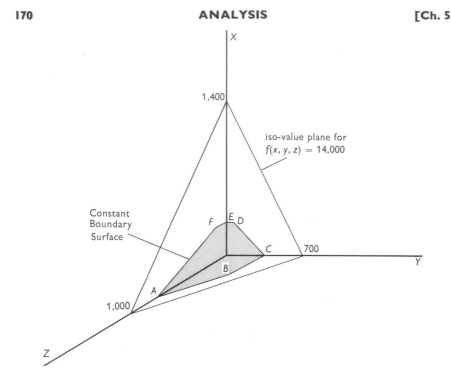

Figure 5–6. Plot of iso-value plane with boundary surface for $f(x, y, z)$.

5–5. SIMPLEX SOLUTION

One of the most significant developments in the history of operations research, if not the most significant, is the development of the simplex analytical technique to allow solution of linear programming problems formulated as is our example problem. The simplex technique was originated by G. B. Dantzig.[3]

The material given in the remainder of this section will allow the reader to develop some of the scheduling solutions arrived at in Chapter 6. In no way is it intended to make him an expert in the use of the simplex algorithm. If the problem does not contain within its solution problems of degeneracy, non-feasible origin, or other unusual situations which preclude the direct use of the material to follow, then this material should suffice to allow the problem to be solved. The reader confronted with a problem insolvable by this material is referred to the references at the end of the chapter for operations research texts which cover the material more fully. A rather clear yet concise treatment is given in Richmond.[4]

For clarification the problem we attacked graphically and which we will now solve by the simplex was:

Objective Function:

$$f(x, y, z) = 10X + 20Y + 14Z$$

Maximize, subject to constraints:

$$X \leq 300$$

$$2X + 2Y \leq 700$$

$$2X + Y + Z \leq 700$$

The first step in the simplex is to rewrite the constraint *inequalities* to make them *equalities*. This is accomplished with the addition of *slack variables* S_i:

$$X + S_1 = 300$$

$$2X + 2Y + S_2 = 700$$

$$2X + Y + Z + S_3 = 700$$

Now we solve for these slack variables:

$$S_1 = 300 - X$$

$$S_2 = 700 - 2X - 2Y$$

$$S_3 = 700 - 2X - Y - Z$$

We are now ready to write down the *initial tableau* for the simplex technique. This is accomplished by developing a matrix with column headings referencing constant values in the objective function and constraint equations, C, and also the variables; X, Y, Z. The rows are sequentially labelled $f(x, y, z)$ and in sequence by the slack variables. Now we fill in the matrix elements corresponding to the row 1 column designation. There is no constant coefficient in the objective function so element $f(x, y, z)/C$ will have a zero entered. This will be followed by the X, Y, and Z coefficients given in $f(x, y, z)$ of 10, 20, and 14. This same procedure is repeated for rows S_1, S_2, and S_3 with the result shown in Table 5–1. The analogy should be clear between the equations and tableau, both given in Table 5–1. The constant value of 0 for $f(x, y, z)$ indicates the initial tableau is for the origin in the graphical situation, with a value for $f(x, y, z)$ of 0. Also, the row variable constant values indicate the contribution of X, Y, and Z to $f(x, y, z)$. Since we do not yet have X, Y, or Z as a row variable this again indicates an

Table 5-1

Initial Simplex Tableau

	C	X	Y	Z	
f(x,y,z)	0	10	20	14	
S_1	300	-1	0	0	
S_2	700	-2	(-2)	0	Pivot
S_3	700	-2	-1	-1	Element

Initial tableau based on equations:

$$f(x,y,z) = 10X + 20Y + 14Z$$
$$S_1 = 300 - X$$
$$S_2 = 700 - 2X - 2Y$$
$$S_3 = 700 - 2X - Y$$

origin situation. The simplex iterative procedure will interchange slack variables S_i with X, Y and/or Z as needed to maximize $f(x, y, z)$.

Richmond[4] gives a rather good presentation of the interchange process, from which the following is paraphrased. This interchange process is triggered by finding a *pivot* element in the matrix. The pivot element occurs in the *column* with the *largest positive* $f(x, y, z)$ value and the *variable row* which has the *smallest absolute ratio* of *row constant, C,* divided by the corresponding *negative pivot column* value in that row. The pivot column for the initial tableau is Y, which has the largest positive $f(x, y, z)$ value, that of 20. The two row ratios would be

$$S_2: \ 700/-2 = |350|$$

$$S_3: \ 700/-1 = |700|$$

Remember, only *negative pivot column* values can be considered for pivot elements. The smallest absolute ratio occurs in row S_2 so the *pivot element* is S_2/Y, and the variables S_2 and Y are *interchanged*, bringing Y into the solution. The next iteration therefore has columns headed C, X, S_2 and Z, and rows labelled $f(x, y, z)$, S_1, Y, and S_3. The *element* values in the new tableau are found as follows:

1. *Pivot Element*—reciprocal of previous value. This is $1/-2$ or -0.5 in our problem.

2. *Other Pivot Row Elements*—previous value divided by *absolute* value of the pivot element. For our case with *initial* tableau element

designations these would be

$$S_2/C:\ 700/|-2| = 350$$

$$S_2/X:\ -2/|-2| = -1$$

$$S_2/Z:\ 0/|-2| = 0$$

3. *Other Pivot Column Elements*—previous value divided by value of pivot element. Note that pivot element sign is taken into consideration. For the example we have, using the initial tableau element designations:

$$f(x,\ y,\ z)/\ Y:20/-2 = -10$$

$$S_1/\ Y:0/-2\ = 0$$

$$S_3/\ Y:-1/-2 = 1/2$$

4. *Remaining Elements*—For a particular element E_{ij} with current value V_{ij} define the element in the row i and the pivot column to be C_i. Also, define the element in column j and the pivot row to be R_j. Then the new value for element E_{ij} will be

$$V_{ij} - \frac{(C_i)(R_j)}{\text{Pivot Element}}$$

For example, consider element S_3/C, with current value of 700. C_i would be -1 found in S_3/Y. R_j has a value 700 located in S_2/C. The new value for S_3/C is then

$$700 - \frac{(-1)(700)}{-2} = 350$$

The completed *new* tableau is shown in Table 5–2. *Remember*, designations S_2 and Y have now been *interchanged*.

This procedure is now repeated using the second tableau to form a third tableau. The overall process is continued until all *variable* values in the $f(x,\ y,\ z)$ row are *negative*. Since $f(x,\ y,\ z)/Z$ is $+14$ we do not yet have an optimum solution. Before continuing to a third tableau though, let us interpret Table 5–2. $f(x,\ y,\ z)$ now has a value of 7,000. The C values of X, Y, or Z indicate the variable values of X, Y, Z that contribute to the 7,000 value for $f(x,\ y,\ z)$. Since Y is the only one of the three with a C value, we see that 350 units of Y give $f(x,\ y,\ z)$ a value of 7,000. Since the coefficient of Y in the objective function was 20, this is certainly correct.

Table 5-2

Tableau for Iteration Two

	C	X	S_2	Z	
$f(x,y,z)$	7,000	-10	-10	14	
S_1	300	-1	0	0	
Y	350	-1	-1/2	0	New
S_3	350	-1	1/2	(-1)	Pivot Element

Another interesting point is to check this with the graphical boundary surface shown previously in Figure 5-5. We can see that the simplex procedure has taken us, on this first iteration, to the *highest* $f(x, y, z)$ breakpoint adjacent to the origin. Subsequent iterations will move toward the optimum in the same manner. Since we know the optimum lies at point B on the boundary surface, we should expect the *next* iteration to be the *final* iteration.

This third iteration is shown in Table 5-3 using the pivot element of S_3/Z from Table 5-2. This of course transposes S_3 and Z and in the third iteration both Y and Z contribute to the solution. Since all $f(x, y, z)$ variables are now *negative* an optimum has been reached. The optimum value for $f(x, y, z)$ is as expected the same as was found by the graphical solution: 11,900 with $Y = 350$ and $Z = 350$.

To summarize the simplex process, a gross flow chart of the procedure is given in Figure 5-7. Not mentioned, though, is the possibility of

Table 5-3

Final Simplex Tableau

Since all $f(x,y,z)$ variables negative, optimum is reached.

	C	X	S_2	S_3
$f(x,y,z)$	11,900	(-24)	(-3)	(-14)
S_1	300	-1	0	0
Y	350	-1	-1/2	0
Z	350	-1	1/2	-1

Maximum $f(x,y,z)$ in $f(x,y,z)/C$ = 11,900

Y contribution in Y/C = 350

Z contribution in Z/C = 350

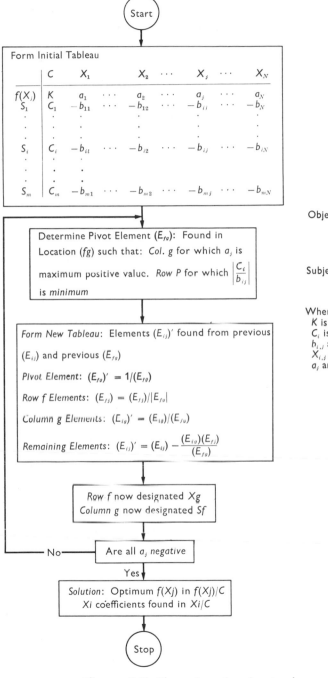

Objective Function:

$$f(x_1, x_2, \ldots, x_j, \ldots, x_N)$$
$$= \sum_{j=1}^{N} a_j x_j + K$$

Subject to:
$$C_i + \sum_{j=1}^{N} b_{i,j} X_{i,j}$$
$$i = 1, 2, \ldots, M$$

Where:
K is objective function constant
C_i is constraint i constant
$b_{i,j}$ are constraint i coefficients
$X_{i,j}$ are problem variables
a_j are required coefficients

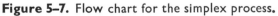

Figure 5–7. Flow chart for the simplex process.

minimizing a function. If this is required then it can be accomplished by changing the signs on all objective function components and then maximizing the result. Again, it should also be mentioned that pitfalls such as degeneracy, non-feasible origin point, and others could crop up. The reader is referred to the references for complete simplex coverage.

5–6. THE TRANSPORTATION ALGORITHM

In certain scheduling problems, such as will be covered in Chapter 7, there frequently arises the problem where products, X, have to be shipped from several sources, i, to several destinations, j, with varying i to j transportation costs C_{ij}, for the movement of a unit X_{ij}. The most obvious source/destination situation would be that of several manufacturing plants supplying a restricted number of warehouses. This problem and others that are similar will be treated in Chapter 7, based on the *transportation algorithm*. The transportation problem can be set up for solution by the simplex procedure, but we will treat it as a solution in its own right. The optimization objective if the C_{ij} are cost values will be to *minimize* overall costs. Conversely, we will see that it is just as easy to *maximize* profit if the C_{ij} are designated profits rather than costs.

Mathematically, with source and destination constraints considered, the transportation problem can be stated:

Objective Function: Minimize (maximize) $Y = \sum\limits_{i=1}^{M} \sum\limits_{j=1}^{N} X_{ij}C_{ij}$, subject to

$$\sum_{i=1}^{M} X_{ij} \leq A_i$$

$$\sum_{j=1}^{N} X_{ij} \geq B_j$$

where X_{ij} are units shipped from i to j

C_{ij} is unit cost for shipping from i to j

A_i are units available at source i

B_j are units required at destination j

$i = 1,2, \ldots , M - 1, M$ sources

$j = 1,2, \ldots , N - 1, N$ destinations

In general, $\sum\limits_{i=1}^{M} A_i = \sum\limits_{j=1}^{N} B_j$. If source units do not exactly match destination units then matching is forced through the use of a dummy source or destination as we will see.

The solution approach is quite straightforward. A matrix, $[MN]$, of C_{ij} values is available. Given also are A_i available items at each source and B_j units required for each destination. The solution objective is to find an assignment of X_{ij} values that satisfy the A_i, B_j requirements and that also satisfies the objective function. Initially, the iterative solution approach will be given at the same time as an example problem is solved. A simplified, or shortened, procedure will then be given, followed by a discussion of problems and ramifications that may be encountered or desired. Finally, in order to tie together the *transportation algorithm* material, as with the simplex procedure, a flow chart representing the procedure will be presented.

A matrix of *cost* values, C_{ij}, is given in Table 5–4 for 5 source locations i and 3 destinations j. M is now stipulated at 5 and N at 3. Also, 71 units X are available at the sources and 71 units are given as the destination capacities:

$$\sum_{i=1}^{M} A_i = \sum_{j=1}^{N} B_j = 71$$

The A_i and B_j values are given with the C_{ij} cost values in the problem initial tableau, Table 5–4.

In Table 5–4 no X_{ij} values have been inserted as yet since none have been determined. The first step in actually obtaining a solution is to obtain a *first feasible solution*. This will be accomplished initially using the northwest corner rule, attributed by Churchman *et al.*[2] to G. B. Dantzig.[3] The top-left element is designated the *northwest corner* and as many X_{ij} values are assigned to this A_1/B_1 position as possible, subject only to the minimum A_1 or B_1 capacity. This is 12 units, limited by the source availability from A_1 which is 12 units. Since this satisfies A_1, element values $X_{1,2}$ and $X_{1,3}$ are set to zero. If B_1 rather than A_1 were satisfied, then the next assignment would have been to X_{12}, and all $X_{2,1}$, $X_{3,1}$, $X_{4,1}$ and $X_{5,1}$ values would have been set to zero.

Since the B_1 value of 25 has not yet been satisfied, 13 units are assigned as $X_{2,1}$ which when added to the $X_{1,1}$ value of 12 now satisfies B_1. This does not satisfy the A_2 capacity of 15, so 2 units are assigned as $X_{2,2}$. This same overall procedure is continued, moving gradually

Table 5-4

"Given" Data for Transportation Algorithm Example

	Destinations			
	B_1	B_2	B_3	A_j
A_1	6	10	5	12
A_2	8	4	9	15
A_3	7	5	8	19
A_4	10	4	9	14
A_5	12	6	15	11
B_j	25	30	16	$71 = \Sigma B_j = \Sigma A_j$

Note: Matrix elements contain

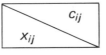

which will occasionally be designated by: $X_{ij}{}^{C_{ij}}$

from the *northwest corner* to the *southeast*, resulting in the first feasible solution given in Table 5–5.

The cost for this assignment, $\sum\limits_{i=1}^{M} \sum\limits_{j=1}^{N} X_{ij} C_{ij}$ is

$$(12)(6) + (13)(8) + (2)(4) + (19)(5) + (9)(4)$$
$$+ (5)(9) + (11)(15) = 525$$

Now, solution NW I needs to be tested to see if the 525 units are optimum. This would be coincidental as the northwest corner approach is designed only to give one possible starting solution out of many. The solution is optimal if moving X_{ij} values into *current zero values of* X_{ij} will not decrease the overall cost. For example, $X_{1,2}$ is currently zero. It can be seen that moving the 2 units $X_{2,2}$ into $X_{2,1}$ position giving a total of $X_{2,1}$ of 15 units, will allow 2 units $X_{1,1}$ to be moved to

Table 5–5

First Feasible Solution (NW I) to Example Problem via the "Northwest Corner" Rule

	B_1	B_2	B_3	
A_1	6 12	10 0	5 0	12
A_2	8 13	4 2	9 0	15
A_3	7 0	5 19	8 0	19
A_4	10 0	4 9	9 5	14
A_5	12 0	6 0	15 11	11
	25	30	16	71

$X_{1,2}$. However, what is the change in cost? If a unit $X_{1,1}$ is moved to $X_{1,2}$ the resultant change in cost is an increase of $(10 - 6)$, or 4 cost units. Moving a unit $X_{2,2}$ to $X_{2,1}$ also gives an increase of 4 units by $(8 - 4)$. The overall *unit cost* change is 8. Moving two X units would of course give an *increase* of 16 cost units. Needless to say, nothing should be moved into element A_1/B_2.

The basic procedure then is to evaluate all changes in cost Δ_k, created by moving units as just discussed into element positions where X_{ij} is currently zero. Therefore, k will range from $k = 1, 2, \ldots, K$ where K is the total number of X_{ij} values which are currently zero. If any Δ_k value is negative, indicating a decrease in cost, then the optimum solution has not been reached and the X_{ij} shift should be made which realizes the *maximum* decrease in cost, or maximum $(-\Delta_k)$. Determining feasible shifts can be a bit of a problem, but basically the process is as follows.

A shift is feasible if a closed path can be made consisting only of *vertical* and *horizontal* segments from a zero X_{ij} element value through elements containing *only non-zero* X_{ij} values, back to the original element. In order for this itself to be realizable, there has to exist $(M + N - 1)$ non-zero X_{ij} elements for which a closed-loop path can *not* be made through only non-zero X_{ij} values. Let us clarify, using the initial solution given in Table 5–5. If element A_1/B_2 had a non-zero $X_{1,2}$ value then the path A_1/B_2: A_1/B_1: A_2/B_1: A_2/B_2: A_1/B_2 would be a closed path of *only* non-zero X_{ij} values. As will soon be seen, this would not allow shifting to all zero elements through only non-zero elements under the $(M + N - 1)$ constraint. Table 5–5 has 7 non-zero X_{ij} values which corresponds to $(M + N - 1)$, or $(5 + 3 - 1)$, and none can be in a closed-loop path of only non-zero X_{ij} values, so we may proceed.

We have already seen the allowable shift into element A_1/B_2 giving an *increase* of 8 cost units. How about element A_5/B_1, which also contains a zero $X_{5,1}$ value? The closed path containing A_5/B_1 is shown in Figure 5–8. Paths like these can frequently be hard to find, but if $(M + N - 1)$ elements contain non-zero X_{ij} values, each of which cannot be in a closed path formed only by non-zero X_{ij} values, then such a path can be found. The cost changes are shown on the closed path arrows in Figure 5–8, giving an overall *decrease* in cost of 2 cost units. The maximum number of units that can be shifted on this path is 9, limited by element A_4/B_2. Needless to say, these closed-path shifts force the A_i and B_j constraints to be maintained. In a closed path there will be a minimum of two "*from/to*" moves. The minimum "*from*" X_{ij} value will be the maximum number that can be shifted in the whole path. From Figure 5–8, the "from" elements are A_2/B_1, A_4/B_2, and A_5/B_3 with X_{ij} values of 13, 9, and 11, respectively. Thus 9 was the maximum shift. The iterations leading to the optimum minimum cost schedule for the example problem are given in Tables 5–6 through 5–11. Under each iteration tableau is given all possible Δ_k

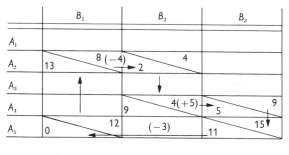

Overall cost change: $-3 -4 +5 = -2$

Figure 5–8. Closed path containing zero $X_{5,1}$ element.

Table 5-6

Initial Tableau NW I for Example Problem

	B_1	B_2	B_3	
A_1	12^6	0^{10}	0^5	12
A_2	13^8	2^4	0^9	15
A_3	0^7	19^5	0^8	19
A_4	0^{10}	9^4	5^9	14
A_5	0^{12}	0^6	11^{15}	11
	25	30	16	71

Possible Δ_k Shifts Leading to NW II Tableau (Δ_8* is Optimum Shift with 9 units maximum):

1. Δ_1 for X_{12}: $X_{11} \rightarrow X_{12}$; $X_{22} \rightarrow X_{21}$; $\Delta_1 = (10 - 6) + (8 - 4) = +8$
2. Δ_2 for X_{13}: $X_{11} \rightarrow X_{13}$; $X_{43} \rightarrow X_{42}$; $X_{22} \rightarrow X_{21}$;
$$\Delta_2 = (5 - 6) + (4 - 9) + (8 - 4) = -2$$
3. Δ_3 for X_{23}: $X_{22} \rightarrow X_{23}$; $X_{43} > X_{42}$; $\Delta_3 = (9 - 4) + (4 - 9) = 0$
4. Δ_4 for X_{31}: $X_{32} \rightarrow X_{31}$; $X_{21} \rightarrow X_{22}$; $\Delta_4 = (7 - 5) + (4 - 8) = -2$
5. Δ_5 for X_{33}: $X_{32} > X_{33}$; $X_{43} \rightarrow X_{42}$; $\Delta_5 = (8 - 5) + (4 - 9) = -2$
6. Δ_6 for X_{41}: $X_{42} \rightarrow X_{41}$; $X_{21} \rightarrow X_{22}$; $\Delta_6 = (10 - 4) + (4 - 8) = +2$
7. Δ_7 for X_{51}: $X_{53} \rightarrow X_{51}$; $X_{21} \rightarrow X_{22}$; $X_{42} > X_{43}$;
$$\Delta_7 = (12 - 15) + (4 - 8) + (9 - 4) = 2$$
8. Δ_8 for X_{52}: $X_{53} \rightarrow X_{52}$; $X_{42} \rightarrow X_{43}$; $\Delta_8 = (6 - 15) + (9 - 4) = -4$*

cost shifts and the maximum $(-\Delta_k)$ shift that forces the move to the subsequent iteration. The shorthand notation, $X_{ij}^{C_{ij}}$, is used in these tableaus for simplicity. The author has found that this notation is quite beneficial in manual solutions. The Δ_k values are shown with complete calculations for the *first two* iterations to help clarify the shifts. Only the Δ_k values themselves are given in the later iterations enabling the reader to practice the calculations for himself.

Table 5-7

Tableau NW II for Example Problem

	B_1	B_2	B_3	
A_1	12^6	0^{10}	0^5	12
A_2	13^8	2^4	0^9	15
A_3	0^7	19^5	0^8	19
A_4	0^{10}	0^4	14^9	14
A_5	0^{12}	9^6	2^{15}	11
	25	30	16	71

Possible Δ_k Shifts Leading to NW III Tableau (Δ_2* is Optimum Shift with 2 units maximum):

1. Δ_1 for X_{12}: Δ_3 for X_{23}; Δ_4 for X_{31}; unchanged from previous tableau:

$$\Delta_1 = +8$$
$$\Delta_3 = 0$$
$$\Delta_4 = -2$$

2. Δ_2 for X_{13}: $X_{11} \to X_{13}$; $X_{53} \to X_{52}$; $X_{22} \to X_{21}$;

$$\Delta_2 = (5-6) + (5-15) + (8-4) = -6*$$

3. Δ_3 for X_{23}: $X_{22} \to X_{23}$; $X_{53} \to X_{52}$; $\Delta_3 = (9-4) + (6-15) = -4$
4. Δ_5 for X_{33}: $X_{32} \to X_{33}$; $X_{53} \to X_{52}$; $\Delta_5 = (8-5) + (6-15) = -6$
5. Δ_6 for X_{41}: $X_{43} \to X_{41}$; $X_{21} \to X_{22}$; $X_{52} \to X_{53}$;

$$\Delta_6 = (10-9) + (4-8) + (15-6) = +6$$

6. Δ_7 for X_{42}: $X_{43} \to X_{42}$; $X_{52} \to X_{53}$; $\Delta_7 = (4-9) + (15-6) = +4$
7. Δ_8 for X_{51}: $X_{52} \to X_{51}$; $X_{21} \to X_{22}$; $\Delta_8 = (12-6) + (4-8) = +2$

The second tableau, Table 5–7, had two optimum shifts, Δ_2 and Δ_5. A logical choice would be to use the shift with the most units being feasible to shift. Since this was two in both cases, the first Δ_k was used.

NW III, Table 5–8, gives an example of a *degenerate* condition. There are 6 non-zero X_{ij} values, which is of course less than the required ($M + N - 1$) number. To alleviate this situation, one zero X_{ij} is

Table 5-8

Tableau NW III for Example Problem

	B_1	B_2	B_3	
A_1	10^6	0^{10}	2^5	1
A_2	15^8	δ^4	0^9	15
A_3	0^7	19^5	0^8	19
A_4	0^{10}	0^4	14^9	14
A_5	0^{12}	11^6	0^{15}	11
	25	30	16	71

Possible Δ_k Shifts Leading to NW IV Tableau (Δ_4* is Optimum Shift with 15 units maximum):

1. Δ_1 for X_{12}; Δ_4 for X_{31}; Δ_8 for X_{51} unchanged from previous tableau:

$$\Delta_1 = +8$$
$$\Delta_4 = -2* \text{ (15 units maximum shift)}$$
$$\Delta_8 = +2$$

2. Δ_2 for X_{23} = 0
3. Δ_3 for X_{33} = 0
4. Δ_5 for X_{41} = 0
5. Δ_6 for X_{42} = -2 (0 units shift due to δ in A_2/B_2)
6. Δ_7 for X_{53} = +9

changed to δ, signifying a minuscule value. This X_{ij} value is treated as a non-zero value when calculating Δ_k's but in any *actual* unit shifts it reverts to a zero value. The A_iB_j element has to be chosen in accordance with original rules (a closed-loop path cannot be made by non-zero X_{ij} values only). The logical element is to choose the *minimum-cost* element that satisfies this criterion. Thus, X_{22} was changed from 0 to δ for this purpose in Table 5–8.

In Tableau NW III both Δ_4 and Δ_6 have cost decreases of 2. However, Δ_6 requires a shift *out* of A_2/B_2 which has δ units. This does not allow

Table 5-9

Tableau NW IV for Example Problem

	B_1	B_2	B_3	
A_1	10^6	0^{10}	2^5	12
A_2	0^8	15^4	0^9	15
A_3	15^7	4^5	0^8	19
A_4	0^{10}	0^4	14^9	14
A_5	0^{12}	11^6	0^5	11
	25	30	16	71

Possible Δ_k Shifts leading to NW V Tableau (Δ_6* is Optimum Shift with 4 units maximum)

1. Δ_5 for X_{41} is same as Δ_5 in previous tableau. $\Delta_5 = 0$
2. Δ_1 for $X_{12} = +6$
3. Δ_2 for $X_{21} = +2$
4. Δ_3 for $X_{23} = +4$
5. Δ_4 for $X_{33} = +2$
6. Δ_6 for $X_{42} = -4$*
7. Δ_7 for $X_{51} = +4$
8. Δ_8 for $X_{53} = -2$

any units to be shifted so Δ_4 is optimum in this tableau, with a 15-unit move.

Finally, Table 5–11 gives the optimum solution after five iterations. It is not possible to move any units into any zero X_{ij} value with a decrease in cost so the minimum cost situation has been achieved. Because there are several values of zero it follows that different schedules will realize the same overall cost of 419. For example, since Δ_2 is zero, having $A_1/B_2 = 4$, $A_1/B_3 = 8$, $A_3/B_2 = 14$, and $A_4/B_3 = 0$ would achieve the same cost. This would allow for some flexibility in scheduling.

Table 5-10

Tableau NW V for Example Problem

	B_1	B_2	B_3	
A_1	6^6	0^{10}	6^5	12
A_2	0^8	15^4	0^9	15
A_3	19^7	0^5	0^8	19
A_4	0^{10}	4^4	10^9	14
A_5	0^{12}	11^6	0^{15}	11
	25	30	16	71

Possible Δ_k Shifts Leading to NW VI Tableau (Δ_2* is Optimum Shift with 6 units maximum)

1. Δ_4 for X_{33}; Δ_5 for X_{41}; are same as in previous tableau:

$$\Delta_4 = +2$$
$$\Delta_5 = 0$$

2. Δ_1 for $X_{12} = +10$
3. Δ_2 for $X_{21} = -2$*
4. Δ_3 for $X_{23} = 0$
5. Δ_6 for $X_{32} = +4$
6. Δ_7 for $X_{51} = 0$
7. Δ_8 for $X_{53} = +4$

5-7. EFFICIENT INITIAL FEASIBLE SOLUTION

Anybody with a glimmer of imagination will realize that the solution to this example problem could have been speeded up with a better initial solution. After all, our initial $\sum_{i=1}^{M} \sum_{j=1}^{N} X_{ij}C_{ij}$ of 525 was 20 percent greater than the optimum. A cost sensitivity approach, commonly called Vogel's approximation, can be used to get a more efficient starting solution.

Table 5-11

Tableau NW VI for Example Problem

	B_1	B_2	B_3	
A_1	0^6	0^{10}	12^5	12
A_2	6^8	9^4	0^9	15
A_3	19^7	0^5	0^8	19
A_4	0^{10}	10^4	4^9	14
A_5	0^{12}	11^6	0^{15}	11
	25	30	16	71

Possible Δ_k Shifts:

1. Δ_1 for X_{11} = +2
2. Δ_2 for X_{12} = 0
3. Δ_3 for X_{23} = 0
4. Δ_4 for X_{32} = +2
5. Δ_5 for X_{33} = 0
6. Δ_6 for X_{41} = +2
7. Δ_7 for X_{51} = +2
8. Δ_8 for X_{53} = +4

Since all $\Delta_k \geq 0$ this is an optimum solution with:

$$\sum_{i=1}^{M} \sum_{j=1}^{N} c_{ij} X_{ij} = (12)(5) + (6)(8) + (9)(4) + (19)(7) + (10)(4)$$
$$+ (4)(9) + (11)(6) = 419$$

Basically, all that is required is a determination of the difference between the minimum and next-to-minimum cost for each row and column. In Table 5–4, for example, the difference for row 1 would be $(6 - 5)$ or 1. For row 2, a value of $(8 - 4)$, or 4, is realized. Assignment is made to that element first which has the *highest* "sensitivity" value. Then the second assignment is to the element with the next highest, and so on. This process minimizes the cost increase possible when not assigning to the lowest cost elements early in the game.

Let's apply this approach to the original example data given in Table 5–4. This is repeated in Table 5–12, with sensitivity values (S_i and S_j) added. Assignment is made to elements according to the largest S_i or S_j value. If a tie occurs in S_i or S_j it is suggested that the element with minimum C_{ij} be utilized.

The initial feasible solution is given in Table 5–13, and was arrived at as follows. Row A_5 has the largest "sensitivity" value, 6, and so the initial assignment is made to X_{52} which has the *minimum* cost in row A_5. The maximum that can be assigned is 11 units. Since no more units can be assigned in row A_5, X_{51} and X_{53} are set to zero. The next largest S value is an S_i of 5, controlled by element A_4/B_2. If 14 units, the capacity for A_4, are assigned, the total for B_2 is still only (11 + 14), or 25, which is less than the 30 capacity. So, 14 units are assigned X_{42}, and X_{41} and X_{43} are then set to zero as row A_4 capacity is satisfied.

The next highest S value is still an S_i value, controlled by element A_2/B_2. Already 25 units have been assigned to B_2 out of a capacity of 30, so 5 more are now assigned to A_2/B_2. Since B_2 is now satisfied, A_1/B_2 and A_3/B_2 are set to zero. The fourth highest S value is now a column S_j value controlled by element A_1/B_3. The full 12 units from source A_1 can be absorbed by B_3 so these are assigned. Accordingly, A_1/B_1 is set to zero.

Now, only four elements are to be assigned: A_2/B_1, A_2/B_3, A_3/B_1, and A_3/B_3. Calculating an S value for only these elements will show that all have a value of 1. A logical step is to then assign *first* to the lowest remaining C_{ij} element. This is A_3/B_1. The full 19 units from A_3 can be assigned, necessitating X_{ij} of zero for A_3/B_3. A_2/B_1 and A_2/B_3 now have X_{ij} values assigned according to the B_1 and B_3 capacities.

The cost value is found to be

$$\sum_{i=1}^{M} \sum_{j=1}^{N} X_{ij} C_{ij} = (12)(5) + (6)(8) + (5)(4) + (4)(9) + (19)(7)$$

$$+ (14)(4) + (11)(6) = 419$$

This is the solution obtained as optimum with five iterations from the "northwest corner" solution! Therefore, much can be gained through getting an initial feasible solution by the "efficient" procedure. A general flow chart of the overall procedure is given in Figure 5–9. An

Table 5-12

Original Example Data from Table 5-4, with Sensitivity Values Added

	B_1	B_2	B_3		S_j
A_1	6	10	5	12	$6 - 5 = 1$
A_2	8	4	9	15	$8 - 4 = 4$
A_3	7	5	8	19	$7 - 5 = 2$
A_4	10	4	9	14	$9 - 4 = 5$
A_5	12	6	15	11	$12 - 6 = 6$
	25	30	16	71	
S_j	$7 - 6 = 1$	$4 - 4 = 0$	$8 - 5 = 3$		

Table 5-13

Initial Tableau Using "Efficient" Starting Procedure

	B_1	B_2	B_3	A_i	S_j
A_1	6 / 0	10 / 0	5 / 12	12	1
A_2	8 / 6	4 / 5	9 / 4	15	4
A_3	7 / 19	5 / 0	8 / 0	19	2
A_4	10 / 0	4 / 14	9 / 0	14	5
A_5	12 / 0	6 / 11	15 / 0	11	6
B_j	25	30	16	71	
S_j	1	0	3		

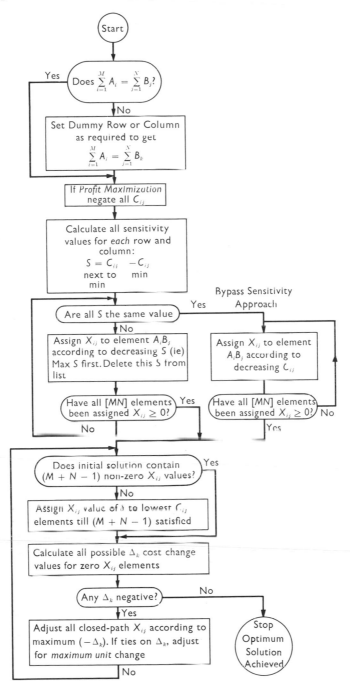

Figure 5–9. Flow chart giving the transportation procedure.

even more efficient procedure for large problems would be to recompute the efficiency values, S, after *each* element assignment.

Before concluding this section about the transportation algorithm we should consider two more items, both of which have rather simple solutions. These will be the case where $\sum_{i=1}^{M} A_i \neq \sum_{j=1}^{N} B_j$, and also the case where *maximization* of *profit* rather than minimization of cost is desired.

5–8. VARIATIONS

In our example problem we had $\sum_{i=1}^{M} A_i = \sum_{j=1}^{N} B_j = 71$. Suppose instead, that B_3 has a capacity of 20 instead of 16 while all other values remain the same. Now $\sum_{i=1}^{M} A_i = 71$ but $\sum_{j=1}^{N} B_j = 75$. The solution is to add a *dummy* source with a 4-unit availability. The costs for this dummy source are all set to the *same* value. Arbitrarily we will set them at zero and *not* use them when assigning sensitivity values.

Table 5–14

Initial Solution for $\sum_{i=1}^{M} A_i \neq \sum_{j=1}^{N} B_j$ Case

	B_1	B_2	B_3	A_i	S_j
A_1	6 / 0	10 / 0	5 / 12	12	1
A_2	8 / 6	4 / 5	9 / 4	15	4
A_3	7 / 19	5 / 0	8 / 0	19	2
A_4	10 / 0	4 / 14	9 / 0	14	5
A_5	12 / 0	6 / 11	15 / 0	11	6
Dummy	0	0	0	4	–
B_j	25	30	20	75	
S_j	1	1	3		

The solution procedure is now *exactly* as before. The initial tableau is given in Table 5–14 for this new case. As might be expected, this solution is exactly the same as the previous problem and therefore optimum. Demand B_3 is not satisfied by 4 units. This same approach would have been used if $\sum_{i=1}^{M} A_i > \sum_{j=1}^{N} B_j$, except that a dummy demand would have been stipulated.

Suppose the C_{ij} figures were *profits* instead of cost? One logical way to approach the problem is to negate the C_{ij} values and treat it as a cost minimization problem. This would be logical from a computer solution point of view. Another way, say manual, is to realize that the values are profits and when a closed-loop path from and to a zero X_{ij} value is made, instead of moving units into a zero X_{ij} position when the change represents a decrease in cost, the change is made for an increase in profit.

This concludes the *transportation algorithm* material. Two scheduling problems using this algorithm are given in Chapter 7, and can easily be solved using the material just covered.

5-9. CONCEPTS OF DYNAMIC PROGRAMMING

By far the simplest way to introduce the concepts of dynamic programming is with a network scheduling problem. This is actually accomplished in this manner when network scheduling and routing is presented in Chapter 7. In fact, the scheduling material solvable by a dynamic programming approach is quite self-explanatory in Chapter 7, at least from the author's viewpoint. Since though, dynamic programming is an optimization approach used in this text and since a great variety of problems can be molded to its use, it is felt that a brief discourse on the basic philosophy should be presented at this time, which in line with the material so far will be oriented to the optimization of mathematical equations of the form, $f(x, y, z \cdots)$.

The *simplex technique* and the *transportation algorithm* were developed for a special category of problem. Not so with dynamic programming, developed by R. Bellman.[1] Here is an approach, or philosophy, for which a wide diversification of problem categories can be applicable, if the analyst has the ability to see how the problem may be defined to fit the approach. Thus, in Chapter 7 we will see application to network routing problems, production scheduling, and combinatorial analysis. Further historical examples are discussed, but not solved, in Chapter 7.

As far as our utilization of dynamic programming is concerned, we will consider it a *complete enumeration* approach. Actually, not *all* possible solutions are enumerated, but the end result is the same as if all possible situations were so evaluated. This approach will be discussed with an example problem.

Suppose for some reason that we have the following somewhat trivial problem:

Maximize $f(x, y, z) = xy^2 + z^3$, subject to

$$x + y + z \leq 17$$

$$x = 7, 8, 9, 10 \quad \text{or} \quad 11$$

$$y = 3, 4, 5$$

$$z = 1, 2, 3, 4$$

The problem will be worked in what is called *stages*, with intermediate computations being made at each stage. The objective function, $f(x, y, z)$, is calculated *partially* at each stage, with the optimum partial $f(x, y, z)$ from the previous stage being used in the calculations for the current stage. The trick is to decide what are stages. In calculating $xy^2 + z^3$ we could first enumerate all *feasible* x-values. The next stage could consider all the feasible values of y^2 in conjunction with the previous stage x values. The optimum values for this stage would be the intermediate $f(x, y, z)$ calculation of xy^2 subject to the four given constraints. Finally, the third stage would add feasible z^3 values to the stage two optimum. Granted, this approach may seem cumbersome for this simple problem, but it has its advantages.

Stage I of the solution is given in Figure 5–10. The ordinate indicates the feasible x values, which are integers between 7 and 11. The abscissa

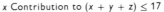

x Contribution to $(x + y + z) \leq 17$

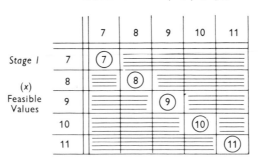

Figure 5–10. Feasible contributions of x to $f(x, y, z) = xy^2 + z^3$.

designation shows the x contribution to the constraint $(x + y + z) \leq$ 17. Finally, the element values in this first tableau are the contribution of the stage variable to the objective function. Needless to say, for x, this need not have been written down, as the contribution is simply the allowable x value. The *optimum* contribution to $f(x, y, z)$ for the particular abscissa combinations are circled. Since there is only one possibility for each combination, each of these is optimum. Ergo, the diagonal elements are circled. These will be used in the next iteration, stage II. Stage II will now have all feasible values of y as the ordinate designation with $(x$ and $y)$ contributions to $(x + y + z) \leq$ 17 as the abscissa labels. These are depicted in Figure 5–11. The minimum $(x + y)$ abscissa value is 10 due to the minimum x and minimum y being 7 and 3 respectively. The maximum is the sum of the allowable maximum x and maximum y. Consider only the row with a y value of 3. If x and y are to total 10 then the previous stage value of x would be 7. Thus we get the values in the northeast corners of each element. Since the contribution of x and y to $f(x, y, z)$ is xy^2 each element (ij) value is composed of (y_i^2) multiplied by the previous stage x value, indicated in each element's little box. The first element for $y = 3$ and $(x + y) = 10$ has a value of $(3)^2(7) = 63$. After each element contribution has been found then the *maximum* in each column is circled and only those values are used in stage III. This example was listed as trivial as it should be obvious that the higher y values would

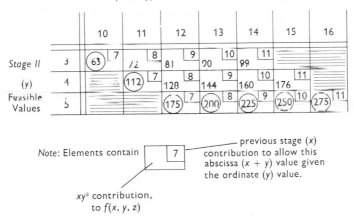

Figure 5–11. Contributions of feasible combinations of x and y to $f(x, y, z) = xy^2 + z^3$.

dominate xy^2. The shaded elements are those non-feasible due to the size restrictions on x and y.

Finally, stage III is given in Figure 5–12. The minimum feasible $(x + y + z)$ is 11, formed by the sum of the minimum x, y, and z values allowable. The value 17 is maximum since that was forced by the initial constraint. The little boxes in each element now contain the value of $(x + y)$ needed to go with each z value to form a particular contribution to $(x + y + z)$. The actual entries in the elements will be $f(x, y, z)$ complete. For example consider the $(x + y + z)$ combination of 15, which from Figure 5–12 we see has a maximum $f(x, y, z)$ value of 226. How was the 226 formed? Given a z of 1, it follows the previous $(x + y)$ to give $(x + y + z)$ of 15 has to be 14. Going to stage II, we see the *optimum* combination for $(x + y)$ of 14 to be 225. Since the contribution at stage III is z^3 it follows the best $xy^2 + z^3$ for $z = 1$ and $(x + y + z) = 13$ would be 225 + (1)³, or 226.

The overall optimum $f(x, y, z)$ is seen to be 276 for $(x + y + z) = 17$ and $z = 1$. Since $z = 1$ and $(x + y + z) = 17$, it follows that the previous stage value for $(x + y)$ had to be 17 − 1, or 16. Going to stage II we see that the y values contributing to the optimum xy^2 for

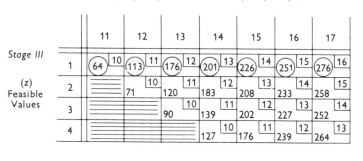

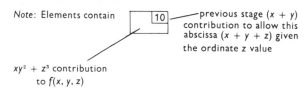

Figure 5–12. Contributions of feasible combinations of x, y, and z to $f(x, y, z) = xy^2 + z^3$.

$(x + y) = 16$ was 5. Therefore x was 11. And the solution to the problem is

$$x = 11$$
$$y = 5$$
$$z = 1$$

with maximum $f(x, y, z) = xy^2 + z^3 = (11)(5)^2 + (1)^3$
$$= 276$$

However, not only do we have the overall optimum, we have the optimum for any $(x + y + z)$ between 11 and 17. For $(x + y + z) = 14$, in iteration III, the optimum $f(x, y, z)$ is 201 for $z = 1$. The optimum $(x + y)$ would be at $(14 - 1)$, or 13, which from iteration II we see had a contribution from $y = 5$. Since $(x + y)$ is 13 and y itself is 5, then x has to be 8. Therefore, if the constraint had been $(x + y + z) = 14$, the solution would be

$$x = 8$$
$$y = 5$$
$$z = 1$$

and maximum $f(x, y, z) = xy^2 + z^3 = (8)(5)^2 + (1)^3 = 201$.

Therefore, the dynamic programming approach allowed all feasible intermediate optimum solutions to be generated and using only the optimum conditions reduced the *overall* combinations needed to be studied. For example, iteration two has 15 possible combinations of x, y contributing to $f(x, y, z)$. Only 7 though were used in conjunction with z to find the overall minimum. In addition, alternate solutions to the overall optimum are readily available. Also, the *minimum* is just as easy to calculate as the *maximum*. This is shown in Figure 5–13. Iterations one and two from the maximization process will not change. However, instead of circling the maximums in stage II we circle the *minimum* xy^2 values and use those in stage III. The minimum $f(x, y, z)$ would be formed by

$$z = 1$$
$$y = 3$$
$$x = 7$$

for

$$f(x, y, z) = xy^2 + z^3 = (7)(3)^2 + (1)^3 = 64$$

which is found in the northwest element of stage III.

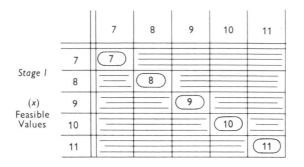

$(x + y)$ Contribution to $(x + y + z) \leq 17$

	10	11	12	13	14	15	16
Stage II							
3	63	72	81	90	99		
(y) Feasible Values 4		112	128	144	160	176	
5			175	200	225	250	275

Feasible $(x + y + z) \leq 17$

	11	12	13	14	15	16	17
Stage III							
1	64	73	82	91	100	177	276
(z) 2		71	80	89	98	107	184
Feasible Values 3			90	99	108	117	126
4				127	136	145	154

Figure 5–13. Minimum $f(x, y, z) = xy^2 + z^3$ subject to prior constraints.

REFERENCES CITED

1. BELLMAN, R., *Dynamic Programming*, Princeton University Press, Princeton, New Jersey, 1957.
2. CHURCHMAN, C. W., ACKOFF, R. L., and ARNOFF, E. L., *Introduction to Operations Research*, John Wiley and Sons, New York, N.Y., 1957.
3. DANTZIG, G. B., in *Activity Analysis of Production and Allocation*, Koopmans, T. C. (ed), Cowles Commission Monograph No. 13, John Wiley and Sons, New York, N.Y., 1951.

4. RICHMOND, S. B., *Operations Research for Management Decisions*, The Ronald Press Company, New York, N.Y., 1968.
5. SHAPIRO, J. M. and WHITNEY, D. R., *Elementary Analysis and Statistics*, C. E. Merrill Books, Inc., Columbus, Ohio, 1967.
6. WILDE, D. J. and BEIGHTLER, C. S., *Foundations of Optimization*, Prentice-Hall, Inc., Englewood Cliffs, N.J., 1967.

FURTHER READING

DANTZIG, G. B., *Linear Programming and Extensions*, Princeton University Press, Princeton, N.J., 1963.
FRAZER, J. R., *Applied Linear Programming*, Prentice-Hall, Inc., Englewood Cliffs, N.J., 1968.
LLEWELLYN, R. W., *Linear Programming*, Holt, Rinehart and Winston, New York, N.Y., 1964.
HOWARD, R. A., "Dynamic Programming," *Management Science*, Vol. 12, No. 5, January 1966.
WHITE, D. J., *Dynamic Programming*, Holden-Day, San Francisco, Calif., 1969.

PROBLEMS

A. *Classical Optimization*

1. For each of the functions in Problems a through f classify whether a maximum, minimum, and inflection point exists or not, while completely identifying these points.

a. $f(t) = 35 + 16.5t - 40t^2 + 3t^3$

b. $f(t) = 15t^2 - 3t^3 + 6$

c. $f(t) = \sin(x)$

d. $f(t) = \cos(x)$

e. $f(t) = 3t - 15t^2 + 2t^3$

f. $f(t) = 5 - 15t - 30t^2 + 10^3$

2. Determine whether the following dual-variable functions have a maximum or minimum. If yes, what values of x and y give this condition?

a. $f(x, y) = 15 - 3x^2 - y^2$

b. $f(x, y) = 3x^2 + y^2 - 15$

c. $f(x, y) = 10x + 15y - 17$

B. *Linear Programming*

3. Use the graphical approach to maximize $f(x, y) = 3.5x + 7.0y$ subject to:

$$x \leq 20$$
$$y \leq 15$$
$$3x + y \leq 68$$

4. Use the simplex algorithm to solve Problem 3.

5. Use the graphical approach to maximize $f(x, y, z) = 5x + 32y + 15z$ subject to:

$$x \leq 15$$
$$x + 2y + 3z \leq 175$$
$$2x + y \leq 84$$

6. Use the simplex algorithm to solve Problem 5.

7. Maximize $f(w, x, y, z) = 3w + 15x + 10y + 8z$ subject to:

$$3w + x \leq 27$$
$$y + 3z \leq 38$$
$$4w + 15x + 2y \leq 53$$

C. *Transportation Algorithm*

8. Consider the following source/destination cost data, C_{ij}, and source and demand values A_i and B_j:

	B_1	B_2	B_3	B_4	B_5	B_6	A_i
A_1	8	6	4	10	9	7	30
A_2	3	8	5	6	10	10	40
A_3	5	7	4	6	8	10	12
A_4	15	12	4	6	10	15	15
A_5	7	9	8	4	7	5	16
B_j	18	20	12	16	14	30	

a. Using the "efficient" initial solution approach, determine the *minimum* cost schedule.

b. By what percent does the *initial* tableau using the "northwest corner" rule miss the optimum cost value found in part a?

9. Assume the C_{ij} values given in Problem 8 are *profit* values. Find that schedule which *maximizes* profit.

D. *Dynamic Programming*

10. Find the x, y, and z values that minimize $f(x, y, z) = x^2y - z^2$ subject to:

$$\cdot x + y + z \geq 19$$
$$x = 4, 5, 6, \text{ or } 7$$
$$y = 11, 12, \text{ or } 13$$
$$z = 1, 2, 3, \text{ or } 4$$

11. Maximize $f(x, y, z)$ in Problem 10.

12. (a) For your answers to Problems 10 and 11, are there any combinations of x, y, and z which achieve both a *maximum* $f(x, y, z)$ and a *minimum* $f(x, y, z)$ for a given $(x + y + z)$ value?

(b) From your answers to Problems 10 and 11, are there any combinations of x, y, and z which allow the *maximum* $f(x, y, z)$ to be at least 3 times the minimum $f(x, y, z)$ for a given $(x + y + z)$ value?

6

Scheduling: Limited-Capacity Analysis

Never in the field of human conflict was so much owed by so many to so few.

WINSTON CHURCHILL, 1941

6–1. CRITICAL RESOURCE ALLOCATION

Scheduling problems come from many sources and have numerous categories and solutions. Complete books* have been devoted to the subject *in toto* so it follows that two or three chapters in this text can only be introductory, certainly not all-inclusive. However, as presented in Chapter 1, scheduling plays an important part in a variety of systems problems. Resource limitations force elongated network schedules. It was shown in Chapter 2 that network scheduling has applicability for a wide grouping of problems. Sequencing problems arise in operating rooms, airplane landing patterns, computer center program-run scheduling as well as the more mundane job sequencing in a factory situation. The scheduling chapters will utilize and develop certain schedule solution techniques. These will *not* have universal applicability but the intention is to show how solution techniques may be developed, sometimes from a most inductive

---

* For example, two are: Conway, R. W., Maxwell, W. H., and Miller, L. W., *Theory of Scheduling*, Addison-Wesley Publishing Company, Reading, Mass., 1967. O'Brien, J. J. (ed.), *Scheduling Handbook*, McGraw-Hill Book Company, New York, N.Y., 1969.

approach. In a few instances, utilization will be made of some Chapter 5 optimization material.

The present chapter will be constrained to include scheduling problems which have a capacity restriction of some kind. Granted, all scheduling problems may be considered in this category, especially when *time* restrictions are certainly a capacity limitation. Be that as it may, this first scheduling chapter will be devoted to scheduling where a capacity restriction of some kind exists.

We will start with the topic of *limited resource allocation* which stems directly from Chapter 2. This provides a logical link between the *planning* and *analysis* functions. Following the topic of resource allocation will be the traditional *line balancing* problem where the limitation usually is one of operators or production capacity. It will be seen that the same approach can be made to the line balancing problem as can be applicable to resource allocation. In fact, one aspect of the line balancing problem may be considered a resource allocation problem with the limited resource being people. Finally, the *process capacity* problem will be presented which allows for graphical optimization in the reduced case, and application of the simplex in the larger problem. The case problem for this chapter will be an extension of Chapter 2's Far East housing project, this time with resource limitations considered.

In Chapter 2, Section 2–6, a hypothetical resource allocation problem was posed for the critical path network repeated in Figure 6–1A with an associated Gantt chart schedule given in Figure 6–1B. The problem asked the question as to what would happen if all of the activities in the network needed one type of resource, say a fork-lift truck, and only three are available. Since for a 16-day schedule activities *G*, *D*, *B*, and *F have* to be accomplished simultaneously for at least four days it follows that a *minimum* of *four* trucks would be needed. This assumes that a truck cannot be shared between activities. The four trucks come about because the four parallel activities, *G*, *D*, *B*, and *F*, *each* need a truck at the same time. The logical way to find the minimum schedule with three fork-lift trucks would be to start activity *F* at time period 9, necessitating an elongation of the project to 17 days. An economic decision can now be made as to whether an additional truck (rent or from another project?) can be justified for cutting the schedule one day to the supposedly cost-minimum 16 days. This schedule, which satisfies *both* the network precedence requirements imposed by Figure 6–1 and the fork-lift resource limitation, is shown in Figure 6–2. It should

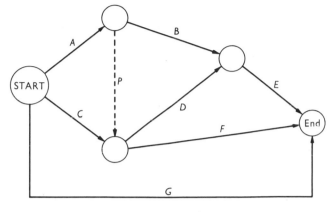

A. Network
(From Figure 2-6)

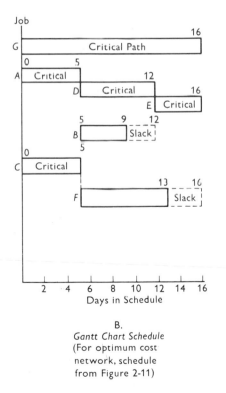

B.
Gantt Chart Schedule
(For optimum cost
network, schedule
from Figure 2-11)

Figure 6–1. Network and Gantt chart schedule for initial resource allocation problem.

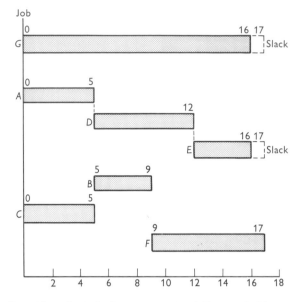

Figure 6–2. Feasible schedule for network of Figure 6–1A given a resource limitation of three trucks with one required for each resource.

be noted that no critical path now exists in the strict definition framework given in Chapter 2. Because of the resource constraints, though, activities *C* and *B cannot* be slipped or four resources would be required on day 9.

This solution probably seems obvious with such a problem. What if the network were much more complex? What if *multiple* resources were critical? What if a *computer solution* were desired? All questions are valid and are difficult to answer. First of all, let's look at the complex, single-resource computer-oriented questions first. Maybe a solution here will give us a clue as to how to tackle the multiple resource problem.

The possible combinations of paths in a complex network makes the *optimum* solution, or minimum length schedule, very difficult to attain. One solution approach is to use a *heuristic* solution technique. A heuristic approach may be defined as one where a set of decision steps leads to a possible optimum solution but does not guarantee such a solution. A good solution can be expected from such a scheme. A typical resource allocation heuristic algorithm was developed by Brooks for a single-resource situation.

6–2. BROOKS' ALGORITHM *

The Brooks' Algorithm (BAG) is interesting in many ways, not the least of which is that it encompasses some of the attributes of digital computer simulation and also those of certain line-balancing heuristic algorithms.

The line-balancing similarity comes through the manner utilized to determine which activities should receive limited resources first. The simulation similarity arises with the technique of looking ahead to when the next change in resource status will take place rather than evaluating this status at every time period. This latter minimizes the number of iterative steps required.

The steps required to assign the single resource with BAG are as follows (for convenience, Table 6–1 gives the tabular results of these steps for the network of Figure 6–1 with three resources available):

1. Develop the project network as with the critical path procedure, identifying activities and their required times.

2. Determine for each activity the maximum time it controls through the network on any one path. This would be like calculating the

---

* Brooks, G. H., "Algorithm for Activity Scheduling to Satisfy Constraints on Resource Availability," unpublished paper dated September 17, 1963. Permission to utilize the algorithm was granted by Dr. Brooks.

Table 6–1

**Brook's Algorithm Solution to Limited Resource
Example with Three Units of Resource**

		G	A	C	D	B	F	E	
ACTIVITY DATA	Activity								
	Duration	16	5	5	7	4	8	1	PROJECT COMPLETION TIME
	ACTIM	16	16	16	11	8	8	4	
	Resources required	1	1	1	1	1	1	1	
	TEARL	0	0	0	5	5	5	12	
	TSTART	0	0	0	5	5	9	12	
	TFIN	16	5	5	12	9	⑰	16	
ALGORITHM ITERATION RESULTS	TNOW	0		5		9	12		
	Resources available	3 2 1 0		2 1 0		1 0	1 0		
	ACT. ALLOW.	G A C		D B F		F	E		
	Iteration No.	1		2		3	4		

critical path time through the network assuming that the starting node for each activity being analyzed is the network starting node. This activity control time will be designated ACTIM for convenience.

3. Rank these in decreasing ACTIM sequence, as in Table 6–1. Ties are ranked in any order. ACTIM for activity A is found by summing the times for activities A, D, and E, which gives 16 days. The duration and resources required for each activity are self-explanatory. The rows titled TEARL, TSTART, TFIN, and TNOW need a little explanation:

    a. TEARL is the earliest time it is possible, due to precedence and time limitations, to schedule each activity. The actual time will be equal to or later than TEARL. TEARL equals the *latest* TFIN time for *all immediate predecessor* activities.

    b. TSTART is the *actual* start time of the activity. If there are no resource limitations then TSTART would always equal TEARL.

    c. TFIN is the completion time of each activity. This equals the activity of TSTART added to the activity duration time.

    d. TNOW is the time at which resource assignments are *now* being considered. *Initially* TNOW equals zero but subsequently equals the lowest TFIN time.

4. We are now ready to sequence the activities according to resource constraints. TNOW is set at 0. The allowable activities (ACT. ALLOW.) to be considered for scheduling at TNOW of zero are those activities that would have a critical path method starting time of 0, namely activities G, A, and C. These are placed in the ACT. ALLOW. row, sequenced in decreasing ACTIM order. In this example, G, A, and C all have the same ACTIM and so can be sequenced in any order. In the resources available column the resources initially available are placed, namely 3.

5. Determine if the first activity in ACT. ALLOW., G, can be assigned. It can, as three resources are available and G requires only one. Also, no predecessor limitations foul the picture. A line is struck through G to indicate assignment and the number of resources available is decreased by one to a value of 2, since G required one resource. TSTART for activity G is set at the current TNOW and the TFIN is set at TSTART plus activity G's duration time. Now it is necessary to determine if activity G being completed will allow another activity to be feasible at some future time. With G it is not, as G is itself an entire critical path. This same process is repeated for the remainder of ACT. ALLOW. activities until the resources available are depleted. In our case, all activities G, A, and C could be assigned a TSTART of zero. From the network of Figure 6–1 it is seen that assigning activity A allows activity B to be scheduled a TEARL of 5 time units later

(activity A's TFIN). Similarly, activities D and F can be assigned a TEARL which is the latest of A and C's TFIN times. Note that if activity A had required too many resources to allow assignment at TNOW of 0, we would still see if activity C could be assigned.

6. TNOW is raised to the next TFIN time which happens to be 5, the completion times of both activities A and C. The resources available at TNOW of 5 is set to the number remaining after assigning resources at TNOW equal to zero (0 in this case), added to the number of resources freed due to activity completion at the new TNOW (2 in this case). ACT. ALLOW. we now set at those not assigned at the previous TNOW (none in our case), added to those which have a TEARL equal to TNOW (D, B, and F).

7. Repeat this assignment process until *all* activities have been scheduled. The latest TFIN gives the duration of the project, which is 17 time units as expected in this example.

As a further example, Table 6–2 gives the assignment if only two resource units are available. The time assignment is found to be 25 days, quite an extension from 17 with three resources. It is left to the reader to determine whether or not the schedules realized in Tables 6–1 and 6–2 are optimum or not. Section 6–11 will present a continuation of Chapter 2's case problem which has a relatively complex network to which we will apply a variant of Brooks' algorithm to multiple resource problems.

Table 6–2

Brook's Algorithm Solution to Limited Resource Example with Two Units of Resource

	Activity	G	A	C	D	B	F	E	
ACTIVITY DATA	Duration	16	5	5	7	4	8	4	**PROJECT COMPLETION TIME**
	ACTIM	16	16	16	11	8	8	4	
	Resources required	1	1	1	1	1	1	1	
	TEARL	0	0	0	10	5	10	20	
	TSTART	0	0	5	10	16	17	20	
	TFIN	16	5	10	17	20	(25)	24	
ALGORITHM ITERATION RESULTS	TNOW	0		5	10	16	17	20	
	Resources available	ⱦ0		⅄0	⅄0	⅄0	⅄0	⅄0	
	ACT. ALLOW.	₲ A̶ C		₵ B	₱ B F	₿ F	F̶	E	
	Iteration No.	1		2	3	4	5	6	

The operation of the heuristic algorithm shows several pertinent points that may be helpful in designing such a procedure. *First*, it is logical. It just plain makes sense to assign activities on the basis of the time that they control through the network. This insures, for example, that critical path activities are assigned first. *Second*, the *next event* procedure of looking ahead to see when the next change will occur in resource status makes the actual work involved in using the algorithm as simple as possible. Third, it iteratively approaches a solution. This makes each stage of the solution relatively simple to apply as well as orienting the solution to possible computer manipulation. These three characteristics of logic, simplicity of application, and computer orientation should be paramount when designing heuristic algorithms for complex problem solution.

William Gleeson (of Honeywell) has suggested to the author that optimality might be guaranteed if assignment were based on some criterion other than ACTIM, or the time each activity controls through the network. This certainly might be the case if another criterion dominates. Gleeson suggested that *time* and *resource* for an activity should be considered and suggested for each activity that the activity time multiplied by the resource requirement for the activity be considered in a manner analogous to ACTIM. For example, consider the network given in Figure 6–3, which we will schedule using ACTIM and also using each activity (time)(resource) value, which will be designated as ACTRES. Table 6–3 gives the allocation by ACTIM while Table

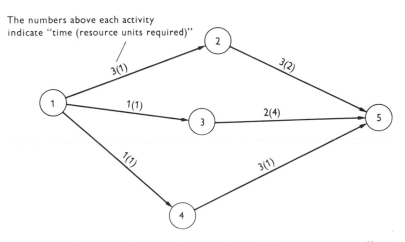

Figure 6–3. Network to allow evaluation of two different resource allocation criteria.

Table 6–3

Resource Allocation by ACTIM for Network Given in Figure 6-3; Total Resources Limited to Five Units

	Activity	1–2	1–4	1–3	2–5	4–5	3–5	
ACTIVITY DATA	Duration	3	1	1	3	3	2	
	ACTIM	6	4	3	3	3	2	
	Resources required	1	1	1	2	1	4	
	TEARL	0	0	0	3	1	1	
	TSTART	0	0	0	3	1	6	PROJECT COMPLETION
	TFIN	3	1	1	6	4	⑧	TIME
ALGORITHM ITERATION RESULTS	TNOW	0			1		3	4	6
	Resources available	~~5~~ ~~4~~ ~~3~~ 2			~~4~~ 3		~~4~~ 2	3	~~5~~ 1
	ACT. ALLOW.	~~1–2~~; ~~1–4~~; ~~1–3~~			~~4–5~~; 3–5		~~2–5~~; 3–5	3–5	~~3–5~~
	Iteration No.	1			2		3	4	5

6–4 gives a similar allocation using ACTRES. For each case, five units of the resource are available.

The schedule using ACTIM gives a total duration of 8 time units while by ACTRES an overall duration of 6 time periods is achieved. First of all, it is now obvious that Brooks' algorithm is not optimum, as mentioned earlier. A rather significant improvement of 25 percent by ACTRES is achieved.

Table 6–4

Resource Allocation by ACTRES for Network Given in Figure 6-3; Total Resource Limited to Five Units

	Activity	1–2	1–3	3–5	2–5	1–4	4–5	
ACTIVITY DATA	Duration	3	1	2	3	1	3	
	ACTRES	9	9	8	6	4	3	
	Resources required	1	1	4	2	1	1	
	TEARL	0	0	1	3	0	1	PROJECT
	TSTART	0	0	1	3	0	3	COMPLETION
	TFIN	3	1	3	⑥	1	⑥	TIME
ALGORITHM ITERATION RESULTS	TNOW	0			1		3	
	Resources available	~~5~~, ~~4~~, ~~3~~, 2			~~4~~,0		~~5~~, ~~3~~, 2	
	ACT. ALLOW.	~~1–2~~; ~~1–3~~; ~~1–4~~			~~3–5~~; 4–5		~~2–5~~; ~~4–5~~	
	Iteration No.	1			2		3	

Now, a brief change in the network data given in Figure 6–3 has an interesting result. Change activity 4-5's time duration to 7 time units, rather than the original 3. Leave everything else as given in Figure 6–3. The scheduling results using ACTIM and ACTRES are as given in Tables 6–5 and 6–6. Now ACTIM gives a more optimum solution, and only one data change was made. This pinpoints the complexity inherent in resource allocation optimization. Also, keep in mind that only *one* resource has been considered—usually far from a realistic condition. The Gantt schedules for the four resource allocation results are given for comparison reasons in Figure 6–4. ACTRES places emphasis on early assignment of activities which have heavy resource requirements for long periods of time. This is certainly a highly practical consideration. However, it is seen from the second example (Tables 6–5 and 6–6) that critical path activities may not be assigned in some optimal ordering using ACTRES. Activity 4-5, for example, was delayed in start for two time units even though it was a critical path item. These two time units are exactly the time length advantage ACTIM had over ACTRES. Without complete possible schedule enumeration, an impossibility for realistic projects even with digital computers, some optimal algorithm would have to incorporate a *criteria decision step* to determine the best criteria for optimality. This is a very difficult task. Again, it should be recalled that we have not yet considered *multiple* resource requirements.

Table 6–5

Resource Allocation by ACTIM for Network Given in Figure 6–3; Activity 4-5 Duration Changed to 7 Time Units. Total Resources Limited to 5 Units

	Activity	1–4	4–5	1–2	1–3	2–5	3–5	
ACTIVITY DATA	Duration	1	7	3	1	3	2	
	ACTIM	8	7	6	3	3	2	
	Resources required	1	1	1	1	2	4	
	TEARL	0	1	0	0	3	1 PROJECT	
	TSTART	0	1	0	0	3	6 COMPLETION TIME	
	TFIN	1	8	3	1	6	⑧	
ALGORITHM ITERATION RESULTS	TNOW		0		1		3	6
	Resources available		5̶ 4̶ 3̶ 2		4̶ 3		4̶ 2	4̶ 0
	ACT. ALLOW.		1̶-̶4̶; 1̶-̶2̶; 1̶-̶3̶		4̶-̶5̶; 3-5		2̶-̶5̶; 3-5	3̶-̶5̶
	Iteration No.		1		2		3	4

Table 6-6

Resource Allocation by ACTRES for Network Given in Figure 6-3; Activity 4-5 Duration Changed to 7 Time Units. Total Resources Limited to 5 Units

	Activity	1-2	1-3	1-4	3-5	4-5	2-5	
ACTIVITY DATA	Duration	3	1	1	2	7	3	
	ACTRES	9	9	8	8	7	6	
	Resources required	1	1	1	4	1	2	
	TEARL	0	0	0	1	1	3	
	TSTART	0	0	0	1	3	3	PROJECT COMPLETION → TIME
	TFIN	3	1	1	3	(10)	6	
ALGORITHM ITERATION RESULTS	TNOW			0		1	3	
	Resources available			~~5~~ ~~4~~ ~~3~~ 2		~~4~~ 0	~~5~~ ~~4~~ 2	
	ACT. ALLOW.			~~1-2; 1-3; 1-4~~		~~3-5;~~ 4-5	~~4-5;~~ 2-5	
	Iteration No.			1		2	3	

One way out of this dilemma might be to consider some *combination* of criteria. As an example, Mason[6] suggested a combination of ACTIM and ACTRES that for simplicity we will designate as TIMRES for time resource combination. One possibility is to add the ACTRES and ACTIM criteria together for TIMRES, as shown in Table 6–7. For the first example, it is found that TIMRES has *exactly* the same activity sequence as ACTRES and so the activity schedule will be the same. ACTRES was optimum in that case, and so, therefore, would be TIMRES. In example two, the TIMRES activity sequence differs from ACTIM in that activities 2-5 and 3-5 are reversed in the last two positions and 4 5 and 1-2 are also reversed a little higher in the sequence. The TIMRES schedule is calculated for this case in Table 6–8.

Interestingly enough, this schedule is the same as the previous best schedule by ACTIM, but if all the completion times are added, it is found that the TIMRES sum is one unit less than ACTIM, allowing for a recuperation maybe from possible schedule slippage. In no way is TIMRES to be construed as being better than ACTIM or ACTRES. However, if ACTIM or ACTRES tend to outweigh one or the other, then TIMRES should be able to *automatically* pick it up. In a similar fashion it might be beneficial to incorporate quantification of other possible criteria. One word of caution should be made regarding the use of some combinatorial decision criteria, such as TIMRES. Because ACTRES is

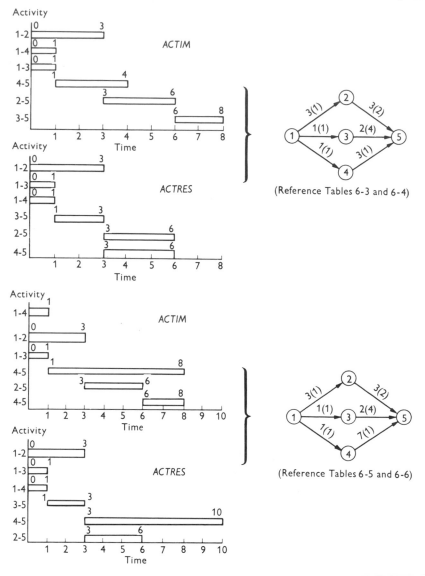

Figure 6–4. Gantt chart summary of example resource schedules.

formed by multiplying activity resource requirements by activity time it will usually dominate ACTIM. Somehow they should be similarly scaled. In our examples the resource requirements were so low that ACTRES scaling was quite similar to ACTIM. When this is not the case putting the rank for ACTIM, ACTRES, TIMRES, or whatever, on

Table 6–7

Calculation of Resource Allocation TIMRES
Criteria from Previous Examples

Example Number 1:

Activity	ACTIM	ACTRES	TIMRES
1–2	6	9	15
1–3	3	9	12
3–5	2	8	10
2–5	3	6	9
1–4	4	4	8
4–5	3	3	6

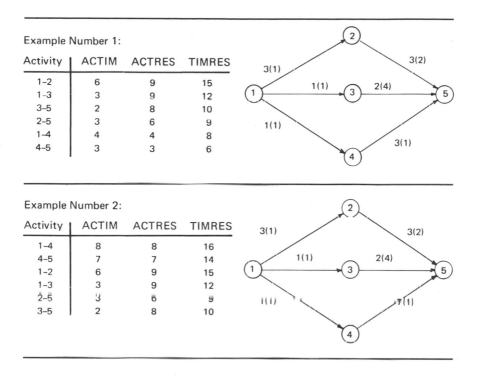

Example Number 2:

Activity	ACTIM	ACTRES	TIMRES
1–4	8	8	16
4–5	7	7	14
1–2	6	9	15
1–3	3	9	12
2–5	3	6	9
3–5	2	8	10

a 0–100 scale would solve this. Table 6–9 shows this for the ACTIM, ACTRES, and TIMRES values given originally in Table 6–7, Example 2. Their scaled values would be used in activity sequencing for resource assignment. It is seen that ranking over the range 0–100 TIMRES will give an activity priority sequence 1-4, 1-2, 4-5, 1-3, 3-5, 2-5. This is exactly the same priority sequence generated by the original TIMRES. However, frequently with large resource requirements per activity this would not be so.

6–3. MULTIPLE RESOURCES

The multiple resource allocation problem can get out of hand very easily when one considers that many resources in conjunction with

Table 6-8

Resource Allocation by TIMRES for Data
Given in Table 6-7, Example Two

	Activity	1-4	1-2	4-5	1-3	3-5	2-5	
ACTIVITY DATA	Duration	1	3	7	1	2	3	
	TIMRES	16	15	14	12	10	9	
	Resources required	1	1	1	1	4	2	
	TEARL	0	0	1	0	1	3	
	TSTART	0	0	1	0	3	5	
	TFIN	1	3	8	1	5	8	
ALGORITHM ITERATION RESULTS	TNOW	0			1	3		5
	Resources available	~~6~~ ~~4~~ ~~3~~ 2			~~4~~ 3	~~4~~ 0		~~4~~ 2
	ACT. ALLOW.	~~1-4~~; ~~1-2~~; ~~1-3~~			~~4-5~~; 3-5	~~3-5~~; 2-5		2-5
	Iteration No.	1			2	3		4

precedence requirements can really give many possible schedule combinations. However, one tabular computer-oriented approach by Mason[6] as an extension of Brooks' algorithm gives an excellent *simple* heuristic approach to getting a good schedule. This is basically a four-step procedure. The steps will be given at the same time as a very simple network two-resource problem is solved. This same procedure

Table 6-9

Scaling Combinatorial Resource Assignment Criteria to
Allow Compatible Mating. Original ACTIM, ACTRES and TIMRES
Data from Table 6-7, Example Two

Activity	Non-Scaled Criteria			Scaled on Range Equals 0-100		
	ACTIM	ACTRES	TIMRES	ACTIM	ACTRES	TIMRES
1-4	8	8	16	100	89	189
4-5	7	7	14	88	78	166
1-2	6	9	15	75	100	175
1-3	3	9	12	38	100	138
2-5	3	6	9	38	67	105
3-5	2	8	10	25	89	114

will then be applied in the case problem solution of the Far-East Housing Project originally presented in Chapter 2. This will be a 13-resource item problem and will be solved manually to demonstrate its simplicity of application.

Consider the project given in Figure 6–5. The following steps will indicate the scheduling procedure for the project activities, with the problem being worked as each step is given.

Step One: Test the resource requirements for each activity against resources available to see if any schedule is feasible. This step hopefully is obvious. If any activity requires more resources than are totally available then it is impossible to schedule that activity. In the example problem there are 3 units of resource A and 4 units of resource B. The maximum requirement by any activity is 3 of each. The requirements are feasible and we can continue. This step in a computer program would allow a check of the data input to be made for correctness.

Step Two: Compute ACTIM or other decision criteria for each activity, working backwards from the terminal node of the network.

This allows the maximum path length for *each* activity to be automatically calculated somewhat in the critical path manner described in Chapter 2. For the current example this would be:

Activity	ACTIM
3–4	4
2–4	3
1–3	5
1–2	5

For further explanation, consider the network in Figure 6–6 with times but not resource requirements given for each activity. The time given in the squares by each node represents the *longest* path to that node working from the last node, which is considered to have a time of 0. ACTIM for each activity equals that activity's ending node time value added to the activity time. Activity 2-4 has an ACTIM of 10 (the ending node value) + 5 (activity length). Similarly, activity 2-3 has an ACTIM of 6 + 4, or 10. This latter case shows the danger in assuming ACTIM is the activity leading node time value, which it is in some cases but not in others. Continuing with the original example:

Step Three: Rank the activities according to ACTIM in a decreasing sequence.

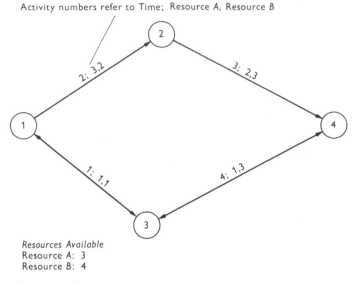

Activity numbers refer to Time; Resource A, Resource B

Resources Available
Resource A: 3
Resource B: 4

Figure 6–5. Project for two-resource assignment example.

Again, this is an obvious step by now, but would require a computer sort in a programmed algorithm. Our example sequence would be:

Activity	ACTIM	
1–2	5⎫	Requires some decision
1–3	5⎭	for computer sequence.
3–4	4	
2–4	3	

Activities 1-2 and 1-3 have the same ACTIM. Nothing has been said yet as to what criteria to use in breaking the tie. We will use the criterion of "longest activity first" in this case on the assumption that shorter activities will be easier to assign later. Many other criteria, such as

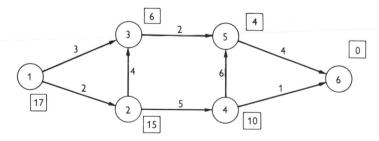

Figure 6–6. Computing ACTIM for a network.

"most resource requirement" could be considered. The validity of "longest activity first" will be shown later in this example's solution.

Step Four: Construct work table and follow-through solution.

The work table will be a little simpler than the tabular presentation used earlier for single resource allocation. The allowable activities, TNOW and certain other data will not be included. The solution will progress down the work table with respect to time until a final solution and project time has been achieved. This solution is given in Table 6–10. A few pertinent comments regarding this solution are given below and correspond to the *time* column of the work table.

> Time 0: Starting resource values of 3 and 4 are first given. Highest ACTIM activity (1-2) is scheduled, which depletes resource A. If any starting activity had required *no* resource A then possibly it could have also been scheduled at time zero. Now time is incremented to 2 the next immediate activity completion time.
>
> Time 2: Activity 1-2 resources returned to available pool. Next activities in ACTIM sequence assigned according to resource requirements. Time incremented to next immediate activity completion time—activity 1-3 completes at time period 3. This overall process continued until all activities assigned. No activity can be brought into the ranked decision set until all immediate predecessors have been assigned.

One last comment on the example. Figure 6–7 gives the Gantt chart solution for the example just as solved, and also for the case where the ACTIM tie was not broken by longest activity first. In this latter case the schedule was one time period longer than the optimum.

6–4. RESOURCE BALANCING

Not quite as systems oriented, maybe, is the resource balancing problem. It does allow a rather orderly transition into the specialized *production* topic of *line balancing*. Resource balancing is an interesting topic in its own light and will be briefly presented only from a single product point of view.

In considering *single resource* allocation only, two scheduling approaches may be considered:

A. Determine the *minimum time* schedule for a particular project given a specified number of resource units available, with that resource being critical. This is the problem just tackled.

B. Given a specified *time length* for a particular project, determine the *minimum* number of resource units required to allow the project

Table 6-10

Working Table for Solution of Two-Resource Example Problem

Time	Activity	Duration	Start	Finish	Available		ACTIM-Ranked
					Resource A	Resource B	Allowable Activities
0	-	-	-	-	3	4	
0	1-2	2	0	2	0	2	1-2; 1-3
2	1-2	-	-	-	3	4	
2	1-3	1	2	3	2	3	1-3; 2-4
2	2-4	3	2	5	0	0	
3	1-3	-	-	-	1	1	None
5	2-4	-	-	-	3	4	3-4
5	3-4	4	5	9	2	1	
9	3-4	-	-	-	3	4	Project Complete

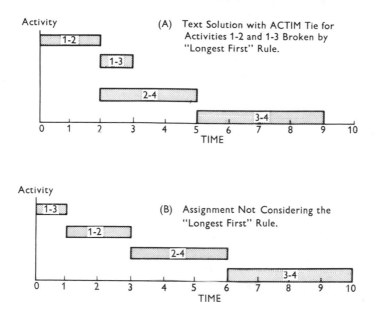

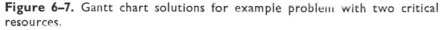

Figure 6–7. Gantt chart solutions for example problem with two critical resources.

to be realized within its time constraint. This will be the *resource balancing* problem.

It should be apparent that the *resource balancing* problem is an iterative variant of the initial *resource scheduling* problem and one way to tackle the problem would be to repetitively solve the resource scheduling problem, starting with some upper or lower bound on the resource level, and then iterate the resource schedule algorithm by either increasing or decreasing the resource level as applicable until the "optimum" resource level is determined. Possibly the best approach would be to determine the *minimum* feasible resource level for the project under some logical assignment criterion. The easiest way to do this would be to start with the *maximum* resource level required by any one activity. The time to complete the project with this resource level would then be computed. If this time is equal to or less than the stipulated project time, the resource balance is completed. If not, then the resource level is increased by one and the process repeated until the project time is equal to or less than stipulated. Needless to say, if the resultant resource level is greater than possibly available, the project stipulated time is infeasible.

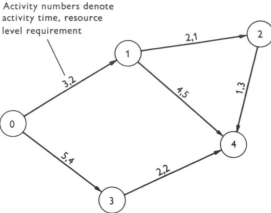

Figure 6–8. Network for resource balancing example.

As an example, consider the network given in Figure 6–8. A required completion date indicates the project length should be 10 time periods. What is the minimum resource level to achieve this? We start with the lower bound resource level at 5, otherwise activity 1-4 could not be accomplished. Using ACTIM as the resource assignment criteria, we get the iterative solution given in Table 6–11. Iteration one, with a resource level of 5 units, gives a schedule of 15 time periods, much greater than the stipulated 10. Iteration two, with a resultant 11 time periods, is getting close. Finally, iteration 3 gives the required resource balance of 7 units to get the project accomplished in 10 time periods.

Multiple resources can be handled in exactly the same way, with *each* iteration being handled as we tackled multiple resources earlier. Different assignment criteria, such as TIMRES, could be incorporated exactly as before. A flow chart is given for a possible solution to the multiple-resource allocation balancing problem in Figure 6–9. A single resource problem would naturally be a limiting case. Similarly, the resource allocation problem discussed initially would be a single-iteration through the flow chart.

6–5. THE LINE–BALANCING PROBLEM

An example of *limited-capacity scheduling* is the traditional manufacturing line-balancing problem. As implied in its name, the line balancing problem is pretty well restricted to *production* problems, particularly those of *mass production*. The *limited-capacity* aspects come

Table 6-11

Iterative Resource Balancing for Project Depicted in Figure 6-8 with Time Stipulation of Ten Units

	Activity	0–3	0–1	1–4	1–2	3–4	2–4	
Iteration 1	ACTIM	7	7	4	3	2	1	
	Duration	5	3	4	2	2	1	
	Resources Req'd	4	2	5	1	2	3	
	TEARL	0	0	8	8	5	14	Completion with 5 Resources
	TSTART	0	5	8	12	5	14	
	TFIN	5	8	12	14	7	(15)	
	TNOW	0	5	7	8	12	14	
	Resources Avail.	5̸ 1	5̸ 3̸ 1	3	5̸ 0	5̸ 4	5̸ 2	
	ACT. ALLOW.	0̶–̶3̶;0–1	0̶–̶1̶;3̶–̶4̶	–	1̶–̶4̶;1–2	1̶–̶2̶	2̶–̶4̶	

	Activity	0–3	0–1	1–4	1–2	3–4	2–4	
Iteration 2	TEARL	0	0	3	3	5	5	Completion with 6 Resources
	TSTART	0	0	5	3	0	9	
	TFIN	5	3	9	5	(11)	10	
	TNOW	0	3		5		9	
	Resources Avail.	6̸ 2̸ 0	2̸ 1		6̸ 1		6̸ 4̸ 1̸	
	ACT. ALLOW.	0̶–̶3̶;0–1̶	1–4;1̶–̶2̶		1̶–̶4̶;2–4;3–4		3–4;2–4	

	Activity	0–3	0–1	1–4	1–2	3–4	2–4	
Iteration 3	TEARL	0	0	3	3	5	5	Completion with 7 Resources
	TSTART	0	0	5	3	6	9	
	TFIN	5	3	9	5	7	(10)	
	TNOW	0	3		5	7	9	
	Resources Avail.	7̸ 3̸ 1	3̸ 2		7̸ 2̸ 0	2	7̸ 4	
	ACT. ALLOW.	0̶–̶3̶;0–1̶	1–4;1̶–̶2̶		1̶–̶4̶;3̶–̶4̶;2–4	2–4	2̶–̶4̶	

about from the fact that given a restricted number of operators, or work stations, it is possible to determine a *schedule* of operations required within the production line for each work station that allows the production rate to be maximized. Conversely, it is possible, given a restricted production rate, to determine the minimum number of work stations required to do the job. Certain line balancing heuristic solution techniques have applicability in the more general resource allocation problem. This will be seen as we apply the *ranked positional weight*

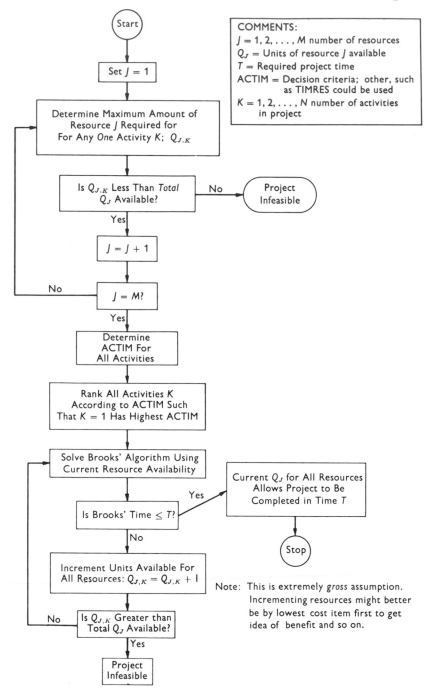

Figure 6–9. Flow chart for multiple resource balancing.

approach to line balancing. The resource allocation material presented earlier in this chapter used an identical approach.

The origin of the line balancing problem came from *assembly line* operations. The problem was to determine the *grouping* of tasks that an operator could accomplish before the item being assembled was moved to the next operator in the line for further work. These groupings of tasks had to take into consideration the rate at which parts were required to be produced and also precedence restrictions enforced by the production sequence. For example, suppose the assembly of a desk lamp involves the following operations:

1. Assemble base to stem. (3 minutes)
2. Insert electrical switch in stem. (4 minutes)
3. Install bulb in stem. (1 minute)
4. Install shade on stem. (2 minutes)
5. Pack. (4 minutes)

(This is quite naive but it is designed only to make a point.) Let's assume that the five operations have to be performed in the sequence given, such that item 1 *has to* precede item 2, item 2 *has to* precede item 3, and so on.

The time to produce one item governs the operator work assignment and is classified as the *cycle time*. The cycle time is a function of the production rate. For example, if the production rate is 60 units per hour then the cycle time would be 1 minute per unit. For the lamp problem the production rate is given at 12 units per hour, with a corresponding cycle time of 5 minutes per unit. The minimum number of operators would be *four*. One operator would do operations 3 and 4 while the other three operators would each perform one of the remaining operations. An operator could *not* perform both operations 1 and 4, even though the total work time would be 5 minutes, as they are separated by two other operations, which indicates that the intervening operations *have* to be performed before operation 4 can be accomplished.

One problem in this assignment could come about if, for some obscure production reason, installing the bulb in the stem and installing the shade on the stem has to be accomplished in different rooms. This physical separation would preclude one operator performing the two operations and five operators would now be required. Therefore, in addition to the precedence limitations, physical separations have to be considered. Similarly, if two different operators require different *skill* requirements, say electrician and welder, then this presents a separation of a different kind. These latter separation restrictions are commonly called *zone* restrictions.

The rather complex line balancing problem now boils down to the following. Knowing the operations required in a particular assembly task and knowing their precedence and zone restrictions, determine an optimal operator/operation(s) assignment to allow a particular cycle time to be met. Actually, as with resource allocation, this can be broken into two problems, one of which can be solved by iteratively solving the other:

1. Given a required *cycle time*, find the *minimum number* of *operators* required to perform the operations in an assembly task, knowing each operation's time, precedence, and zone status.

2. Given a specified *number* of *operators*, determine the *minimum* cycle time in which an assembly can be produced, knowing each operation's time, precedence, or zone status.

To further generalize, a grouping of operations will be classified as a work *station* where usually one operator will be assigned to a station. The following symbology will be used in the solutions to the line balancing problem:

1. Let t_i be the time for the ith operation 0_i in the assembly task. $i = 1, 2, 3, \ldots, N$.
2. Let C be the cycle time.
3. Let S_k be the set of operations in the Kth work station. $k = 1, 2, 3, \ldots, M$.
4. Let T be the overall time available for the sequence of assembly required.
5. Let Q be the production quantity required in T. Therefore $C = T/Q$.

The restrictions for assignment of operations to stations, other than precedence or zone, has to include:

1. $1 \leq M \leq N$
   The number of stations cannot be greater than the number of operations. Also the minimum number of stations is one.
2. $T_i \leq C$
   No operation time may be greater than the cycle time (unless multiple operators are allowed per operation). Implicit in this restriction is that the accumulation of operation times per station cannot exceed the cycle time.

6–6. HELGESON-BIRNIE (H-B) SOLUTION

One of the earliest heuristic approaches to line balancing was proposed by Helgeson and Birnie.[3] Their approach assigned operations to stations in an order that corresponds to the length of time each controls through the remainder of the network. This is directly comparable to the resource allocation ACTIM procedure. The only difference is that *all* succeeding operations are considered in the ranking, not just those on the longest path emanating from the operation in question. The sum of the times of those operations controlled in this manner by a particular operation is defined as the *positional weight*. Ranking operations in *decreasing* sequence according to their positional weights leads to the technique designation of *ranked positional weight technique*. Of course, as operations are assigned to stations, cognizance has to be taken of the precedence and zoning restrictions. The latter is very simple. Since a zone includes only operations that may be combined with each other, having separate line balance solutions for each zone solves the restriction. However, one complication of this is with operations that can be in one of several zones.

Rather than dream up a line balancing example to demonstrate the H-B solution, we will utilize one that Wester and Kilbridge presented as a realistic case problem in the *Journal of Industrial Engineering*.[8] This problem presented a two-line situation, but in order to simplify the presentation we will only utilize one of the lines. It still incorporates all the features one would expect in a line balancing problem.

The problem is one of assembling television sets. The portion of the line under consideration is shown in Figure 6–10, along with a *precedence network* showing all work operations to be accomplished. The precedence network has all the same connotations associated with network development as given in Chapter 2. The major difference, which is minor, lies in the fact that the nodes are themselves operations with arrows representing precedence. The problem is complicated by the fact that there are two sides to the conveyor line, so activities required on one side of the line cannot be mixed with those required on the other side. Otherwise, the operator would be climbing over the conveyor periodically. Similarly, operations requiring the front of the set facing the operator cannot be mixed with those requiring the set's back, unless the operator is to physically rotate the set. In addition, the test station presents a process separation whereby operations preceding the test station cannot be mixed with those following.

At first glance it would seem that grouping all operations together as one set which require work at the front of the set, and those which require work at the back as another set, with separate balances accomplished for each set, would be a start. Also, a third set would be the

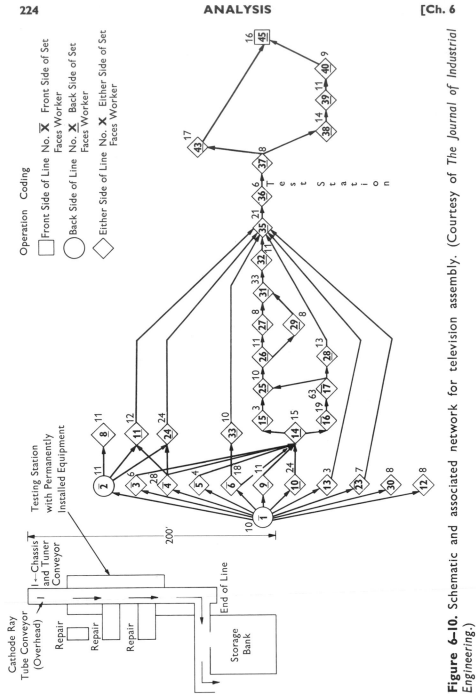

Figure 6–10. Schematic and associated network for television assembly. (Courtesy of *The Journal of Industrial Engineering.*)

operations *after* the test station. This simple approach breaks down when a *front* operation intervenes between a series of *back* operations, or vice versa. A case in point with the network of Figure 6–10 is that operations 14 and 25 cannot be combined because operations $\overline{16}$ and $\overline{17}$ intervene. Similarly, $\overline{6}$ and $\overline{16}$ cannot be combined because of 14. Paradoxically though, $\overline{23}$ and $\overline{16}$ can be combined and so can $\overline{23}$ and $\overline{6}$, but as just mentioned, not $\overline{6}$ and $\overline{16}$. Thus the problem becomes more complex. Zone groupings can be as given in Table 6–12. The three operations requiring a firm *front* or firm *back* of the line position are not distinguished from the others in this vein as the others can either be in the back or the front. A solution to the line balancing problem is now to group operations together only if their zone relationship allows, and by some assignment decision rule. As mentioned the H-B assignment

Table 6–12

Allowable Zones for Example Line Balancing Problem

Operation	Allowable Zones	Operation	Allowable Zones
$\overline{1}$	A*	$\overline{16}$	D
$\overline{2}$	A	$\overline{17}$	D
$\overline{3}$	A	25	C
$\overline{4}$	A	28	C
5	A	26	C
$\overline{6}$	A	27	C
9	B	29	C
10	B	31	C
13	A or B or C or D	32	C
$\overline{23}$	A or D	35	C
30	A or B or C or D	36	C
12	A or B or C or D	37	E
8	B or C	38	E
11	B or C	43	E
24	B or C	39	E
33	B or C	40	E
14	B	45	E
15	B or C		

*Only operations with the same alphabetic zone
can be combined in the same section.

Table 6-13

Calculation of Operation Positional Weights for Example Problem

Operation	Positional Weight (PW)
45	16
40	25
39	36
38	50
43	33
37	75
36	81
35	102
32	113
31	146
29	154
27	154
26	173
25	183
28	115
17	259
16	278
15	186
14	296
33	112
24	126
11	114
8	11
12	8
30	8
23	109
13	105
10	320
9	307
6	324
5	300
4	360
3	302
2	160
1	491

decision rule assigns operations in accordance to the amount of time each operation controls through the network.

The first step, once the precedence network is developed, is to compute the positional weight for each operation. This is the cumulative sum of all operation times that follow the particular operation, added to the particular operation's duration time. Operation 38 would have a positional weight of 50, which is the sum of the times for elements 38, 39, 40, and 45. Similarly, 37 has a positional weight of 75, which corresponds to the positional weight for 38 added to the times for operations 43 and 37. All operation positional weights are found similarly, working back from the end of the network. The results of this step are given in Table 6–13. Ranking the operations in decreasing positional weight sequence gives the H-B *ranked positional weight* sequence of Table 6–14. Operations are assigned to stations in this sequence, subject of course to zoning restrictions, and cycle time limits.

Assuming a cycle time of 84 (one that Wester and Kilbridge found to have a remarkably good fit) the first operation to be assigned would be 1̄

Table 6–14

Ranked Operations by Positional Weights (Table 6-13)

Operation	Rank	Operation	Rank
1̄	1	28	19
4̄	2	11	20
6̄	3	32	21
10	4	33	22
9	5	2̄3̄	23
3̄	6	13	24
5̄	7	35	25
14	8	36	26
1̄6̄	9	37	27
1̄7̄	10	38	28
15	11	39	29
25	12	43	30
26	13	40	31
2̄	14	45	32
29	15	8	33
27	16	12	34
31	17	30	35
24	18		

Table 6–15

Use of the H-B Algorithm To Assign Operations in a Line Problem

C = 84

Station	Operation	Operation Time	Cumulative Station Time	Comments
1	$\overline{1}$	10	10	$\overline{1}$ has highest positional weight 10; 9 in wrong zone.
	$\overline{4}$	28	38	
	$\overline{6}$	18	56	
	$\overline{3}$	6	62	
	$\overline{5}$	4	66	
	$\overline{2}$	11	77	
	$\overline{23}$	7	84	Station 1 time = C; STOP.
2	10	24	24	10 highest positional weight operation not yet assigned.
	9	11	35	
	14	15	50	
	15	3	53	14 and 25 in different zones— assign 15.
	24	24	77	
	13	3	80	All other allowable operations force station 3 time > 84; STOP
3	$\overline{16}$	19	19	
	$\overline{17}$	63	82	
4	25	10	10	
	26	11	21	
	29	8	29	
	27	8	37	
	31	33	70	
	28	13	83	All other allowable operations force station 4 time > 84; STOP
5	11	12	12	
	32	11	23	
	33	10	33	
	35	21	54	
	36	6	60	
	8	11	71	
	12	8	79	All other allowable operations force station 5 time > 84; STOP

Table 6-15 (*Continued*)

Station	Operation	Operation Time	Cumulative Station Time	Comments
6	30	8	8	No other operations can combine.
7	37	8	8	
	38	14	22	
	39	11	33	
	43	17	50	
	40	9	59	
	45	16	75	All operations assigned.

with a station 1 cumulative time of 10. The next to be assigned are $\bar{4}$ and $\bar{6}$. The next operations to be assigned, by positional weight, should be 10 and 9. These are in different zones from $\bar{1}$, $\bar{4}$, and $\bar{6}$ and so cannot be assigned at this time. The next element that is satisfactory is $\bar{3}$ which accumulates the station time to 15. This process continues until $C \leq 84$ with no more operations feasible to assign. The first element *not yet assigned* in the ranked positional weight sequence is assigned to station 2. This process continues until all operations have been assigned, as is shown in Table 6–15.

The result is painful. Stations 1, 2, 3, 4, 5, and 7 have quite a balanced work load. Station 6 would only be working about 10 percent of the time. The answer is to try to get six stations instead of the seven. This is not so obvious. One answer, which requires decreasing the production rate, is to increase the cycle time to 85. Now operation 13 could be transferred from station 2 to station 5 (just before operation 35). Now station 6's operation 30 can be safely placed in station 2.

Actually the Helgeson-Birnie approach usually gives a good balanced workload. However, it is computer oriented and it is heuristic, so an optimum is not necessarily achieved. Mansoor suggested an improvement to the B-H approach which will guarantee optimality.[5] Unfortunately, the combinations of elements that might have to be tackled would make it somewhat non-feasible for large networks. Another way to tackle the problem, as with resource allocation, is to use a different decision criterion for operation assignment.

Several papers have been published giving heuristic solutions to the line balancing problem. Frequently, it is found that examples are given with the procedure for which an excellent solution is achieved. However, alternating the examples with solutions sometimes realizes a solution which is certainly not optimum. The moral of course is that the one unique heuristic algorithm for line balancing just does not exist, as was found with resource allocation. Orienting the technique for computer solution, as with the H-B technique, requires a simplification that might occasionally give poor results, as with the problem just investigated. The analyst should take the solution and attempt to generate a better one by induction, if possible.

A possible improvement on the H-B approach, at least for the given problem, will be presented to show how an algorithm might be developed. The approach will utilize some of the ideas found in the H-B method, Mansoor's approach, and one developed by Kilbridge and Wester.[4] The latter was *not* computer oriented but required an analyst's perception for solution. The philosophy of the approach will entail:

1. Operations that have heavy precedence responsibility (several operations dependent) should be scheduled early.
2. In line with 1, a fallacy of the H-B approach is that an operation with a large associated time might take precedence over one with heavy dependence responsibilities, if several of the dependent operations are small in time. For example, in the previous problem, if operation 12 had a time of 84, it would have had an assignment capability over operation *37* even though *37* has 5 subsequent operations and 12 none.

6–7. IMPROVED PROCEDURE

The steps involved in the new solution will be:

1. Develop the precedence network in the normal manner.

2. Assign *precedence zones* from left to right. Re-draw the network with all operations being assigned the latest precedence zone possible. This will insure that operations with few dependencies will at least be considered for assignment late in the schedule.

3. Within each precedence zone rank operations from maximum to minimum duration times. This will insure that the largest operation will be considered first, giving the chance for a better combination of smaller operations later. This was one problem with the previous H-B solution.

4. Assign operations by the following sequence, conforming to process zone restrictions:
    a. Leftmost zone first.
    b. Within a zone, assign according to largest operation first.

5. At the end of each *station* assignment decide if the time utilization

is acceptable. If not, check *all* operations whose predecessor relations have been satisfied. Determine if changing these for any operation(s) within the station whose predecessor zone(s) are equal to or earlier than the operations being considered for entry into the station, will increase the utilization. If yes, make the change.

This will be clarified in the example problem.

The network given in Figure 6–10 will be re-evaluated using the new procedure. The solution will be given in the same order as the given procedural steps. Operations after the test station will *not* be considered as they form a distinct separate balance.

Step 1: The network was developed in Figure 6–10.

Step 2: The network, redrawn according to precedence zones, is given in Figure 6–11.

Step 3: Operation priorities, according to decreasing operation times within zones, are given in Table 6–16.

Step 4) Assignment of operations to stations is given in Table 6–17
Step 5) with appropriate comments.

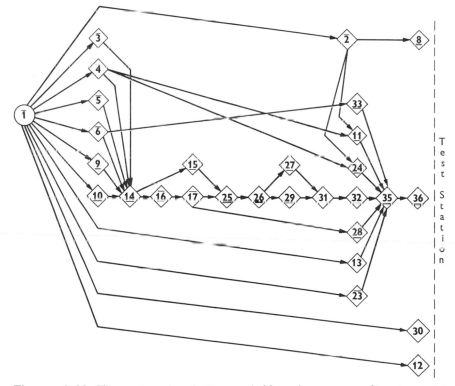

Figure 6–11. The network of Figure 6–10 redrawn according to zone precedence characteristics.

Table 6–16

**Sequencing of Elements According to Zone
Precedence Characteristics and Decreasing
Times Within Zones**

Zone	Elements Within Zone Ranked According to Decreasing Time →
1	T
2	$\overline{4}$; $\underline{10}$; $\overline{6}$; $\underline{9}$; $\overline{3}$; $\overline{5}$
3	$\underline{14}$
4	$\overline{16}$
5	$\overline{17}$; $\underline{15}$
6	$\underline{25}$
7	$\underline{26}$
8	$\overset{\frown}{27}$; 29
9	$\underline{31}$; $\overline{2}$
10	$\underline{24}$; $\underline{28}$; $\underline{11}$; $\underline{32}$; $\underline{33}$; $\overline{23}$; 13
11	$\underline{35}$
12	$\underline{36}$; $\underline{8}$; $\overset{\frown}{30}$; 12

The assignment turns out to be the same as determined by Wester and Kilbridge, although the sequence to get them is a little different. Only one station change had to be made to improve the utilization. The advantage of attempting to improve only the last *station* balance according to some acceptable utilization factor has to lie with the fact that each station should have only a few operations within it, and relatively few operations should be eligible for switching into the station. Thus, possible improvements should be readily apparent, as in the example. A *disadvantage* in attempting to optimize each station as the balances are made accrues due to the fact that the good combinations of large and small operations might be used early in the balance, forcing possible bad balances later in the line. Needless to say, the method just generated does not guarantee optimality, although solutions should be good solutions approaching optimal, and might well be optimal. A possible *production line* schematic using the solution is given in Figure 6–12.

The only measure of a good station balance that we discussed was that of *cumulative time utilization*. The most utilized method, which is directly analogous to cumulative time utilization, is that of station

Table 6-17

Line Balance for Example Problem Using Developed Heuristic Approach

Station	Operation	Operation Time	Cumulative Operation Time	Comments
1	$\overline{1}$	10	10	
	$\overline{4}$	28	38	
	$\overline{6}$	18	56	
	$\overline{3}$	6	62	
	$\overline{5}$	4	66	
	$\overline{2}$	11	77	
	$\overline{23}$	7	84	Perfect balance—forget step 5
2	10	24	24	
	9	11	35	
	14	15	50	
	~~15~~	~~3~~	~~53~~	25 not with 14 in zone
	24	24	~~77~~ 74	
	~~13~~	~~3~~	~~80~~	
	33	10	84*	Perfect balance; exchange 33 for 15; 13
3	$\overline{16}$	0.19	0.19	
	$\overline{17}$	0.63	0.82	
4	15	3	3	
	25	10	13	
	26	11	24	
	27	8	32	
	29	8	40	
	31	33	73	
	32	11	84	
5	28	13	13	
	11	12	25	
	13	3	28	
	35	21	49	
	36	6	55	
	8	11	66	
	30	8	74	
	12	8	82	

*After operation 13 assigned, the available operations not assigned but whose predecessors have been completed are: 8; 11; 16; 13; 23; 30; 12; 33.

Exchanging 33 for 15 and 13, neither of which affect the assignment of 33, realizes a station increase of 7 time units.

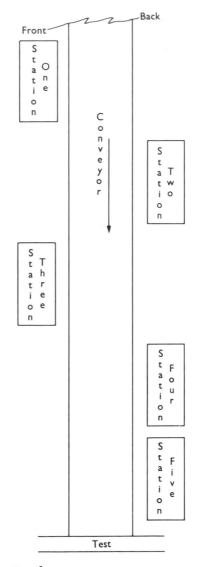

Figure 6–12. Schematic of station arrangement corresponding to balance determined in Table 6–17.

efficiency. Station efficiency is calculated by

$$\text{S.E.} = \left[\frac{\sum\limits_{i \in k} T_{i,k}}{C} \right] \left[100 \right] \%$$

where $\sum T_{i,k}$ designates the cumulative sum of the operation times within the Kth station. The maximum S.E. is, of course, 100 percent when the sum of the operation times within the station equals cycle time.

Similarly, line efficiency is found with:

$$\text{L.E.} = \left[\frac{\sum\limits_{i=1}^{N} T_{i}}{(M)(C)} \right] \left[100 \right] \% \tag{6–1}$$

where M was earlier designated as the number of stations within the line, and N is the total number of operations to be balanced. If a variety of line balances are made for a variety of cycle times, a saw-tooth curve for line efficiency is realized, somewhat as shown in Figure 6–13. Theoretically, the range of cycle times would be such as to allow a range of 1 up to N stations. N stations would be realized when only one operation is in each station and 1 station occurs if all operations can be included in one station. The efficiency drops when $(K - 2)$ stations increases to $(K - 1)$ because, from Equation 6–1, $\sum\limits_{i=1}^{N} T_{i}$ does not change, but $(M)(C)$ increases as a function of M. The "optimum" balance for a *specified* number of stations would occur at the line

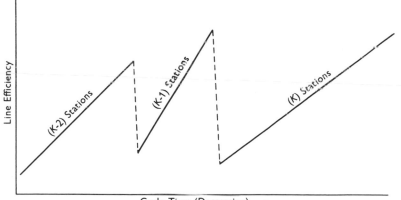

Figure 6–13. Saw tooth characteristic of line efficiency vs. cycle times.

efficiency peak for that number of stations, as this would occur at the lowest cycle time. This, of course, would give the highest production rate for that number of stations.

Finally, a few comments are in order regarding the state of the art in line balancing research. Even though production lines may be considered to have completely deterministic times, this may not be the case. In the mechanized line where line balancing may be utilized to determine automatic operations to be scheduled between transfer mechanisms, the deterministic concept may be valid. In operator-controlled situations, such as stacking in the manufacture of semiconductor devices, this would tend to not be the case. Moodie and Young considered the possibility of line balancing where the operator times were random variables.[7]

Also, multi-product situations have not been considered. Random entry by a variety of products into a line leads to another interesting line balancing problem. This was considered by Deutsch in his doctoral dissertation.[2] The discrete situation solution we developed demonstrated at least how a good solution may be evolved for a highly complex problem by an almost common sense approach.

6–8. LIMITED PROCESS CAPACITY

Scheduling products within a production facility where capacity limitations exist at various processing points within each product's sequence, both from a time and output capacity view, was one of the earlier linear programming examples. Simple problems, with two or three products only, may be attacked graphically. More complex problems can be tackled using the *simplex* approach given in Chapter 5. Two production problems will be presented, with two and four products respectively to be scheduled. This will allow the advantages and disadvantages of graphical solutions to be first presented, while the four-product problem forces the use of the simplex.

For the first example, consider that a company has been manufacturing 100 units of Product A (Q_A) per year and 100 of Product B (Q_B). Each of these products has to go through a sequence of four processes in order to be manufactured, and each process has 2,000 hours available for utilization by both products per year. Market surveys indicate that a relatively unlimited production of Product A could be absorbed by the consumer, but Product B has a limit of 175 units per

Table 6-18

**Hours per Unit Required
in Each Process**

	Product	
Process	A	B
1	3	10
2	8	7
3	6	8
4	4	2

year. Management wonders if the best utilization of current processes are being made.

The hours per unit that each product requires in each process are given in Table 6-18. Profit for Product A (Z_A) has been found to be $250 per unit and for Product B (Z_B) to be $300. A restatement of the problem posed in the first paragraph would be to find the schedule of product mix that maximizes profit, and compare it with the existing schedules.

The problem may be formulated for linear programming solution by:

Objective Function: Maximize $(250)(Q_A) + (300)(Q_B) = Z$ subject to:

$$3Q_A + 10Q_B \leq 2,000$$
$$8Q_A + 7Q_B \leq 2,000$$
$$6Q_A + 8Q_B \leq 2,000$$
$$4Q_A + 2Q_B < 2,000$$
$$Q_B \leq 175$$

The objective function tells us that we want to maximize the combined profits of products A and B. The first four constraint equations tell us that the combined number of hours spent by the two products in each process may not exceed 2,000 hours for each process. The fifth constraint indicates that the market capacity for product B is 175 units per year. A graphical portrayal of the five constraints is given in Figure 6-14.

The constraint lines for a particular process represent the locus of all possible combinations of products per year manufactured in that particular process. For example, consider process 3 with the constraint of $6Q_A + 8Q_B \leq 2,000$. Two points are needed to describe the boundary line representing this constraint. If Q_B is 0, then 333 units of A could be

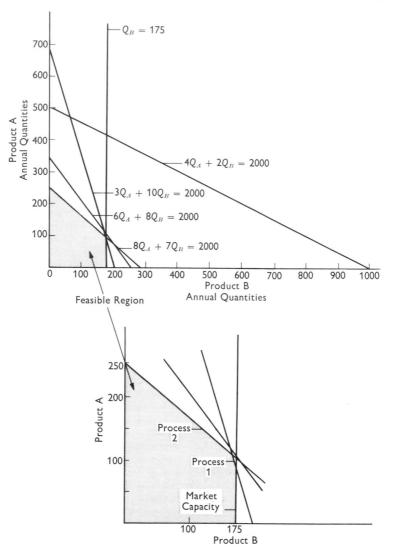

Figure 6–14. Graphical representation of constraints for example one.

manufactured. Similarly, if Q_A is 0, 250 units of B are possible. Connecting these two points on the graph represents the constraint for process 3. For this process only, combinations of products A and B may be produced that graphically fall on or below this line. However, any points below indicate this process is below capacity. Figure 6–14 shows us that the two limiting processes, as far as products A and B are concerned, are processes 1 and 2, and the market capacity for product

B. Any combination of products A and B that graphically falls in the shaded area bounded by processes 1 and 2, and the market capacity of B, is a feasible level of production. In other words, with the given conditions these quantities of the two products can be produced.

The profit level for any of the feasible combinations is also a linear function, as described by the original objective function. Isometrically, this is shown in Figure 6–15. The fact that for each process the profit Z is a linear function can be shown by:

1. $Z = Q_A Z_A + Q_B Z_B$, where Z_A and Z_B are profits per unit and are constants.
2. Each process boundary was defined by a linear equation. For example process 2 was defined by: $8Q_A + 7Q_B = 2,000$ so $Q_A = 250 - \frac{7}{8}Q_B$
3. Substituting this into the Z formula gives: $Z = (250 - \frac{7}{8}Q_B)(Z_A) + (Q_B)(Z_B)$ which is a linear function in terms of Q_B.

Therefore, the profit has to be maximum at one of the *end-points* of the process boundary line, a fundamental tenet of linear programming. This is shown by the profit plane of Figure 6–15. What it also tells us is that, once we have the feasible region defined, as in Figure 6–14, the maximum profit can be found algebraically by determining the profits only at *process boundary breakpoints*.

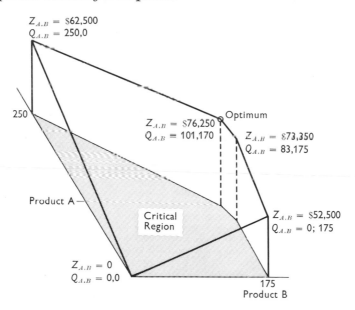

Figure 6–15. Profit-plane for critical region in example one problem.

6–9. ALGEBRAIC SOLUTION

In the critical region, Figure 6–15, there are four breakpoints, not counting 0, 0. Two are obvious: $Q_A = 250$, $Q_B = 0$; and $Q_A = 0$, $Q_B = 175$. The quantities at the other two breakpoints can be found by solving the two intersecting processes in each case simultaneously. Going up from $Q_B = 175$, the first intersection is between *process 1* and the Q_B market capacity line. At this point $Q_B = 175$. We know process 1 is defined by

$$3Q_A + 10Q_B = 2{,}000$$

So

$$Q_A = \frac{2{,}000 - (10)(175)}{3} = 83$$

The profit at this point is found from

$$Z = (Q_A)(Z_A) + (Q_B)(Z_B)$$
$$Z = (83)(250) + (175)(300) = \$73{,}350$$

Moving along the feasible region boundary, the next breakpoint is between process 1 and process 2, each defined respectively by

$$3Q_A + 10Q_B = 2{,}000$$

and

$$8Q_A + 7Q_B = 2{,}000$$

Solving simultaneously, $Q_A = 101$ and $Q_B = 170$. The profit at this point is now

$$Z = (101)(250) + (170)(300) = \$76{,}250$$

The other two breakpoints realize profits as

1. $Q_B = 175$: $Z = (175)(300) = \$52{,}500$
2. $Q_A = 250$: $Z = (250)(250) = \$62{,}500$

And so algebraically we realize the·same schedule as was found graphically in Figure 6–15. Manufacture 101 units per year of product A and 170 units of product B.

Another way to pinpoint the graphical solution more rapidly is to plot iso-profit lines on the critical region, as shown in Figure 6–16. An iso-profit line is defined as one on which, for any combination of products manufactured, the profit is the same. Two such lines are

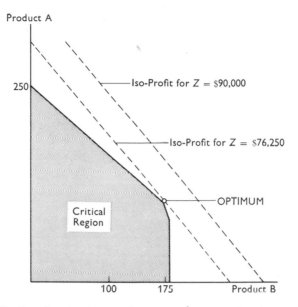

Figure 6–16. Graphical solution for example one using iso-profit lines.

shown in Figure 6–16, for $Z = \$90,000$ and $Z = \$76,250$. The fact that these iso-profit lines are parallel can be shown:

1. When $Q_B = 0$; $Z = (Q_A)(Z_A)$.
2. When $Q_A = 0$; $Z = (Q_B)(Z_B)$; since iso-profit means a constant Z:
3. $(Q_A)(Z_A) = (Q_B)(Z_B)$.
   But the slope of an iso profit line is Q_A/Q_B so:
4. Slope $= Q_A/Q_B = Z_B/Z_A$
   Since Z_B/Z_A is constant ($300/250 = 1.2$ in example one) the iso-profit lines have to be parallel.

The optimum profit point on the critical region is found by finding the point on the critical region through which an iso-profit line will pass, without passing through any other part of the critical region—not counting the 0, 0 point. The iso-profit lines increase in value as they are moved out from the 0, 0 points and so the line farthest from the origin that still touches the critical region has to define the maximum profit point.

Finally, the simplex solution for this problem is given in Table 6–19. The reader is referred to Chapter 5 for review of the simplex procedure if this solution method seems a little fuzzy. The original tableau was

Table 6-19

Simplex Solution for Example One

I.

	C	Q_A	Q_B	
Z	0	250	300	
S_1	2000	-3	-10	
S_2	2000	-8	-7	
S_3	2000	-6	-8	
S_4	2000	-4	-2	
S_5	175	0	(-1)	→Pivot 1

II.

	C	Q_A	S_5	
Z	52,500	250	-300	
S_1	250	(-3)	10	→Pivot 2
S_2	775	-8	7	
S_3	600	-6	8	
S_4	1,650	-4	2	
Q_B	175	0	-1	

III.

	C	S_1	S_5	
Z	73,330	-83.3	530	
Q_A	83	-0.33	3.33	
S_2	108	2.67	(-19.67)	→Pivot 3
S_3	100	+2.00	-12.00	
S_4	1,317	+1.33	-11.33	
Q_B	175	0	-1	

IV.

	C	S_1	S_2	
Z	76,240	-10.98	-27.1	OPTIMUM
Q_A	(101)	0.12	-0.17	Q_A = 101
S_5	5.49	0.14	-0.05	Q_B = 170
S_3	34.11	0.37	0.61	Z = \$76,240
S_4	1,254.80	-0.21	0.58	
Q_B	(170)	-0.14	0.05	

formulated from the original objective function and constraints:

Objective Function: Maximize $(250)(Q_A) + (300)(Q_B) = Z$, subject to

$$3Q_A + 10Q_B \leq 2{,}000$$
$$8Q_A + 7Q_B \leq 2{,}000$$
$$6Q_A + 8Q_B \leq 2{,}000$$
$$4Q_A + 2Q_B \leq 2{,}000$$
$$Q_B \leq 175$$

Adding slack variables where required to remove the inequalities and then solving for Z and these slack variables we get

$$Z = 250Q_A + 300Q_B$$
$$S_1 = 2{,}000 - 3Q_A - 10Q_B$$
$$S_2 = 2{,}000 - 8Q_A - 7Q_B$$
$$S_3 = 2{,}000 - 6Q_A - 8Q_B$$
$$S_4 = 2{,}000 - 4Q_A - 2Q_B$$
$$S_5 = 175 - (1)Q_B$$

When comparing the simplex solution with the critical region given in Figure 6–14 it is seen that the original tableau of course represents the origin point $(Q_A = 0; \ Q_B = 0)$. Tableau II gives $Z = \$52{,}500$ for $Q_B = 175$ and $Q_A = 0$. The third tableau continues along the boundary region to give $Z = \$73{,}330$ for $Q_A = 83$ and $Q_B = 175$. Finally, the bottom tableau gives the optimum solution at $Q_A = 101$ and $Q_B = 170$: $Z = \$76{,}240$.

The original question asked if the current schedule of 100 units of product A and 100 of product B is optimum. Obviously not, as the annual profit would be \$55,000 as contrasted to a possible optimum of \$76,240. Figure 6–14 shows an obvious fallacy in the original $Q_A = 100$: $Q_B = 100$ production scheme. It is far below capacity. If 100 units of B were required, A would be limited by process 2 and could have a production level of:

Process 2: $8Q_A + 7Q_B = 2{,}000$
$$8Q_A + (7)(100) = 2{,}000$$
$$Q_A = 1{,}300/8 = 162 \text{ units}$$

Adding the extra 62 units of A to the schedule would realize an *added* profit of $(62)(250)$ or \$15,400. A similar analysis fixing product A at 100 units per year would show that product B could be produced at 170 units—the optimum calculated earlier.

So, several ways for attacking the two-product process capacity problem have been given. Data are now readily available to allow determination of the various process utilizations assuming the optimum profit schedule is maintained. In turn, this will give an idea of process capacity available for sub-contracting, other product manufacture, and so on. Similarly, data are on hand to show which processes it might be advantageous to expand to increase profit. Figure 6–14, for example, shows that processes 4 and 3 would not be expanded initially. Figure 6–16 tells us, by looking at the iso-profit lines, that trying to increase the market for product B alone will not be fruitful. It is left to the reader to show that if only one process can be expanded, that this should be process 2. Unfortunately, as products in the scheduling problem increase, the usefulness of the graphical approach decays. In fact, if there are four products it is hopeless.

6–10. FOUR-PRODUCT EXAMPLE

Four products are to be shipped, with unlimited demand for each. The products cannot exceed 2,000 pounds in weight and cannot exceed 1,000 cubic feet in volume. The potential profits for products A, B, C, and D are 10, 20, 30, and 25 dollars per unit. The volumes and weight per unit are given in Table 6–20. The problem can be re-stated mathematically, if we wish to maximize the profit:

Objective Function: Maximize $Z = 10Q_A + 20Q_B + 30Q_C + 25Q_D$ subject to:

$$3Q_A + 6Q_B + 4Q_C + 2Q_D \leq 1,000$$

$$5Q_A + 4Q_B + 2Q_C + 6Q_D \leq 2,000$$

Needless to say, a graphical solution is now impossible. The simplex solution is given in Table 6–21 and follows exactly the procedure

Table 6–20

Unit Data for Example Two

	Product			
	Q_A	Q_B	Q_C	Q_D
Volume/unit, ft.^{3}	3	6	4	2
Weight/unit, lb.	5	4	2	6

Table 6–21

Simplex Solution for Example Two

I.		C	Q_A	Q_B	Q_C	Q_D	
	z	0	10	20	30	25	
	S_1	1000	-3	-6	(-4)	-2	Pivot 1
	S_2	2000	-5	-4	-2	-6	

II.		C	Q_A	Q_B	S_1	Q_D	
	z	7500	-12.50	-25.0	-7.50	10.0	
	Q_C	250	-0.75	-1.5	-0.25	-0.5	
	S_2	1500	-3.50	-1.0	0.50	(-5.0)	Pivot 2

III.		C	Q_A	Q_B	S_1	S_2	
	z	10,500	19.50	-27.00	-6.50	-2.00	OPTIMUM
	Q_C	(100)	-0.40	-1.40	-0.30	0.10	Q_C = 100
	Q_D	(300)	-0.70	-0.20	0.10	-0.20	Q_D = 300
							Z = $10,500

utilized in the last two examples. The solution tells us to ship only two products, C and D, and a profit of $10,500 will be realized.

One interesting aspect of this problem is that it could be worked by solving a series of two simultaneous equations. When only one constraint is given in a problem of this kind, the solution is found to be only *one* product. Two constraints will lead to a combination of two products or only one, and so on. At the most then, the optimum will be a combination of two products. Since there are three products this means that six combinations of two each are possible. Taking the two constraint equations for just products C and D (assuming $Q_A = Q_B = 0$) we get

$$4Q_C + 2Q_D = 1,000$$

$$2Q_C + 6Q_D = 2,000$$

Solving simultaneously we find

$$Q_D = 300 \text{ units}$$

$$Q_C = 100 \text{ units}$$

The profit is found to be

$$Z = (Q_D)(Z_D) + (Q_C)(Z_C)$$
$$Z = (300)(25) + (100)(30) = \$10,500$$

which is the result found by the simplex. It is left to the reader to check out the other five combinations and the three cases where only one product is produced to show that this result is the optimum. Of course, negative quantities denote infeasible combinations.

6–11. CASE PROBLEM

In Chapter 2 we analyzed a critical path planning project for the erection of two-story prefabricated buildings for a tropical climate, such as Southeast Asia. A feasible range of schedules evolved for this project was found to be 12 days to 25 days, with a total cost range going from \$9,462 to \$7,174 (see Table 2–11). The optimum schedule

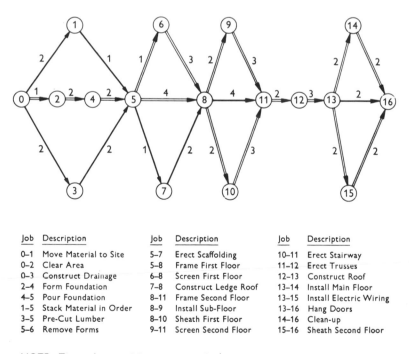

Job	Description	Job	Description	Job	Description
0–1	Move Material to Site	5–7	Erect Scaffolding	10–11	Erect Stairway
0–2	Clear Area	5–8	Frame First Floor	11–12	Erect Trusses
0–3	Construct Drainage	6–8	Screen First Floor	12–13	Construct Roof
2–4	Form Foundation	7–8	Construct Ledge Roof	13–14	Install Main Floor
4–5	Pour Foundation	8–11	Frame Second Floor	13–15	Install Electric Wiring
1–5	Stack Material in Order	8–9	Install Sub-Floor	13–16	Hang Doors
3–5	Pre-Cut Lumber	8–10	Sheath First Floor	14–16	Clean-up
5–6	Remove Forms	9–11	Screen Second Floor	15–16	Sheath Second Floor

NOTE: Times above activity arrows are in days.
        Double-line activities are critical.

Figure 6–17. Case problem network.

for minimum total cost was determined to be 23 days. However, a cursory look at the resources available in line with this 23-day schedule showed several resources to be insufficient to allow the project to be completed within 23 days. This case problem picks up where that problem left off. The multiple-resource extension of Brooks' algorithm will be utilized to find what schedule, using the resources available and activity times generated for the 23 day critical path schedule, would really be feasible.

The 23-day network is given in Figure 6–17. The total resources available and activity resource requirements are given in Tables 6–22 and 6–23 respectively. Implicit in the crashing of a CPM network is the utilization of extra resources to allow the crashing to be accomplished. We will assume, however, that the 23-day CPM schedule has available the number of resources in Table 6–22.

The first solution step is to evolve the activity assignment criteria for each activity. ACTIM will be utilized, though ACTRES and TIMRES would be just as applicable. When using the amount of resource in ACTRES or TIMRES with *multiple* resources, some combination of resources, such as addition, would have to be made for each activity. Some common denominator would have to be utilized

Table 6–22

Resource Availability Sheet for Case Problem

Resource Identification		Available
Number	Description	
01	Flat bed truck	1
02	Concrete mixer	1
03	Truck mounted crane	1
04	Portable scaffolding	3
05	Circular saw	2
06	Small hand tools	3
07	Pick-up truck	1
08	Dump truck	1
09	Front loader	1
10	Road grader	1
11	Electricians	2
12	Carpenters	2
13	Laborers	15

Table 6-23

Job Resource Requirements for Case Problem

		Resource												
Activity		01	02	03	04	05	06	07	08	09	10	11	12	13
I	J	Qty	Qty	Qty	Qty	Qty	Qty	Qty	Qty	Qty	Qty	Qty	Qty	Qty
0	1	1	—	1	—	—	1	1	1	1	—	—	—	6
0	2	—	—	—	—	—	1	—	1	—	1	—	—	4
0	3	—	—	—	—	—	1	—	—	—	1	—	2	6
2	4	1	1	1	—	—	—	—	—	1	—	—	2	4
4	5	—	—	—	—	1	1	—	—	—	—	—	—	10
1	5	—	—	—	—	—	1	—	—	—	—	—	2	6
3	5	—	—	—	1	—	1	—	—	—	—	—	1	4
5	6	—	—	—	1	1	1	—	—	—	—	—	1	2
5	7	—	—	—	1	1	1	—	—	—	—	—	2	2
6	8	—	—	—	1	1	1	—	—	—	—	—	2	4
7	8	—	—	—	1	—	1	—	—	—	—	—	2	4
8	9	—	—	—	1	1	1	—	—	—	—	—	2	6
8	10	—	—	—	1	1	1	—	—	—	—	—	2	6
9	11	—	—	—	1	1	1	—	—	1	—	—	2	4
10	11	—	—	—	1	1	1	—	—	—	—	—	2	6
11	12	—	—	—	1	1	1	—	—	—	—	—	2	6
12	13	—	—	—	1	1	1	—	—	—	—	—	2	6
13	14	—	—	—	1	1	1	—	—	—	—	—	2	6
13	15	—	—	—	1	—	1	—	—	—	—	2	2	2
13	16	—	—	—	—	1	1	—	—	—	—	—	1	2
15	16	—	—	—	1	—	1	—	—	—	—	—	2	6
14	16	—	—	—	—	1	1	—	1	—	—	—	—	4
5	8	—	—	—	1	1	1	—	—	—	—	—	2	8
8	11	—	—	—	1	1	1	—	—	—	—	—	2	8

to allow them to be safely added. A logical one might well be cost of resource since dollars are certainly additive, even though flat bed trucks and circular saws are not.

ACTIM is found by first working backwards through the network, starting at time zero for the last node, and determining the *latest* time any node may occur. This of course is the *longest* path for the project leading to each particular node. These values are shown on Figure 6–18. ACTIM for each activity is now found by adding the activity *end node* time to the particular activity time. These are then sequenced according to decreasing ACTIM time, and the activities assigned in that basic sequence. The activity ACTIM values are given in Table 6–24 sequenced in decreasing order.

The solution to the problem using the multiple-resource solution approach is given in the working table presented in Table 6–25. Rather than laboriously go through the solution step-by-step, comments are given within the table regarding the solution. The Gantt chart schedule is given in Figure 6–19. The resultant time schedule of 43 days is a far cry from the CPM solution of 23 days. The only consolation is that the 43-day schedule is feasible. Contrast this 43-day Gantt schedule with that originally given in Figure 2–23 to see the real effect on time. Some of the steps given in Table 6–25 may seem rather pedestrian, but they are included to allow the resources to be maintained at their correct levels at all times. Running down the *comment* column in the solution it is easy to see which resources create the difficulty. Resource 12 for example is really hurting the schedule. Also, looking down the

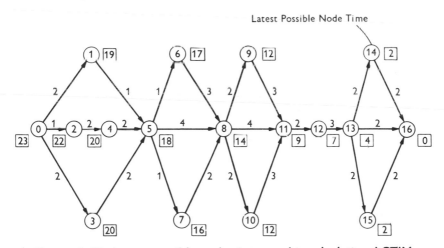

Figure 6–18. Latest possible node times used in calculating ACTIM.

Table 6-24

Case Problem Activities Ranked According to ACTIM

Activity	ACTIM	Reason for Breaking Precedence Tie
0—2	23	
0—3	22*	0—3 is initial event activity.
2—4	22	
0—1	21	
3—5	20*	No reason. Tie-break could be made on
4—5	20	resources required, cost, etc.
1—5	19	
5—8	18*	5—8 is longest duration.
5—6	18	
6—8	17	6—8 is longest duration.
5—7	17	
7—8	16	
8—10	14	No reason; see 3—5.
8—9	14	
8—11	13	
10—11	12	No reason; see 3—5.
9—11	12	
11—12	9	
12—13	7	
13—15	4*	No reason; see 3—5.
13—14	4	
13—16	2*	No reason; see 3—5.
15—16	2*	
14—16	2	

resource columns in conjunction with resource availability allows the utilization to be evaluated. Several resource units are found to be not required.

Finally, one or two salient conclusions might be in order:

1. The procedure is so simple it seems ridiculous. However, it was checked against the results obtained from a commercial resource allocation program and the ACTIM approach achieved exactly the same project length.

2. The author solved the problem under very distracting conditions. The solution was reached in $1\frac{1}{2}$ hours—not bad when one realizes this

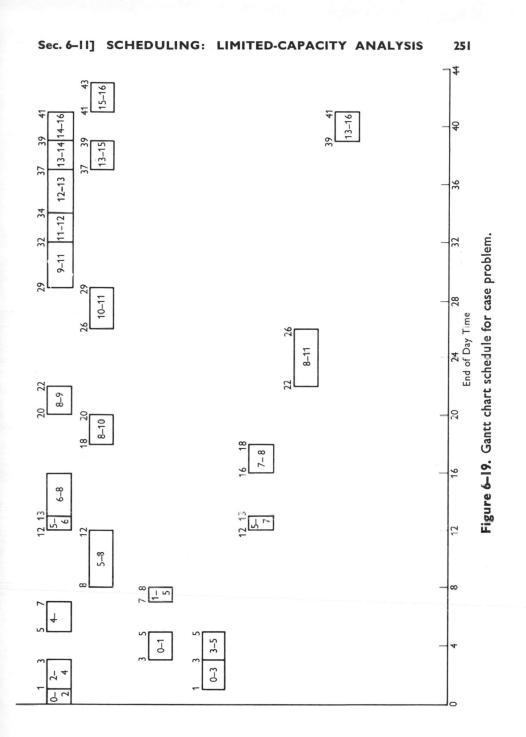

Figure 6–19. Gantt chart schedule for case problem.

Table 6-25

Case Problem Solution

Time	Activity	Duration	Start	Finish	R1	R2	R3	R4	R5	R6	R7	R8	R9	R10	R11	R12	R13	Allow Act. (ACTIM ratio)	Currently
0	—	—	—	—	1	1	1	3	2	3	1	1	1	1	2	2	15	~~0-2~~;0-3;0-1	R10 lack for both 0-3 and 0-1
0	0-2	1	0	1	1	1	1	3	2	2	1	0	1	0	2	2	11		0-2 Resources back
1	0-2	—	—	—	1	1	1	3	2	3	1	1	1	1	2	2	15	~~0-3~~;~~2-4~~;0-1	R10 lack for 0-1
1	0-3	2	1	3	1	1	1	3	2	2	1	1	1	0	2	2	9		
	2-4	2	1	3	1	1	1	3	1	1	1	1	1	0	2	0	5		
3	0-3 / 2-4	—	—	—	1	1	1	3	2	3	1	1	1	1	2	2	16	~~0-1~~;~~3-5~~;4-5	0-3 and R4 Resource back
3	0-1	2	3	5	0	1	0	3	2	2	0	0	0	1	2	2	9		
	3-5	2	3	5	0	1	0	3	1	1	0	0	0	1	2	0	5		R10 lack for 4-5
5	0-1 / 3-5	—	—	—	1	1	1	3	2	3	1	1	1	1	2	2	15	~~4-5~~;1-5	0-1 and 3-5 Resources back
5	4-5	2	5	7	1	1	1	3	2	2	1	1	1	1	2	0	5		
7	4-5	—	—	—	1	1	1	3	2	3	1	1	1	1	2	2	15	1-5	R13 lack for 1-5
7	1-5	1	7	8	1	1	1	3	2	2	1	1	1	1	2	2	9		4-5 Resources back
8	1-5	—	—	—	1	1	1	3	2	3	1	1	1	1	2	2	15	~~5-8~~;5-6;5-7	1-5 Resources back
8	5-8	4	8	12	1	1	1	2	1	2	1	1	1	1	2	0	7		R12 lack for 5-6 and 5-7
12	5-8	—	—	—	1	1	1	3	2	3	1	1	1	1	2	2	15	~~5-6~~;5-7	5-8 Resources back
12	5-6	1	12	13	1	1	1	3	2	2	1	1	1	1	2	1	13		
	5-7	1	12	13	1	1	1	2	2	1	1	1	1	1	2	0	11		
13	5-6 / 5-7	—	—	—	1	1	1	3	2	3	1	1	1	1	2	2	15	~~6-8~~;7-8	5-6 and 5-7 Resources back
13	6-8	3	13	16	1	1	1	3	2	2	1	1	1	1	2	0	11		R12 lack for 7-8

Time	Activity	Dur	Start	Finish												Total	Scheduled	Notes
16	6-8	–	–		1	3	2	3	1	1	1	1	1	2	2	15	~~7-8~~	6-8 Resources back
16	7-8	2	16	18	1	2	1	2	1	1	1	1	1	2	0	11		7-8 Resources back
18	7-8	–	–		1	3	2	3	1	1	1	1	1	2	2	15	~~8-10~~;8-9;8-11	R12 lack for 8-9 and 8-11
18	8-10	2	18	20	1	2	1	2	1	1	1	1	1	2	0	9		8-10 Resources back
20	8-10	–	–		1	3	2	3	1	1	1	1	1	2	2	15	~~8-9~~;8-11;10-11	R12 lack for 8-11 and 10-11
20	8-9	2	20	22	1	2	1	2	1	1	1	1	1	2	0	9		8-9 Resources back
22	8-9	–	–		1	3	2	3	1	1	1	1	1	2	2	15	~~8-11~~;10-11;9-11	R12 lack for 10-11 and 9-11
22	8-11	4	22	26	1	2	1	2	1	1	1	1	1	2	0	7		8-11 Resources back
26	8-11	–	–		1	3	2	3	1	1	1	1	1	2	2	15	~~10-11~~;9-11	R12 lack for 9-11
26	10-11	3	26	29	1	2	1	2	1	1	1	1	1	2	0	9		10-11 Resources back
29	10-11	–	–		1	3	2	3	0	1	1	1	1	2	2	15	~~9-11~~	10-11 Resources back
29	9-11	3	29	32	1	2	2	2	1	1	1	1	1	2	0	9		9-11 Resources back
32	9-11	–	–		1	3	2	3	1	1	1	1	1	2	2	15	~~11-12~~	9-11 Resources back
34	11-12	2	32	34	1	2	1	2	1	1	1	1	1	2	0	9		11-2 Resources back
34	11-12	–	–		1	3	2	3	1	1	1	1	1	2	2	15	~~12-13~~	
37	12-13	3	34	37	1	2	1	2	1	1	1	1	1	2	0	9		
37	12-13	–	–		1	3	2	3	1	1	1	1	1	2	2	15	~~13-15~~;~~13-14~~;13-16	13-15 & 13-14 Resources back
37	13-15	2	37	39	1	2	2	2	1	1	0	1	0	0	2	13		R12 lack for 13-16
37	13-14	2	37	39	1	2	2	1	1	1	1	1	0	0	0	7		
39	13-15	–	–		1	3	2	3	1	1	1	1	1	2	2	15	~~13-16~~;15-16;~~14-16~~	13-14 & 13-15 Resources back
39	13-14	–	–															
39	13-16	2	39	41	1	3	2	2	1	1	1	1	1	2	1	13		R12 lack for 15-16
39	14-16	2	39	41	1	3	2	1	1	1	0	1	1	2	1	9		
41	13-16	–	–		1	3	2	3	1	1	1	1	1	2	2	15	~~15-16~~	13-16 & 14-16 Resources back
41	14-16	–	–															
41	15-16	2	41	43	1	2	1	2	1	1	1	1	1	2	0	9		15-16 Resources back
43	15-16	–	–		1	3	3	3	1	1	1	1	1	2	2	15		PROJECT COMPLETE

PROJECT SCHEDULE

included ACTIM determination. Also, a 24-activity network with 13 resources is not small. Maybe a moral is that *simplicity can be a virtue.*

REFERENCES CITED

1. BROOKS, G. H., "Algorithm for Activity Scheduling To Satisfy Constraints on Resource Availability," unpublished paper dated September 17, 1963.
2. DEUTSCH, DONALD, "A Branch and Bound Technique for Mixed-Product Assembly Line Balancing," unpublished Ph.D. Dissertation, Faculty of Industrial Engineering, Arizona State University, Tempe, Arizona, February, 1971.
3. HELGESON, W. B., and BIRNIE, D. P., "Assembly Line Balancing Using the Ranked Positional Weight Technique," *The Journal of Industrial Engineering.* Vol. XII, No. 6, November–December, 1961.
4. KILBRIDGE, M. D., and WESTER, LEON, "A Heuristic Method of Line Balancing," *The Journal of Industrial Engineering*, Vol. XII, No. 4, July–August, 1961.
5. MANSOOR, E. M., "Assembly Line Balancing—An Improvement on the Ranked Positional Weight Technique," *The Journal of Industrial Engineering*, Vol. XV, No. 2, March–April, 1964.
6. MASON, RICHARD, "An Adaptation of the Brooks Algorithm for Scheduling Projects Under Multiple Resource Constraints," unpublished master's report, Faculty of Industrial Engineering, Arizona State University, Tempe, Arizona, August, 1970.
7. MOODIE, C. L., and YOUNG, H. H., "A Heuristic Method of Line Balancing for Assumption of Constant or Variable Work Element Times," *The Journal of Industrial Engineering*, Vol. XVI, No. 1, January–February, 1965.
8. WESTER, L., and KILBRIDGE, M. D., "Heuristic Line. Balancing: A Case," *The Journal of Industrial Engineering*, Vol. XIII, No. 3, May–June, 1962.

FURTHER READING

CONWAY, R. W., MAXWELL, W. H., and MILLER, L. W., *Theory of Scheduling*, Addison-Wesley Publishing Company, Reading, Mass., 1967.
DAVIS, E. W., "Resource Allocation in Project Network Models,—A Survey," *The Journal of Industrial Engineering*, Vol. XVII, No. 4, April 1966. [This reference contains a good bibliography covering the topic of resource allocation.]
IGNALL, E. J., "A Review of Assembly Line Balancing," *The Journal of Industrial Engineering*, Vol. XVI, No. 4, July–August, 1965. [Contains an excellent review of work accomplished on line balancing prior to 1965.]
O'BRIEN, J. J. (ed.), *Scheduling Handbook*, McGraw-Hill Book Company, Inc., New York, N.Y., 1969.

PROBLEMS

1. An airplane routine maintenance project requires the activities, activity times, and mechanics per activity shown in the following network:

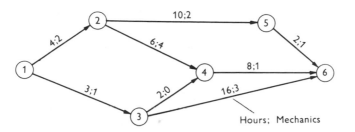

A. Develop the Gantt chart schedule evolved by conventional CPM analysis, without consideration for resource capacity.

B. If four mechanics are available, can the Gantt schedule be met? Justify your answer.

C. Utilize the Brooks algorithm to determine the minimum length (by Brooks) project utilizing a maximum of four mechanics total. Does this seem to be optimum?

D. A mechanic costs the company $27.50 per hour, including overhead, benefits etc. The cost of having an airplane idle in maintenance is $53.00 per hour. (This is a small plane.) What is the number of mechanics required to minimize the overall routine maintenance costs?

2. Given the same network problem as in Problem 1, determine the minimum time schedule with four mechanics, using the decision variable ACTRES and also schedule with TIMRES. How optimum does the Brooks' solution look now?

3. Consider the following project with given activity and resource requirements:

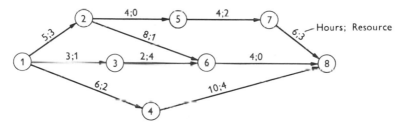

A. Determine the feasible minimum schedule time using both ACTIM and ACTRES, knowing the resource capacity is six units. If ACTIM or ACTRES gives a better schedule, justify why you think this occurred.

B. A fixed time duration of 22 hours is firmed for the project. Use the *balancing* approach to determine the minimum units of resource required for the project.

4. The airplane project given in Problem 1 actually requires mechanics, electricians, and laborers, as follows:

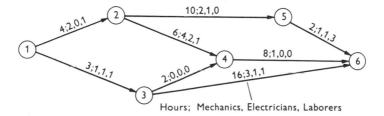

Use ACTIM to determine the minimum-length schedule given a total of four mechanics, two electricians, and three laborers.

5. The following precedence network and line balancing operation times were developed by Moodie and Young [Reference 7].

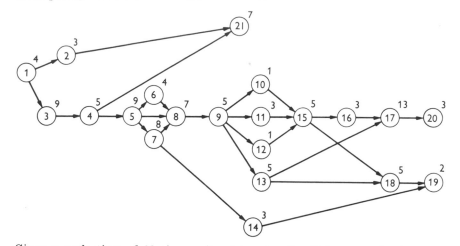

Given a cycle time of 21 time units, determine the Helgeson and Birnie line balance. Does this seem optimum?

6. For the same network, use the text-developed line balancing method balance. (*Note:* You should be able to achieve a line efficiency of 100%.)

7. Two products are manufactured through two processes with the following hours required in each process per product:

	Q_A	Q_B
Process 1	10	20
Process 2	18	15

Profit figures for A and B are $40 and $38, respectively. In addition, Product A has a market limitation of 10 units per month and B has one of 12 units. Process 1 has 180 hours per month available for the two products combined and process 2 has 200 hours.

A. Determine graphically the production schedule that maximizes monthly profit.

B. Check your solution with the simplex solution.

C. If one, and only one, process can be expanded, what would you recommend?

D. If a subcontract requires process 2 for 10 hours per month and will realize a net profit of $150 per month, what schedule would you suggest for products A and B production?

8. Five products are produced through two processes with the following hours required in each process per product:

	Q_A	Q_B	Q_C	Q_D	Q_E
Process 1	5	4	6	3	2
Process 2	2	3	4	2	5

Profit figures for products A, B, C, D, and E are 50, 60, 40, 30, and 20 dollars per unit. Monthly hours available are 100 for each of the processes. Demand is unlimited for each of the products. Determine the production schedule that maximizes profit.

7

Route Scheduling

*To everything there is a season, and a time
to every purpose under the heavens.*

ECCLESIASTES

7–1. DEFINITIONS

The introductory quote would have unique applicability to fore-casting (seasonal variations have to be considered), inventory control (which as we will see can be construed as a special case of scheduling), and also scheduling itself. The problem with scheduling, as with all the other functions, is to determine the best time to assign a start for those items requiring scheduling. Time may be construed as being the place that an item has in a particular *sequence*. The sequence does not itself denote the item *time*, but it of course will eventually dictate the time, once other items in the sequence have been accomplished.

This chapter will be devoted to *routing* problems, Chapter 8 to sequencing problems. Routing will be defined to mean the *path* that has to be taken in order to get something from one place to another with some criterion of optimality involved. This criterion may be minimization of the distance or cost, or maximization of profit, among others. The sequencing problem will be concerned with the *order* in which several things are accomplished with the objective being a minimization of the time which *all* the things take for completion, or some similar criterion. The first scheduling problem will be our old friend (by now), the *network* scheduling problem.

This will allow the practical concepts of dynamic programming to be introduced. This topic will then be utilized in multi-stage scheduling problems.

7–2. NETWORK ROUTING

Consider the simple network given in Figure 7–1. The nodes represent physical locations and the numbers above arrows represent some measure of the value or cost of transportation between the physical locations, with arrows of course representing a relationship between two locations. Suppose, first of all, that the numbers represent miles between adjacent cities joined by the arrows above which the numbers appear. What is the shortest distance from the western city at node 1 to *any* eastern city, represented by nodes 7, 8, or 9? With such a small network all possible path combinations can easily be enumerated and the minimum picked. With a more complex network this would not be as feasible. So we will attack the problem in a logical fashion, node by node. Since we want to go from node 1 initially, a logical start might be to pick the minimum path emanating from node 1. Then the minimum would be taken from the resultant nodes until a path is determined to an eastern location. Using this philosophy the path would be

1–5	4 miles
5–7	2 miles
Total path	6 miles

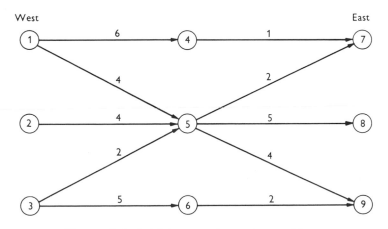

Figure 7–1. Initial network routing problem.

which is certainly the minimum path from node 1 to any eastern node. Suppose we wanted the longest path from node 1 to any eastern node. Using the same logic we would take the path

1–4	6 miles
4–7	1 mile
Total path	7 miles

Which certainly is *not* the longest path from node 1 to any eastern node. Why not? By discounting path 1–5 we have eliminated several path combinations, any one of which might be the optimum. The next logical approach then is to work *backwards* from the eastern nodes, determining the minimum (maximum) value at the intermediate nodes (4, 5, 6), and then using these values, determine the optimum at the starting nodes. For example, the *maximum* path would be found by

A. Maximum at node 4: path 7–4: 1*

B. Maximum at node 5: path 7–5: 2
 path 8–5: 5*
 path 9–5: 4

C. Maximum at node 6: path 9–6: 2*

The result of the first decision set has been achieved. Using the results of the decision set, the maximum path from node 1 can be determined:

Maximum of: (Node 4 maximum + path 4–1) = 1 + 6 = 7
and (Node 5 maximum + path 5–1) = 5 + 4 = 9*

The results of the second decision set show us that the longest path from node 1 to any eastern node is 9. Working forward from node 1 we find that path was formed by 1–5 and 5–8. Finding the minimum path in the same fashion we find that nodes 4 and 5 have minimum values of 1 and 2 respectively, through paths 7–4 and 7–5. The minimum from node 1 is then the minimum of

(Node 4 minimum + path 4–1) = 1 + 6 = 7
and (Node 5 minimum + path 5–1) = 2 + 4 = 6*

And the correct minimum path through 7–5, 5–1 is found.

Now let us consolidate what has gone into the solution technique:

1. By working *backward*, *all* possible combinations are enumerated.

2. At each *intermediate* point in the solution an optimum is determined. This optimum is then utilized in finding subsequent intermediate (or final) optimum solutions. This allows the potential

number of possible solutions to be reduced significantly at each decision point.

3. This approach may be utilized equally as well for minimization as for maximization problems.

Finally, it should be self-explanatory that we have been using the *dynamic programming* approach presented in Chapter 5. Groupings of locations (nodes) may be considered as *stages*, and so the network routing problem is certainly a *multi-stage scheduling* problem.

To wind up the network routing material prior to leading into further considerations of multi-stage scheduling, consider the more complex network shown in Figure 7–2. It might be mentioned at this time that an excellent, more rigorous treatment of network analysis by dynamic programming, and dynamic programming as an optimization technique, is presented in Chapter 8 of *Foundations of Optimization* by Wilde and Beightler.[7]

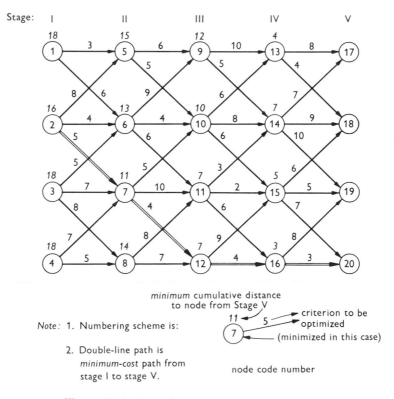

Figure 7–2. Complex transportation network.

The numbers between nodes might represent some cost coding with nodes being some physical location. The problem could be to determine the route from any stage I location to one at stage V that minimizes the accumulated path cost. This may seem a peculiar problem but it certainly exists in ship-line situations. A freighter going from Liverpool to a Gulf Coast port for example, will not necessarily guarantee to a passenger at which port he will disembark, say Gulfport, New Orleans, or Houston.

The solution for *minimizing* the accumulated path cost is given in Table 7–1. This is presented in tabular format which will be maintained in the next section covering multi-stage scheduling. Figure 7–2 shows above each node the accumulated minimum time through its and all preceding stages. The minimum cost is seen to be 16 coming from node 2. The tabular format of Table 7–1 will be a little clearer with regard to deciding the path to take for node 2 to a stage V node in order to achieve the 16 cost units.

Refer to Table 7–1 results. The stage IV results are predicated on an initial cost of 0 at any stage V node. If some penalty were required at one or more nodes, this certainly could be added. The ten entries in the stage IV tableau gives *all* possible path lengths to stage IV from stage V. This can be seen from Figure 7–2 as there are ten paths from stage IV to stage V. Considering only node 14 in stage IV, it can be seen that accumulations from stage V of 7, 9, and 10 are possible, depending on whether the path is from node 17, 18, or 19. The minimum of these is 7, which is starred in the stage IV tableau to indicate this is the accumulation that will be used in the stage III tableau. So, out of the ten paths in the stage IV tableau, only the 4 optimum will be considered for use in the next stage, cutting out 60 percent of the possible initial paths.

Continue to the stage III tableau, and node 10 in particular. Node 10 is fed from nodes 13, 14, and 15. The path cost for node 13 to node 10 is 6 units (from Figure 7–2). Add to this the minimum node 13 accumulated cost of 4 (from stage IV tableau) and an accumulated minimum cost through stage III to node 10 is 10 cost units. Similar calculations are accomplished for the cases where node 10 is fed from nodes 14 and 15. The minimum turned out to be the 10 cost units calculated from node 13, so that 10 value is starred. This process is continued through stage I to get the minimum possible paths from stage V through any node in stage I. The minimum values correlate nicely with those realized on the network in Figure 7–2.

Table 7-1

Tabular Solution Minimizing Transportation Costs for the Network Given in Figure 7-1

		Minimum Accumulation At Following Stage K Node:			
		13	14	15	16
From Stage	17	8	7*	—	—
(K+1) Node:	18	4*	9	6	—
K = Stage IV	19	—	10	5*	8
	20	—	—	7	3*
		9	10	11	12
	13	14	10*	—	—
	14	12*	15	10	—
Stage III	15	—	11	7*	14
	16	—	—	9	7*
		5	6	7	8
	9	18	21	—	—
	10	15*	14	15	—
Stage II	11	—	13*	17	15
	12	—	—	11*	14*
		1	2	3	4
	5	18*	23	—	—
	6	19	17	18*	—
Stage I	7	—	16*	18*	18*
	8	—	—	22	19

*Minimum accumulation at particular *column* node.

The overall minimum is 16 cost units with a path leaving from node 2. What path is taken to stage V to realize this? This is determined by working backwards from stage I. The starred value of 16 cost units for node 2 came from node 7. Find the starred 16 under node 2 in the stage

I tableau, and then move to the left to find the node it came from in stage II, which turns out to be node 7. Now go to node 7 in stage II and the optimum cost units of 11 came from node 12 in stage III. Continuing in this fashion it is found that the optimum path is

Node 2–Node 7–Node 12–Node 16–Node 20

Adding the path costs given in the network of Figure 7–2 shows this of course to be correct. If we had to start at node 3, it is seen for the stage I tableau that two paths give a cost of 18. Tracing back in the fashion just discussed gives these two paths as

Node 3–Node 6–Node 11–Node 15–Node 19

Node 3–Node 7–Node 12–Node 16–Node 20

Both paths of course sum to an accumulated cost of 18 units. The two paths through the tableaus are given in Table 7–2, with optimum entries *only* given for convenience. Finally, if the minimum path to a *specific* ending node (stage V) is required, then the problem should be worked in reverse, starting with stage I and working to stage V.

7-3. MULTI-STAGE SCHEDULING

Many applications for dynamic programming may be found. In Chapter 5, where we were introduced to the topic, its application to the optimization of mathematical expressions was presented. We have just seen in the immediately previous section its applicability to network routing problems. A survey of the literature reveals many interesting applications. Howard defines dynamic programming as a mathematical technique for solving certain types of sequential decision problems.[3] A sequential decision problem is characterized as a problem in which a sequence of decisions must be made with each decision affecting future decisions. As Howard suggests, rarely is an operational situation encountered where the implications of any decision do not extend into the future. One interesting example presented by Larson discusses the use of dynamic programming to the routing of airplanes between airports in order to maximize airplane profit figures.[4] A digital computer program was written to analyze the situation where initially the schedule of flights over the time period to be evaluated is input, as well as estimates of the number of passengers on each flight. The present state of each airplane is given. Constants are specified,

Table 7-2

Optimum Path Determination for the Solution given in Table 7-1, Knowing the Starting Node is Node 3

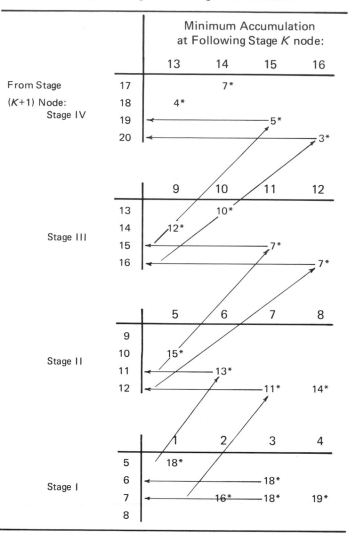

such as when and where an airplane has to have maintenance. The program then determines the order of flights each airplane shall make in order to maximize profit within the constraints. According to Larson, minor modifications allow the program to handle non-integral times of flight between airports, non-integral departure times, possibility of diversion to other airports, varying flight times due to wind, and other such constraints and conditions.

In the concluding chapter of his book, Nemhauser[5] points out the applicability of dynamic programming to *multi-stage inventory models*. The *basic* concepts of the inventory model will be presented later in Chapters 9 and 10. Other potential applications indicated by Nemhauser include a missile control system, resource allocation problems, and multi-stage chemical processes. The objective for the missile guidance system would be to minimize deviations from a desired trajectory. From our discussion in Chapter 3, it then seems logical that dynamic programming should have applicability to the forecasting problem. The objective of the chemical process, typically a reactor process, would be applicable for the resource allocation problem.

The application of dynamic programming to *assortment problems* has been given by White.[6] These problems cover the situation where a decision has to be made regarding the economies of purchasing a variety of applicable sizes of raw material for a particular product. White also discusses an interesting steel rolling application. Several stages are required in a rolling mill, each reducing the steel thickness a certain amount until the final stage reduces the steel to the desired thickness. The use of dynamic progamming in determining the optimum amount of reduction at each stage and in determining the optimum number of stages is given by Professor White.

Finally, before giving a couple of short examples of dynamic programming in the scheduling field, it should be mentioned that historically dynamic programming was developed by Richard Bellman in 1957.[1] The applicability to such a wide grouping of diverse problems makes dynamic programming a true systems discipline. The major difficulty in application is usually found in determining how to manipulate the problem so that it can be approached by dynamic programming. This can be seen by contrasting the problems solved in Chapter 5 with the two to be now presented.

7–4. PRODUCTION-SCHEDULING EXAMPLE

One of the standard types of production-scheduling problem relating to dynamic programming solution is the situation where a product has to be manufactured over a certain number of time periods, with a varying unit cost dependent on the particular time period. This dynamic cost situation might be due to the need for utilization of equipment for other products at varying rates during the scheduling period. Also, if the production units are accumulated and shipped at the end of the scheduling period then inventory holding charges play a part in the cost structure. If products are sold as produced during the scheduling period then income per unit will possibly vary due to seasonal characteristics or due to getting a new product early on the market. We will consider a small problem following the latter case.

Table 7–3 gives the costs estimated in producing zero through five units of a particular product in any of five possible time periods. Costs are estimated for producing *zero* units as a *penalty* for not utilizing the equipment at all. If other products require utilization of the equipment to be scheduled at certain times during the schedule period, then costs might vary due to overtime costs or possibly due to penalties which attempt to prevent production in certain periods, based on profit and cost functions of the other products to be scheduled.

Table 7–4 lists the predicted income per unit figures for the five scheduling periods. Income is not necessarily uniform *within* time periods, possibly due to price breaks. Similarly, income is not constant from period to period due to varying supply and demand characteristics. Also, income per unit might be lower in the early life of the product in order to attempt to capture a market for a new product. Income might also be low at the end of the scheduling period because of a saturated market. This hypothetical example attempts to take into consideration some of these characteristics.

The objective of the problem will be to maximize profit for the product over the entire five scheduling periods. We could just as easily have tackled the minimization of costs or maximization of income. However, from a system objective, maximization of profit is the most logical. Needless to say, the schedules realized for the three possible optimization criteria will be the same only by pure coincidence. One of the academic problems at the end of this chapter suggests that you verify this. Since profit is found by (Income − Costs), a profit matrix in Table 7–5 is formed by subtracting the cost matrix from the profit matrix, and the resultant matrix will be used in the solution of the problem.

This will be accomplished in exactly the same manner as used with the network problem in the previous section. In that problem, geographical sections of the country were classified as stages. The nodes

Table 7–3

Cost Matrix for Production-Scheduling Problem

		Time Period (t) in Which Units (k) Produced				
		A	B	C	D	E
Number of Units (k) Produced in Time Period (t)	0	5	4	3	5	6
	1	15	16	14	18	19
	2	28	32	30	35	30
	3	43	50	48	50	45
	4	60	70	68	63	58
	5	85	93	90	85	83

Table 7–4

Income Matrix for Production-Scheduling Problem

		Time Period (t) in Which Units (k) Produced				
		A	B	C	D	E
Number of Units (k) Produced in Time Period (t)	0	0	0	0	0	0
	1	22	24	27	26	23
	2	44	47	50	48	45
	3	66	70	73	74	67
	4	88	90	95	98	89
	5	110	110	115	118	111

Table 7–5

Profit Matrix for Production-Scheduling Problem

		Time Period (t) in Which Units (k) Produced				
		A	B	C	D	E
Number of Units (k) Produced in Time Period (t)	0	-5	-4	-3	-5	-6
	1	7	8	13	8	4
	2	16	15	20	13	15
	3	23	20	25	24	22
	4	28	20	27	35	31
	5	25	17	25	33	28

Table 7-6
Dynamic Programming Solution to Production Scheduling Problem

Cumulative Units (K)′ from Stage E — STAGE E

Units (K) Produced in Stage E	0	1	2	3	4	5
0	-6*					
1		4*				
2			15*			
3				22*		
4					31*	
5						28*

Cumulative Units (K)′ from Stages D and E — STAGE D

Units (K) Produced in Stage D	1	2	3	4	5	6	7	8	9	10
0	-1	10	17	26	23					
1	2*	12*	23*	30*	39*	36				
2		7	17	28	35	44	41			
3			18	28	39*	46	55	52		
4				29	39*	50*	57*	66*	63	
5					27	37	48	55	64*	61*

Cumulative Units (K)′ from Stages C, D and E — STAGE C

Units (K) Produced in Stage C	6	7	8	9	10	11	12	13	14	15
0	47	54	63	61	58					
1	52*	63*	70*	79*	77	74				
2	50	59	70*	77	86*	84	81			
3	48	55	64	75	82	91*	89	86		
4	39	50	57	66	77	84	93*	91*	88	
5	27	37	48	55	64	75	82	91*	89*	86*

Cumulative Units $(K)'$ from Stages B, C, D and E

Units (K)	11	12	13	14	15	16
Produced in Stage B						
0	87	89	87	85	82	
1	94*	99	101	99	97	94
2	94*	101*	106*	108	106	104
3	90	99	106*	111*	113*	111
4	83	90	99	106	111	113*
5	69	80	87	96	103	108

STAGE B

Cumulative Units Required from All Stages

Units (K)	16
Produced in Stage A	
0	108
1	120
2	127
3	129*
4	129*
5	119

STAGE A

*Items marked with an asterisk denote an *optimum* characteristic at some particular point in the solution.

Shaded area denotes non-feasible conditions.

within the geographical stages represented decision points, as to whether or not they would be taken. Minimization of accumulated distance or cost between specified nodes was the optimization criteria. In this production-scheduling problem, time periods will be stages. Units to be produced within a stage will be equivalent to the nodes in the network situation. And finally, the optimization criterion is one of maximizing profit for a specified accumulation of units.

The sequential steps leading to a solution are shown in Table 7–6. Time period (or stage) E is the last period in the scheduling sequence and period A is the first. As with the network problem we will work backwards, determining the optimum conditions for stage E and progress stage by stage, accumulating unit combinations, until the required number are produced in the five stations. We will assume that 16 units are required through the five periods with a maximum of five units possible in any one of the five scheduling time periods.

The first iteration is for the *final* time period, stage E in Table 7–6. This certainly need not be put in the solution sequence but for the sake of completeness it will be included. Obviously, if 0 through 5 units are produced in this final period then the *accumulation* out of the period has to be 0 through 5 if we are working backwards. The five possible profit figures were obtained from Table 7–5 and fall on the diagonal of the first iteration matrix. All other 30 possibilities are non-feasible and so are shaded. For example, if you produce 3 units it is not possible to get anything but 3 units out. The asterisks indicate that each of the profit figures is optimum for each accumulation listed at the top of the matrix. Again, this is obvious in the first iteration as only one possibility exists for each accumulation.

Continuing backwards through *stage* D we get possible accumulation units for stages D *and* E varying from 1 to 10 units. Actually, this could be 0 to 10, but since we need 16 units after all five periods and the maximum that can be produced in the next three periods is 15 units, it follows the minimum number of units that can be scheduled in stages D *and* E is 1. Let us just consider the accumulation of 5 units as an example in determining profit possibilities. The reader can then verify the profits for the remaining accumulations. If 0 units are produced in stage D, 5 have to be produced in stage E. The optimum profit for 5 units in stage E was found to realize 28 profit units. Table 7–5 tells us that producing zero in stage D will give a profit of −5. The combined profit is 28 − 5, or 23. The remainder of the column profits are found as follows:

Produce in Stage D	Require in Stage E	Gives a Profit of
0 (profit of −5)	5 (profit of 28)	(−5 + 28) = 23
1 (profit of 8)	4 (profit of 31)	(8 + 31) = 39 *
2 (profit of 13)	3 (profit of 22)	(13 + 22) = 35
3 (profit of 24)	2 (profit of 15)	(24 + 15) = 39 *
4 (profit of 35)	1 (profit of 4)	(35 + 4) = 39 *
5 (profit of 33)	0 (profit of −6)	(33 − 6) = 27

* Optimum profit = 39

The optimum profit is 39 and these values are marked by an asterisk (*) to so indicate. Only the values with an asterisk are used in calculating the optimum conditions for stage C to give accumulations for stages C and D and E. For example, suppose we want to find the maximum profit for producing 2 in period C to give a 3-stage accumulation of 7 units. This would require 5 units to be produced in stages D and E with an optimum profit just found to be 39. The profit for 2 in period C is 20, from Table 7–5, so the combined profit is 39 + 20, or 59. This same procedure is followed to stage A, where the maximum profit is found to be 129.

Now, what schedule gives 129 profit units? As with the network problem, we can find this by working from stage A to stage E. It turns out there are three possible solutions, which are given in Table 7–7. From the stage A solution iteration it can be seen that 3 or 4 units in A will give the optimum 129 profit. Consider only the 4. If 16 total units are to be produced and we produced 4 in stage A, then 12 had to be the previous accumulation. The optimum profit for 12 at stage B is 101, achieved if 2 units are produced in B. If 2 are produced in B to give an accumulation of 12, 10 has to be the previous accumulation through stage C. The optimum profit there is 86 for a production of 2 units in stage C. This is again followed and we get 4 units in the stage D and 4 units in stage E. The reader may verify the remaining two schedules given in Table 7–7 by following this same procedure. Of course a verification of arithmetic accuracy may be accomplished by taking the final schedule(s), as in Table 7–7, and then adding the individual profit figures from Table 7–5 to insure that they do add to the supposed optimum total. Finally, in following the five iterations in Table 7–6 and realizing that the profits with asterisks are the only ones considered in the solution, it is seen that in each iteration, except

Table 7-7

**The Three Possible Solutions for Maximizing
Profit for the Production-Scheduling Problem**

Stage A	Stage B	Stage C	Stage D	Stage E

for the first and last, the technique eliminates from consideration many schedules that can not possibly be optimum, thus simplifying greatly the *overall* calculations.

The production example, just presented, showed that when many combinations of solution are possible then dynamic programming is a solution approach that can decrease the number of combinations that have to be examined before a solution is realized. This gives rise to the thought that dynamic programming should be valid for a general class of combinatorial problems. However, it may not be as efficient in terms of effort as certain specialized techniques. As an example, consider a company that has five sub-contracts to make, one each to one of the five companies that bid on the contracts. One and only one contract will be let to each company bidding. The contract bids made by these five companies for the five contracts are given in Table 7-8. Dashes indicate that a particular company declined to bid on a certain contract, as with company B and contracts 1 and 2. The problem is

Table 7-8

Cost Submitted in Bid Form by Five Companies for Five Contracts

Contract	Company				
	A	B	C	D	E
1	80	—	—	200	120
2	150	—	130	190	110
3	95	125	118	180	80
4	130	150	85	200	95
5	115	140	120	160	100

to determine how to assign the contracts to companies so as to minimize total contract costs. This assumes of course that the lowest bid for each contract does not *have* to be accepted.

The problem may be set up by having either contracts or companies as stages. We will utilize contracts as stages and companies as decisions to be optimized *within* stages. The overall solution is given in tabular format in Table 7–9. The first iteration, for stage 5, should be self-explanatory. If we consider only contract 5 there are five potential companies for that contract, with the cost figures given in iteration 1.

Stage 4 gives the cost figures when contracts 4 and 5 are to be assigned. Combinations of two companies each have to be considered for total cost. These combinations given as the top heading in the second iteration are not permutations for they are in effect permuted with the five possible companies for contract 4 given as ordinate headings. For example, consider the possibility of contracts 4 and 5 going to companies A and B. Contract 4 could go to A and 5 to B, or vice versa. If we assign contract 4 to A this gives a cost of 130, from Table 7–8. This forces contract 5 to go to B with a cost, from matrix one in Table 7–9, of 140. The total is 270, which is the 1,1 element cost in the iteration two matrix of Table 7–9. Now, if B is assigned to contract 4, the cost is 150. Assigning A to contract 5 gives a cost of 115, to a total of 265, the value given in position 2,1 of Table 7–9's second iteration.

All other calculations are performed in the same manner. When we get to iteration 5 there is only one possible *combination* of companies. These are *permuted*, though, by fixing in order the five companies for contract 1. If A is assigned contract 1, a cost of 80 is found from Table 7–8. This means that the previous lowest cost for assignment of contracts 2 through 5 to companies B, C, D, and E has to be added to 80. This value is found to be 480 in column 5 of the solution iteration 4, giving a total cost of 560. B and C companies cannot be assigned contract 1, so only two more situations have to be checked—assigning contract 1 to company D or E. Since both realize a minimum cost of 630, the 560 has to be optimum.

What assignment of contracts to companies achieves this? This is solved in exactly the same fashion as the previous production scheduling problem. Iteration 5 assigns contract 1 to A. This came from the optimum to B, C, D, E in iteration 4, which assigned contract 2 to E. This leaves the company combination of BCD, which from iteration 3 has contract 3 assigned to B. Iteration 2 tells us that CD, the only two companies remaining to be assigned, gives contract

Table 7-9

Dynamic Programming Solution to the Contract/Company Problem

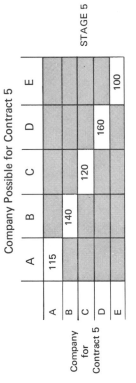

STAGE 5

Company Possible for Contract 5

	A	B	C	D	E
Company for Contract 5 — A	115				
B		140			
C			120		
D				160	
E					100

STAGE 4

Company *Combinations* Possible for Contracts 4 and 5

	A/B	A/C	A/D	A/E	B/C	B/D	B/E	C/D	C/E	D/E
Company for Contract 4 — A	270	250	290*	230						
B	265*				270	310*	250			
C		200*			225*			245*	185*	
D			315			340		320		300
E				210*			235*		215	255*

STAGE 3

Company *Combinations* Possible for Contracts 3 and 4 and 5

	A/B/C	A/B/D	A/C/D	A/B/E	A/C/E	A/D/E	B/C/D	B/C/E	B/D/E	C/D/E
Company for Contract 3 — A	320*	405*	340*	330*	280*	350*				
B	325	415		335			370*	310	380*	
C	383		408		328		428	353		373
D		445	380			390	390		405	365
E				345	280*	370		305*	390	325*

Company *Combinations* Possible for Contracts 2, 3, 4 and 5

	A B C D	A B C E	A B D E	A C D E	B C D E
A	520	455	530	475	
B					
C	535	460	520	460	510
D	510*			470	495
E		430*	515*	450*	480*

Company for Contract 2

STAGE 2

Company *Combination* Possible for Contracts 1, 2, 3, 4 and 5

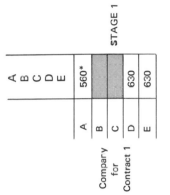

	A B C D E
A	560*
B	
C	
D	630
E	630

Company for Contract 1

STAGE 1

*Optimum conditions

Table 7–10

**Possible Dynamic Programming Schedules
for Contract/Company Problem**

Optimum Solution

Assignment	Cost
Contract 1 → Company A	80
Contract 2 → Company E	110
Contract 3 → Company B	125
Contract 4 → Company C	85
Contract 5 → Company D	160
	560

Alternate 1 (Assign Contract 1 to Company D)

Assignment	Cost
Contract 1 → Company D	200
Contract 2 → Company E	110
Contract 3 → Company A	95
Contract 4 → Company C	85
Contract 5 → Company B	140
	630

Alternate 2 (Assign Contract 1 to Company E)

Assignment	Cost
Contract 1 → Company E	120
Contract 2 → Company D	190
Contract 3 → Company A	95
Contract 4 → Company C	85
Contract 5 → Company B	140
	630

4 to C. This leaves contract 5 for company D. To give the reader a check, schedules when D and E are assigned contract 1 are given in Table 7–10.

Even though this approach to the company/contract problem is *relatively* efficient, eliminating many infeasible combinations as the solution progresses, it is certainly not the most efficient. The highly specialized optimization technique, the *assignment* algorithm, will handle a specific set of problems, of which the company/contract problem is a member, far more easily. The dynamic programming solution does present alternate solutions to the optimum very easily, which may not be so simple with the assignment procedure.

7–5. THE ASSIGNMENT ALGORITHM

As just mentioned, a large class of problems fall into a similar situation as in the previous contract/company example, where the same number of contracts have to be assigned as there are companies to receive them, and one and only one contract goes to each company. Similar situations exist where a certain number of trucks have to go to a certain number of destinations, with the number of trucks equal to destinations. Cost or profits vary with the truck/destination combination. The trick is to optimize truck/destinations with one and only one truck going to a unique destination. Another example would have workers assigned to an equal number of jobs, with a varying worker/job cost. In some ways the problem is highly restricted due to the equality requirement of *sources* and *destinations*, and in the assignment of only one source item to each destination. The *transportation* algorithm discussed in Chapter 5 and briefly in the subsequent section will handle a wider variety of this problem.

As an introduction to the assignment problem we will consider a small problem with most of the peculiarities one would expect to encounter. Then we will tackle the contract/company problem to see if we can verify the dynamic programming solution. Consider first a situation where 3 jobs have to be assigned to 3 work centers, with a varying cost relationship for each job/center combination as given in Table 7–11. The problem is to assign jobs to work centers with the objective of minimizing costs.

Table 7-11

Job/Work Center Costs for
Possible Assignments

Job	Work Center		
	A	B	C
1	5	10	10
2	11	14	6
3	9	10	8

The solution procedure is very simple. Subtract a constant amount from *every* job/work center possible assignment until zero cost appears for a feasible assignment. Needless to say, if the *same* amount is subtracted from *all* possible combinations then the first assignment to get zero cost employs the minimum cost. Unfortunately the *feasible assignment* restriction does not always fall out as we will see, where a *feasible assignment* has a zero in each row and column of the initial problem matrix.

The zero possibilities are forced by subtracting from *each* row element the minimum value in that row, as shown in Table 7–12.

Subtracting a constant from each element in a row does subtract the constant from all job/cost center combinations. This forces at least one zero in each row. Repeating the same procedure for the columns subtracts the minimum in any column from each element in that column to force a chance for at least one zero in every row and column. Table 7–12 shows that a solution did indeed come to the fore in our initial example. Assigning job 1 to center A is the minimum cost job for center A. Similarly in assigning job 2 to center C. The third job is assigned to center B. Needless to say, the sum of the three individual minimum costs has to realize the minimum overall—in this case a cost of 21, going back to the original cost units in Table 7–11. This

Table 7–12

Assignment Solution to Problem Costed in Table 7-11

		A	B	C	
(A)	1	5 − 5 = 0	10 − 5 = 5	10 − 5 = 5	
Job	2	11 − 6 = 5	14 − 6 = 8	6 − 6 = 0	Row
	3	9 − 8 = 1	10 − 8 = 2	8 − 8 = 0	Subtraction

		A	B	C	
	1	0 − 0 = 0	5 − 2 = 3	5 − 0 = 5	
(B)	2	5 − 0 = 5	8 − 2 = 6	0 − 0 = 0	Column
	3	1 − 0 = 1	2 − 2 = 0	0 − 0 = 0	Subtraction

		A	B	C	
	1	0*	3	5	*May Lead to
(C)	2	5	6	0*	Optimum
	3	1	0*	0	Assignment

may also be verified by summing *all* values subtracted for the elements and columns: $5 + 6 + 8 + 2 = 21$.

Maximization. Suppose instead of costs in Table 7–11 we had profits and the objective was to *maximize* profit. This can be handled easily by *reversing* the position each job/center has in a monotonically increasing sequence. For example, in Table 7–11, the job/center combination of 1/A is the minimum and 2/C next to minimum. If they are adjusted so that they are maximum and next-to-maximum respectively, and the other elements adjusted in a similar fashion, minimizing as we did before would in effect develop those assignments which would *maximize* profit. The simplest way to adjust the "cost"

Table 7–13

Assignment for Maximization of Values for Table 7-11 Matrix

Work Center

		A	B	C	
(A)	1	$14 - 5 = 9$	$14 - 10 = 4$	$14 - 10 = 4$	In *maximizing*, first subtract each element value from the original maximum element value. (This maximum value was 14 in Table 7-11.)
Job	2	$14 - 11 = 3$	$14 - 14 = 0$	$14 - 6 = 8$	
	3	$14 - 9 = 5$	$14 - 10 = 4$	$14 - 8 = 6$	

then

		A	B	C	
(B)	1	5	0	0	
	2	3	0	8	Perform normal row subtraction
	3	1	0	2	

and

		A	B	C	
(C)	1	4	0	0*	
	2	2	0*	8	Normal column subtraction.
	3	0*	0	2	

Optimum: Job 3 to Center A
              Job 2 to Center B
              Job 1 to Center C

values is to subtract *each* element value from the maximum matrix value. The resultant matrix is then scheduled to minimize accumulated "costs." This is accomplished in Table 7–13 for the assumption that Table 7–11 values represent *profits* which have to be *maximized*. This maximum "profit" is

Job 3 to center A:	9
Job 2 to center B:	14
Job 1 to center C:	10
	$\overline{33}$

The validity of this solution is apparent after a brief perusal of the original data.

Now, the only problem is that subtraction of constants from rows and columns does not have to lead to at least one zero in each row and column. For example, see a new problem with subtraction results given in Table 7–14. We cannot get a unique zero in each row and column. Job 2 *has* to be assigned to work center A and so does job 3. This of course is a violation of the initial problem stipulation. One way

Table 7–14

Assignment Problem with Non-Optimum Solution
After Initial Row and Column Subtraction

		Work Center			
		A	B	C	
	1	3	8	5	
Job	2	6	14	9	Original Cost
	3	12	18	16	Matrix
		A	B	C	
	1	0	5	2	
	2	0	8	3	Row Subtraction
	3	0	6	4	
		A	B	C	
	1	0	0	0	
	2	0	3	1	Column Subtraction
	3	0	1	2	

Table 7–15

**Two Straight Lines Can Be Drawn
Through all Zeros in Initial Solution from
Table 7–14. Three Are Needed for Optimum**

		Work Center		
		A	B	C
	1	0	0	0
Job	2	0	3	1
	3	0	1	2

to see if a solution has been reached is to draw the minimum number of straight lines through *all* zeros. If this number of lines is less than the number of rows in the matrix, then an optimum solution has not been achieved. This can be seen in Table 7–15.

The procedure to follow in completing the solution is to now take all elements *not* covered by a straight line and subtract from these the minimum of the non-covered element values. This same value is *added* to any element that falls at an *intersection* of straight lines. In Table 7–15 the value of 1 is the minimum of the four *non-covered* elements. This is subtracted from the four elements and then is added to the zero in position 1,1, which is at an intersection of lines. This result is depicted in Table 7–16. Three lines are now needed to cover all

Table 7–16

**Optimum Solution Through
Subtraction/Addition Manipulation**

		Work Center		
		A	B	C
	1	0+1 = 1	0	0
Job	2	0	3 − 1 = 2	1 − 1 = 0
	3	0	1 − 1 = 0	2 − 1 = 1

$\downarrow$

	A	B	C
1	1	0	0
2	0	2	0
3	0	0	1

zeros. Two optimum solutions are possible:

    Job 1—B
    Job 2—C
    Job 3—A
and
    Job 1—C
    Job 2—A
    Job 3—B

Both solutions give a total cost of 29. At first glance this might not seem to be the optimum value. However, with only a 3 × 3 matrix it is possible to see *all* assignments easily by complete enumeration as only six possibilities exist. These are given in Table 7–17, and lo, 29 is optimum. If an optimum solution had not popped out the first time, the subtraction/addition process would have been continued until it did.

Finally, in a large matrix, finding the *minimum* number of lines with which to cross all zeros might be relatively difficult. A series of steps has been developed by Hillier and Lieberman[2] as follows:

a. For each row/column with *exactly* one remaining zero element, reserve that position for an assignment and eliminate other zero element positions in that column/row from further consideration. Repeat for non-reserved positions until all zero elements are either

Table 7–17

**Complete Schedule Enumeration
for Assignment Problem Solved in
Table 7-16**

Company Combination[*]	Cost
ABC	33
ACB	30
BAC	30
BCA	29**
CBA	31
CAB	29**

*Assigning Jobs 1, 2, 3 to companies can be accomplished with the combinations given.

**Optimum.

reserved or eliminated. If an optimal solution is not achieved go to step b. An optimal solution is one where the reserved positions comprise a complete set of assignments.

b. To get the minimum number of straight lines:

1. Put a mark by all rows that do not have assignments.
2. Put a mark by all columns which have zeros in marked rows.
3. Mark all rows that have assignments in marked columns.
4. Repeat steps 2 and 3 until no more rows or columns can be marked.
5. Draw a line through each unmarked row and through each marked column.

Table 7–18

Initial Assignment Solution to the Contract/Company Problem

		Company				
		A	B	C	D	E
C o n t r a c t	1	80	1000*	1000*	200	120
	2	150	1000*	130	190	110
	3	95	125	118	180	80
	4	130	150	85	200	95
	5	115	140	120	160	100

Initial Cost Matrix

(Items marked with asterisks are *arbitrarily large* to prevent non-allowable assignments.)

	A	B	C	D	E
1	0	920	920	120	40
2	40	890	20	80	0
3	15	45	38	100	0
4	45	65	0	115	10
5	15	40	20	60	0

Row Subtraction

	A	B	C	D	E
1	0	880	920	60	40
2	40	850	20	20	0
3	15	5	38	40	0
4	45	25	0	55	10
5	15	0	20	0	0

Column Subtraction

Table 7-19

Finding the Minimum Number of Zero-Covering Lines
Via the Hillier-Lieberman Method

0*	880	920	60	40	(A)	Fix assignments where only one zero in row/column. These are marked by asterisks. Only 4 of 5 needed are made.
40	850	20	20	0*		
15	5	38	40	0		
45	25	0*	55	10		
15	0*	20	0	0		

0*	880	920	60	40	(B)	Mark rows (√) which do not have assignment.
40	850	20	20	0*		
15	5	38	40	0 √		
45	25	0*	55	10		
15	0*	20	0	0		

0*	880	920	60	40	(C)	Mark columns (√) which have zeros in marked rows.
40	850	20	20	0*		
15	5	38	40	0 √		
45	25	0*	55	10		
15	0*	20	0	0		
				√		

0*	880	920	60	40	(D)	Mark rows (√) which have assignments in marked columns.
40	850	20	20	0* √		
15	5	38	40	0 √		
45	25	0*	55	10		(C and D repeated till no more columns and rows can be marked. We have hit this point already.)
15	0*	20	0	0		
				√		

~~0~~	~~880~~	~~920~~	~~60~~	~~40~~	(E)	Draw a line through each unmarked row and each marked column.
40	850	20	20	0* √		
15	5	38	40	0 √		
~~45~~	~~25~~	~~0*~~	~~55~~	~~10~~		
~~15~~	~~0*~~	~~20~~	~~0~~	0		
				√		

This sequence will be discussed with the use of the contract/company problem solved earlier by dynamic programming.

The basic cost matrix for the contract/company problem is repeated in Table 7–18 along with the initial assignment algorithm row and column subtraction steps. The only difference in this initial cost matrix from the original is that the combinations 1/B, 1/C, and 2/B are given a large cost value to prevent assignment as they were not given any cost values in the original due to non-feasibility of assignment. A symbolic symbol is sometimes used and this can be consistently kept track of to insure non-assignment.

Now let us follow the Hillier-Lieberman steps to find the minimum number of straight lines to cover zeros, even though this is quite obviously four. Table 7–19 gives the results of following the basic steps. For convenience, *only* the cost values are given for each matrix. It is found that 4 lines can cover the zeros. Since we have a 5×5 matrix, 5 lines would be needed for a feasible solution.

The minimum non-covered element is 5. This is subtracted from all non-covered elements, and is added to *intersection* elements (1, 5; 4, 5; 5, 5). The new matrix values are given in Table 7–20, with the second matrix indicating a feasible solution of

Contract 1—Company A
Contract 2—Company E
Contract 3—Company B
Contract 4—Company C
Contract 5—Company D

As expected, this is the same solution achieved by dynamic programming, but in this latter case a much more efficient procedure was employed.

As mentioned earlier, the *assignment* algorithm is fine if as many destinations exist as sources, and if one source item can go to only one destination. We will now look briefly at the *transportation* algorithm, which allows this to be relaxed considerably.

7–6. THE TRANSPORTATION PROBLEM

The transportation algorithm was introduced in Chapter 5 as an optimization technique and so not much time will be spent discussing the technique. It is however quite valuable in the scheduling field and so its application to scheduling problems will be briefly considered with two examples.

Table 7-20

Final Assignment Solution for Contract/Company Problem

0	880	920	60	40+5=45	
40−5=35	850−5=845	20−5=15	20−5=15	0	
15−5=10	5−5=0	38−5=33	40−5=35	0	
45	25	0	55	10+5=15	
15	0	20	0	0+5=5	

Company

		A	B	C	D	E
	1	0*	880	920	60	45
	2	35	845	15	15	0*
Contract	3	10	0*	33	35	0
	4	45	25	0*	55	15
	5	15	0	20	0*	0

The assignment algorithm covered those situations where only one source item could go to one destination slot. The transportation procedure will solve a wider class of scheduling problems where instead of a one-to-one assignment, several units of each source item have to be scheduled to a number of destinations, which do not, as in the assignment problem, have to equal the number of sources.

For example, suppose an airline has its airplanes located at four different airports. An urgent recall requires these planes, say fifty-nine in number, to be flown to two refurbishing facilities. One facility can handle twenty-six planes and the other thirty-three. Costs vary for each of the four airports to the two refurbishing locations. How many planes from each airport should be shipped to which location? Schematically, the base data for the problem are given in Figure 7–3. The objective is to find that schedule which minimizes plane-miles in getting the planes from airports to maintenance facilities.

From our Chapter 5 introduction it is apparent that this is a problem suitable to solution by the transportation method. A summary of the "cost" matrix for airport/maintenance facility relationships is given in Table 7–21. "Cost" in this problem of course is measured in terms of miles traveled. Initial assignment of planes to facilities is given in

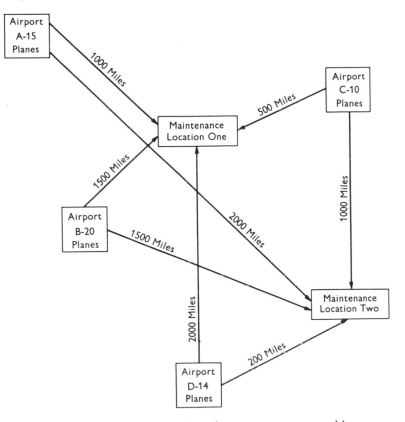

Figure 7–3. Schematic of airplane maintenance problem.

Table 7-21

"Cost" Relationship in Terms of
Miles to Travel Between Airports
and Maintenance Facilities

Airports	M1	M2
A	1000	2000
B	1500	1500
C	500	1000
D	2000	200

Table 7–22

Initial Assignment of Planes to Maintenance Facilities by the "Northwest Corner" Rule

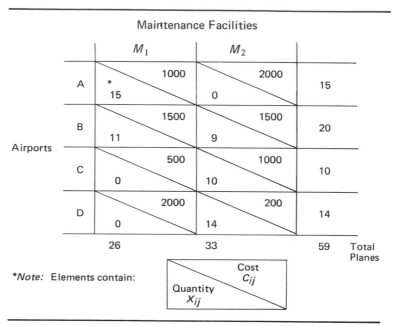

Note: Elements contain:

Table 7–22 using the "Northwest Corner" rule to get started. Since M1 has a capacity of 26 planes, 15 certainly can be scheduled from Airport A to M1. Only 11 of Airport B's 20 planes can go to M1, filling its capacity of 26 planes. Since airplanes to be scheduled equals exactly the capacity in the maintenance facilities, the remaining 33 planes have to be assigned to M2 as given in Table 7–22. Of course, this is probably not optimum as the "Northwest Corner" rule just gives a beginning schedule.

The possible manipulations, moving planes into the zero positions in Table 7–22, gives cost (mileage) changes for a *one plane* shift as follows:

I *A/M2 Position*
   Airport A—One plane $M1$ to $M2$: Cost change is $2,000 - 1,000 = +1,000$; to maintain plane balance, airport B has to shift one plane $M2$ to $M1$ with a cost change of $1,500 - 1,500 = 0$.
   Result: Do not shift anything A/$M2$, due to increase per plane cost of 1,000 miles.

II *C/M1 Position*

Airport C—One Plane $M2$ to $M1$: Cost change is $500 - 1,000 = -500$

To maintain balance, airport B has to shift one plane $M2$ to $M1$ with no cost change.

Result: Savings per plane shift is 500 miles.

III *D/M1 Position*

Airport D—One plane $M2$ to $M1$: Cost change is $2,000 - 200 = +1,800$; to maintain balance, same airport B shift as above $= 0$ change.

Result: Do not shift anything $D/M1$, due to increase per plane cost of 1,800 miles.

The overall result is to shift into the $C/M1$ position. The amount to be shifted is limited by the $C/M2$ element or 10 planes. The result of a 10-plane shift from element $C/M2$ to $C/M1$ and $B/M1$ to $B/M2$ is shown in Table 7–23. Since $A/M2$ and $D/M1$ shifts are not affected by the new shift, an optimum assignment has been realized as follows:

Maintenance Facility $M1$

15 Planes from airport A
1 Plane from airport B
10 Planes from airport C

Maintenance Facility $M2$

19 Planes from airport B
14 Planes from airport D

The total mileage cost, $\sum X_{ij}C_{ij}$, is

$$(15)(1000) + (1)(1500) + (19)(1500) + (10)(500) + (14)(200)$$
$$= 52,800 \text{ plane-miles}$$

This had a very simple solution with only one iteration. What would have happened if the "sensitivity" approach had been used to get an initial solution rather than using the "Northwest Corner" rule? Recall from Chapter 5 the steps required in the "sensitivity" initial assignment:

A. For each row indicate the difference between the lowest and next-to-lowest element costs. This indicates a cost "penalty" if the lowest cost is not used.

B. Repeat step A for each column.

C. Assign units to cells on the basis of the largest "penalty" cost until all units are assigned.

Table 7-23

Optimum Scheduling of Planes to Airports

Maintenance Facilities

Airports	M_1	M_2	
A	1000 / 15	2000 / 0	15
B	1500 / 1	1500 / 19	20
C	500 / 10	1000 / 0	10
D	2000 / 0	200 / 14	14
	26	33	

Table 7-24

Penalty Matrix for Plane/Maintenance Scheduling Problem

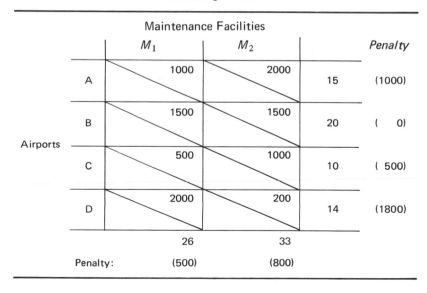

Maintenance Facilities

Airports	M_1	M_2		Penalty
A	1000	2000	15	(1000)
B	1500	1500	20	(0)
C	500	1000	10	(500)
D	2000	200	14	(1800)
	26	33		
Penalty:	(500)	(800)		

As an example, the "cost" matrix only from Table 7–22 is repeated in Table 7–24 with the penalties indicated for rows and columns. The element with the highest penalty, D/M2, should be assigned first. This can take fourteen units. The next-highest penalty element A/M1, is assigned the 15 possible units. The third element according to penalty cost is C/M1. Ten units can be assigned to it. The total assigned to M1 is 25 so far, out of a capacity of 26. D/M1 cannot be assigned any units due to the D/M2 assignment so the remaining one plane is assigned B/M1. This leaves 19 units for B/M2 to satisfy airport B's 20 planes. This *initial* assignment turns out to be also the *optimum* one, saving one iteration from those needed with the "North-west Corner" rule.

It is not always the case in a problem of this kind that the supply and capacity exactly match. Suppose that *both* maintenance facilities could have handled 33 planes, with a total capacity of 66 versus a need for 59 planes. What now would be the optimum plane/maintenance facility schedule? The way to set up the solution matrix is

Table 7–25

Assignment by "Sensitivity" Rule When Maintenance Capacity Is Greater than Airport Supply

		Maintenance Facilities			Penalty
		M_1	M_2		
Airports	A	1000 / 15	2000 / 0	15	(1000)
	B	1500 / 8	1500 / 12	20	(0)
	C	500 / 10	1000 / 0	10	(500)
	D	2000 / 0	200 / 14	14	(1800)
	Dummy	0 / 0	0 / 7	7	(0)
		33	33	66	
	Penalty	(500)	(800)		

with a *dummy* airport having 7 planes so that supply and capacity match. The costs for the *dummy* to the maintenance facilities are set to zero. This new matrix and initial assignment by the "sensitivity" rule are given in Table 7–25. It will be left to the reader to verify that this initial assignment *is* correct, and that it is also optimum. In considering the penalty values to assist in initial assignment, the zero cost for dummies should *not* be used as the lowest cost.

7–7. JOB ASSIGNMENT EXAMPLE

Another standard scheduling problem amenable to solution by the transportation method is an extension of the job/work center problem discussed earlier as an *assignment method* problem. Three jobs had to be assigned, each to one of three work centers. A varying cost relationship existed for each job/work center relationship. However, what if a time restriction exists for the jobs and the time available in each work center varies because of other commitments? The original problem given in Table 7–11 is repeated in Table 7–26 with the addition of time constraints.

The initial solution, by the "sensitivity" rule, is given in Table 7–27. The work hours were assigned elements in the following order according to this solution:

1/A; 3/B; 2/C; 3/A

Table 7-26

Job/Work Center Associated Costs and Time Requirements

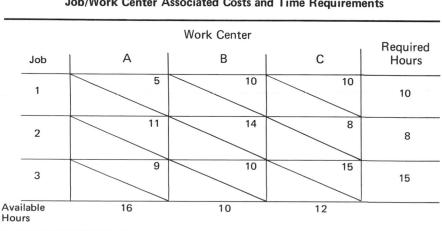

Job	Work Center A	Work Center B	Work Center C	Required Hours
1	5	10	10	10
2	11	14	8	8
3	9	10	15	15
Available Hours	16	10	12	

Table 7–27

Schedule of Jobs to Work Centers According to
"Sensitivity" Rule

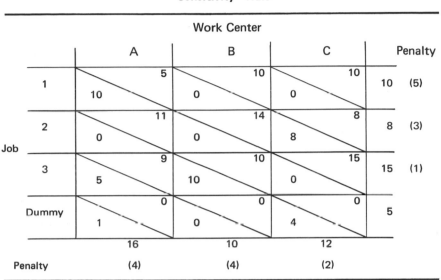

The dummy elements then naturally fell into place. The reader might like to verify both the solution and the fact that it is optimum.

This completes the scheduling material applicable to solution by the transportation algorithm. Many types of problem can be solved by this algorithm, of which two only were looked at. Now we will switch to a rather different and complex scheduling problem, that of sequencing, in Chapter 8.

REFERENCES CITED

1. BELLMAN, R., *Dynamic Programming*, Princeton University Press, Princeton, N.J., 1957.
2. HILLIER, F. S., and LIEBERMAN, G. L., *Introduction to Operations Research*, Holden-Day, Inc., San Francisco, Calif., 1968.
3. HOWARD, R. A., "Dynamic Programming," *Management Science*, Vol. 12, No. 5, January, 1966.
4. LARSON, R. E., *State Increment Dynamic Programming*, American Elsevier Publishing Company, Inc., New York, 1968.
5. NEMHAUSER, G. L., *Introduction to Dynamic Programming*, John Wiley and Sons, Inc., New York, N.Y., 1966.
6. WHITE, D. J., *Dynamic Programming*, Holden-Day, San Francisco, Calif., 1969.

7. WILDE, D. J., and BEIGHTLER, C. S., *Foundations of Optimization*, Prentice-Hall, Inc., Englewood Cliffs, N.J., 1967.

FURTHER READING

RICHMOND, S. B., *Operations Research for Management Decisions*, The Ronald Press Company, New York, N.Y., 1968.

SASIENI, M., YASPAN, A., and FRIEDMAN, L., *Operations Research*, John Wiley and Sons, Inc., New York, N.Y., 1959.

PROBLEMS

1. Consider the following transportation network:

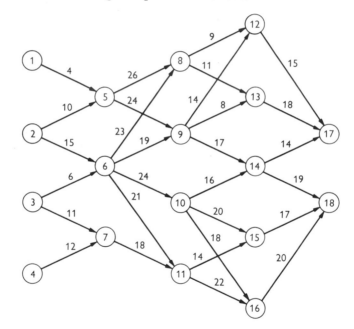

The numbers above the arrows represent some item to be either minimized or maximized.

A. Determine the *minimum* path accumulated from:
   1. Node 1 to node 17 or 18.
   2. Node 2 to node 18.
   3. Node 1 or 2 or 3 or 4 to node 17 or 18.

B. Determine the *maximum* path accumulated from:
   1. Node 1 to node 17 or 18.
   2. Node 1 or 2 or 3 or 4 to node 17 or 18.
   3. Node 2 or 4 to node 17 or 18.

C. If route 9-14 *has to be* taken, determine the minimum path from node 1 or 2 or 3 or 4 to node 17 or 18.

2. Consider the dynamic programming scheduling problem whose cost matrix is given in Table 7–3. Within the same constraints as the text problem *minimize* production costs over the five time periods.

3. Consider the dynamic programming scheduling problem whose *income* matrix is given in Table 7–4. Within the same constraints as the text problem *maximize* income over the five time periods.

4. Discuss your results found in Problems 2 and 3 in light of the text solution to the production scheduling problem to show why profit maximization is the most logical optimization criteria.

5. Consider the contract/company problem whose solution is given in Table 7–9. Management has a cost plus 20% federal contract and being rather deceitful decides to *maximize* contract/company costs. What schedule achieves this? Accomplish this with dynamic programming.

6. Verify your schedule for Problem 6 by the assignment algorithm.

7. Production costs for a product are as follows:

Units Produced	Time Period					
	A	B	C	D	E	F
1	100	120	105	135	150	125
2	190	240	200	280	300	260
3	280	360	350	435	450	400

Fourteen units are required at the end of period F. Inventory charges are made according to the following formula:

$$Y = (20)(t)^{1.3}$$

where Y is the *unit* cost of holding the unit for *complete* periods. For example, an item produced in period B would be held for 4 complete periods, so Y is:

$$(20)(4)^{1.3} = 121 \text{ cost units}$$

Find the production schedule that minimizes the total production cost.

8. Four manual jobs are to be performed by four workers. The expected times for these jobs by the workers are:

Worker	Job			
	A	B	C	D
1	10	15	9	21
2	12	16	15	23
3	8	14	16	22
4	16	20	18	19

Assign jobs to workers (one each) so that overall manufacturing time is minimized.

9. Worker 2 can not be assigned job B in problem 9, and worker 4 can not be assigned job D. What schedule is now realized for minimization of working time?

10. Five movies are to be scheduled by a cinema for one showing apiece. Expected income for each of the movies will vary according to the particular week it is shown due to some weeks having more young (old) people available and so on. These projected dollar incomes are:

	Week Shown				
	May 1	May 8	May 15	May 22	May 29
Walt Disney movie	10,000	11,500	9,000	10,800	8,000
X-rated movie	18,000	19,500	17,000	18,500	19,000
M-rated movie	9,000	7,000	8,500	10,500	9,500
Old-time festival	16,500	18,000	14,000	18,500	15,000
War movie	3,000	2,500	4,200	3,800	4,000

If all movies have to be shown, in what order would you schedule them?

11. Consider a cost matrix as follows:

	Contractor			
	1	2	3	4
A	5	8	10	15
B	12	9	7	11
C	9	12	8	14

Jobs A, B, C are to be assigned to 3 of the 4 contractors. In order to utilize the assignment algorithm, a dummy job, D, is added with a zero cost value for each of the 4 contractors. Now, with this 4×4 matrix find the job/contractor assignment that minimizes total cost.

12. A company has three plants and five warehouses. The warehouses and plants have production values and storage capacities as follows:

Plant	Warehouse
A. 20,000 units	I 8,000 units
B. 15,000 units	II 10,000 units
C. 40,000 units	III 13,000 units
	IV 20,000 units
	V 27,000 units

Costs of shipping (coded) from plant to warehouse are as follows:

	Warehouse				
Plant	I	II	III	IV	V
A	15	8	16	10	11
B	10	17	20	19	14
C	25	14	15	8	15

What is the most economical shipping schedule to get the 75,000 units stored in warehouses? What is the shipping cost (coded) for your schedule?

8

Sequence Scheduling

Good order is the foundation of all good things.

EDMUND BURKE

8–1. SEQUENCING

The sequencing problem is a scheduling problem of some complexity. We will limit our discussion to the job-shop sequencing situation but it should be realized that this basic problem is pertinent to a wide variety of disciplines. The job-shop sequencing problem has several different jobs, each of which consists of several operations which have to be assigned sequentially to a limited number of work centers. The sequence of operations may or may not be the same for each of the jobs. Each operation within the work sequence is assumed to be performed on one unique machine or work center. The requirement of the problem is to determine the order in which the jobs are to be assigned sequentially through the work centers in order to satisfy some criteria of optimality. Several similar types of problem should be readily apparent. Sequencing buses through a maintenance facility with separate bays for separate functions is one. We are all familiar with the typical automobile repair facility that has the same scheduling problem. In a different vein, sequencing medical tests for a group of patients, with each patient requiring different categories of medical test, falls into this problem sphere.

Portions of this chapter were researched by Carolyn L. Hislop in an unpublished report titled "On the Job Shop Sequencing Problem," May 23, 1969, Tempe, Arizona.

In some respects, this sequencing problem is very much akin to the resource allocation problem. Finding the *optimum* sequence is dependent upon the criterion of optimization which itself possibly may be incorrect. Another similarity is that seemingly simple problems can blow out of all proportion as far as solution complexity is concerned. We will look at a few small problems to see why this is so and also to see why the sequencing problem is still the focal point of a large amount of current scheduling research activity.

At first thought it might seem that the most obvious criterion of optimality to use in scheduling a batch of jobs in a job shop facility would be to *minimize* the total time in the job shop for all jobs. This would certainly be laudable if one customer submitted all the jobs and he required the jobs to be completed as soon as possible. If the jobs were submitted by a *group* of customers and each job had a required due date for completion, it might be logical to minimize the total due-date slippage time. This is certainly not the same problem as minimizing total in-shop time. A simple example should clarify this. Consider the times that two jobs take in three work centers, as given in Table 8-1. Each job is assumed to have the same work center sequence having to progress sequentially through work centers 1, 2, and 3.

If the criterion of completing *all* jobs in the minimum total time were formed then the optimum job sequence of *B-A* would be chosen. For only two jobs the only other possible sequence would be *A-B*. The Gantt chart schedules for these two sequences is given in Figure 8-1, and it is seen that sequence *B-A* beats *A-B* by one time unit.

Now suppose the criterion of optimality had been to minimize due-date slippage. If job *A* has a due date, referenced from time zero

Table 8-1

Times for Producing Two Jobs Through Three Work Centers

Work Center	Job	
	A	*B*
1	6	4
2	4	7
3	5	8
Total Job Time	15	19

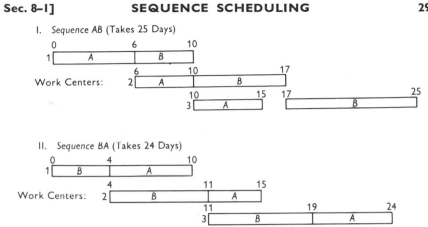

Figure 8–1. Gantt chart schedule for two possible sequences for job data given in Table 8–1.

when both jobs are delivered to the shop, of 16 and B has one of 24, then the sequence A-B would be preferred. The total due date slippage with B-A would be 5 time periods and 1 in the A-B situation.

Conway, Maxwell, and Miller[6] indicate a typical list of sequencing criteria to be minimized or maximized as appropriate:

1. Mean flow-time, or time in shop
2. Mean earliness
3. Mean lateness
4. Mean waiting time
5. Mean number of jobs in the system
6. Machine utilization
7. Cost of delay
8. Cost of lateness
9. Combinations of the above

Eilon gives an interesting example to show the problems involved in sequencing according to some *decision rule* expected to minimize some criterion such as overall time in the shop.[7] Three jobs have to be sequenced through three work centers in the fashion of our earlier two-job example. The appropriate job/work center time data is given in Table 8–2. Obviously six possible sequences of jobs are possible: ABC; ACB; BAC; BCA; CAB; CBA. The sequence that minimizes total shop time for all three jobs is BAC with an overall time of 17 units. The others vary up to 23 units, which will be left to the reader to show. However, the most interesting aspect of this example is that job B, the starting job, has neither the shortest nor largest starting

Table 8-2

Times for Producing Three Jobs Through
Three Work Centers*

Work Center	Job		
	A	B	C
1	1	2	3
2	6	2	3
3	5	6	2
Total Job Time	12	10	8

*From S. Eilon, *Elements of Production Planning
and Control,* Macmillan, New York, copyright © 1962,
Samuel Eilon.

operation time of the three jobs. Yet one criterion recommended for job-shop sequencing, when in doubt, is to schedule that job with the shortest starting time. In resource allocation, a similar problem, we saw that scheduling larger items first might be beneficial. Thus, the sequencing problem looks like one with a large potential for satisfying research.

The first technique for optimizing sequencing problems would be that of *complete schedule* enumeration. This is generally infeasible due to the large number of schedule permutations possible from only a small number of jobs. The Eilon problem with just three jobs had a possibility of six schedules—certainly feasible for evaluation, but very messy if the number of operations within jobs is considerable. If there are N jobs to be scheduled and all possible schedules are enumerated, there are $(N!)$ possible schedules. Ten jobs would require $(10!)$ or 3,628,800 schedules to be evaluated. If one considers the operations, M, involved in each job then the possible sequences, assuming the sequences within jobs not being fixed, will be $(N!)^M$. The most generous conclusion that can be reached concerning complete enumeration for the general sequencing problem is that it ranks as one of the least desirable possibilities.

One way to approach the problem is to use digital computer simulation. By simulating the flow characteristics of the scheduling environment it is possible to evaluate different scheduling rules as to their effect in optimizing the scheduling criteria. One thing that is relatively simple to accomplish with simulation that is rather difficult with analytical approaches is the possibility for bringing in machine and operator failure characteristics and other hard-to-mathematically-model situations.

In the next section we will look at some of the analytical approaches that have been developed for sequencing problems in the last few years. This will give a starting point for the interested reader in developing his own approach. Also, it will indicate a little better the complexity of the problem for analytical solution.

8–2. ANALYTIC METHODS

Many approaches have been developed to enable feasible sequencing schedules to be evolved, in which the optimum will occur. Several articles have reviewed the problem in depth, with excellent bibliographies.[2,10,11] We will be content to only look at the N job/2 or 3 machine problem, and also the 2 job/M machine case.

Optimal solution techniques for the N job/2 or 3 machine problem have been developed by S. M. Johnson[9] which are extremely simple to apply. The structure of the problem is such that the N jobs must go through first machine A and then machine B, all in the same sequence. Only one job can be on one machine at one time. If A_i represents the time for the ith job on machine A and B_i the time for the ith job on machine B then Johnson proved that job i *precedes* job $(i + 1)$ when

$$\text{Min } (A_i, B_{i+1}) < \text{Min } (A_{i+1}, B_i).$$

The optimum sequence is found by repetition of this rule. To simplify matters, Johnson developed the following steps that evolve the optimum solution:

1. List all A_i and B_i in two columns.
2. Scan all A_i and B_i for the minimum time value.
3. If this time is for machine A, place that corresponding job first. If for machine B, place the corresponding job last in the sequence.
4. Repeat steps 2 and 3 after elimination of assigned jobs.
5. If ties exist *within* A_i or B_i, sequence the job with the smallest subscript. If ties exist between A_i and B_i sequence according to A.

As an example consider the 4 job/2 machine problem data given in Table 8–3. The minimum of *all* A_i, B_i values in the original data set is 6 for A_2. Since this is for the first machine in the sequence, job 2 is assigned first in the sequence. When A_2 is eliminated, B_1 is minimum in iteration II. Job 1 is assigned last as this is on the *second* machine in sequence. Finally, iteration III has A_3 minimum with 9 units, and job 3 is therefore scheduled in position 2 of the sequence. Job 4 fills out the sequence in position 3. The Gantt chart solution for this schedule (optimum out of 24 possible) is shown in Figure 8–2. The iteration sequence is given in Table 8–4.

It can be shown intuitively that the resultant schedule depicted in Figure 8–2 is in fact optimum if overall job time is to be minimized.

Table 8–3

**Job/Machine Data for
4 Job/2 Machine Problem**

	Machine	
Job (i)	A_i	B_i
1	8	7
2	6	9
3	9	12
4	14	10

Table 8–4

**Solution to 4 Job/2 Machine Problem
Given In Table 8–3**

Iteration	i	A_i	B_i	Sequence (Job)
I	1	8	7	
	2	6̸	9	
	3	9	10	
	4	14	10	2 _ _ _
II	1	8	7̸	
	2	6̸	9	
	3	9	10	
	4	14	10	2 _ _ 1
III	1	8	7̸	
	2	6̸	9	
	3	9̸	10	
	4	14	10	2 3 _ 1
			Final Sequence:	2 3 4 1

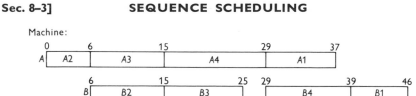

Figure 8–2. Gantt schedule for the 4 job/2 machine problem.

Obviously, the four jobs can be sequenced in any fashion on machine A and the overall time will be the same—37 time units. The *overall possible minimum* would be achieved by scheduling that job on machine B *last* that has the *minimum* B_i so that the overall time is 37 units plus minimum B_i. This is why Johnson's rules call for the minimum B_i to schedule job i last. In our problem the minimum *possible* overall time would be $37 + 7 = 44$ units. The next to the minimum B_i is 9 units, 2 greater than the 7 scheduled last in our solution. Therefore, the minimum if B_1 is not scheduled last in the sequence would be $37 + 9$, or 46 units. This is exactly the schedule we realized and so the sequence has to be optimum.

Before looking at Johnson's modification for N jobs/3 machines, it is pertinent to realize that real world characteristics can play a part in the solution. Two major restrictions pointed out by Churchman[4] concerning the previous problem approach are:

1. There are no completion priorities. No product is needed more quickly than another.
2. It is assumed that in-process storage space is available and the cost of in-process inventory is the same for each job or too small to be taken into account.

8–3. *N* JOBS/3 MACHINES

Johnson extended the 2-machine problem to 3 by showing that job i precedes job j if

$$\text{Min } (A_i + B_i, C_j + B_j) < \text{Min } (A_j + B_j, C_i + B_i)$$

The problem is treated exactly as before after the three columns are reduced to two by the expedient of $A_i + B_i$ being column 1 and $B_i + C_i$ being the other column. Unfortunately, this is guaranteed optimum only if $\min A_i \geq \max B_j$ or $\min C_i \geq \max B_j$, which is rather restrictive. An example is given in Table 8–5 with solution. The Gantt chart solution is given in Figure 8–3 and as with the 2-job

Table 8-5

Example of Optimal Solution for 3 Job/3 Machine Problem

Job (i)	Machine		
	A_i	B_i	C_i
1	8	3	7
2	6	5	5
3	10	4	8

Min $A_i >$ max B_i
6 $>$ 5

i	$A_i + B_i$	$B_i + C_i$	Sequence
1	11	10	
2	11	10	
3	14	12	_ _ 1
1	11	10	
2	11	10	
3	14	12	_ 2 1

Final Sequence: 3 2 1

problem, the fact that this schedule is optimum can be intuitively shown. Since all A_i can be assigned sequentially regardless of order, the *minimum possible* time would be $\sum A_i + \min (B_i + C_i)$. For the problem just solved this would be $24 + 10 = 34$. This is the time achieved by the solution technique.

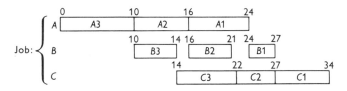

Figure 8–3. Gantt chart schedule for 3 job/3 machine problem.

8–4. 2 JOBS/M MACHINES

Needless to say, solution of the 2 job/M machine problem can be handled easily by the enumeration process if the sequence through the M machines is the same for each job. Only two sequences would be possible—A-B and B-A. If, however, the sequence through machines is fixed for each job but not the same for each job then the problem can get quite difficult. Akers[1] introduced a *graphical* concept which leads to good, but not necessarily optimal, results. Beckman[3] later extended Akers' work and developed an algorithm which does yield an optimum solution.

Akers' technique is as follows:

1. Draw a set of axes with the horizontal scale representing processing time on job 1 and the vertical scale representing processing time on job 2.

2. Lay out the machine times on each axis in the given technological order. Shade the rectangle formed by each start and end times (jobs 1 and 2) for each machine. This will be clarified with an example.

3. Starting at the axes' origin, move to the upper right-hand corner with a path of segments of horizontal and vertical lines, and diagonals with a unit slope. A move to the right (horizontal) indicates job 1 is being processed and one upward indicates job 2 is being processed. A diagonal move indicates *both* jobs are being processed. No movement is permitted through shaded rectangles as this would have both jobs being processed by one machine at the same time.

4. The optimal path is the one that minimizes overall time:

$$\sum \text{Vertical and horizontal segments plus} \sum \frac{diagonal\ segments}{\sqrt{2}}.$$

As much diagonal travel as possible should be aimed at.

5. The solution sequence processes *job 1 before job 2* on all machines appearing *above* the path, and processes job 2 before job 1 if the machine appears below the path.

As an example, consider the 2 job/4 machine data given in Table 8–6. A solution is given in Figure 8–4. Since machines A, B, and C lie above the line, job 1 is processed first on those machines. Job 2 is processed first on machine D. The Gantt chart for this arrangement is given in Figure 8–5. If we take $\sum$ vertical and horizontal segments plus $\sum$ *diagonal segments* for the path length we get

Horizontal:	6
Vertical:	4
Diagonal/$\sqrt{2}$:	10
	20

This of course is the time span given by the Gantt schedule. Instead of actually calculating (diagonal/$\sqrt{2}$) it is easier to sum the vertical *or* horizontal distance moved by the diagonals.

The path given in Figure 8–5 is only one of many possible paths.

Table 8–6

Data for 2 Job/4 Machine Problem

Job 1			Job 2	
Machine Required Sequence	Time		Machine Required Sequence	Time
A	6		A	4
B	1		D	3
C	5		B	2
D	4		C	5
	16			14

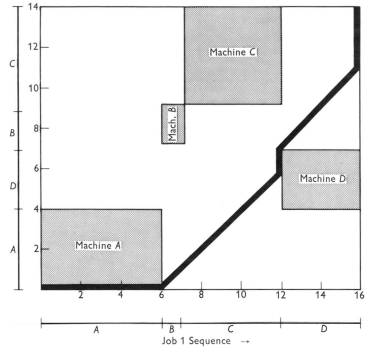

Figure 8–4. Graphical solution to 2 job/4 machine sequencing problem.

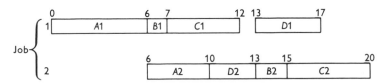

Figure 8–5. Gantt chart schedule for 2 job/4 machine solution.

Finding the correct optimal path can be quite a problem. It is this problem that Beckman attacked.

8–5. BECKMAN SOLUTION

Beckman's technique extends Akers' approach so that several paths are considered, and the optimal one is then selected. The feasible sequences can be enumerated as follows:

1. Perform steps 1 and 2 of Akers' procedure.

2. Draw lines with a unit slope in both directions from the upper left and lower right of each blocked-out area. Lines terminate when they intersect the top or bottom of any other block or when they intersect a hypothetical extension of the top or bottom of each block. If no block is in the lower left-hand corner, draw a line from the origin, terminating as just indicated.

3. Number each line.

4. Start either at the origin or at the upper left or lower right of the "origin" block and move upward and to the right along the lines. When a line terminates, move to the closest diagonal line on either the left or right which will advance the path toward the upper right hand corner.

5. Keep track of the possible paths in a table in a manner that will be indicated with an example.

6. Circle the end-points of the various paths in the table. Select the largest one and trace backwards to determine the component segments.

7. Determine the machine sequence as in Akers' formulation.

8. The optimum time $-\sum$ (required times for job 1) $+\sum$ (required times for job 2) $-$ (largest end-point value from the table). This is obvious as the end-point value denotes the *cumulative* time that both jobs are processed at the same time.

The Akers' example will be repeated with Beckman's solution. Figure 8–6 gives Akers' machine rectangle representations with Beckman's feasible unit slope lines. The feasible solutions (steps 4 and 5) are developed in Table 8–7. The reference numbers allow us to trace back the optimum path. The cumulative distance is simply the accumulated time along a diagonal path. This is either the vertical or horizontal distance taken. Line 2 is the first diagonal taken. It terminates after 5 units. Either line 1 or 5 can be taken to extend the path. Line 1 ends in a cumulative distance of 7 units and line 5 with one of 9. Since these are end points they are circled in the table. Line 7 is another feasible starting diagonal and has an accumulation of 4.

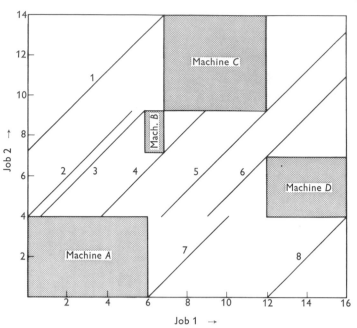

Figure 8–6. Beckman's "Courses of Action" for 2 job/4 machine problem.

The only feasible extension is line 6, which allows an accumulation of 10. In case there is any confusion on this accumulation, let's look at the line 7 and 6 accumulation. Looking at the horizontal times, line 7 goes from 6 to 10, for the 4 accumulation. Line 6 would then go from 10 to 16 giving an added time of 6, for the accumulation of 10.

The optimum diagonal path accumulates to 10, but all three feasible

Table 8-7

**Feasible "Diagonal Trips" from Beckman's
"Courses of Action" (Figure 8–6)**

Reference Number	Cumulative Diagonal Distance	Cumulative Came from Reference Number	Diagonal Number
1	5	0	2
2	(7)	1	1
3	(9)	1	5
4	4	0	7
5	(10)	4	6

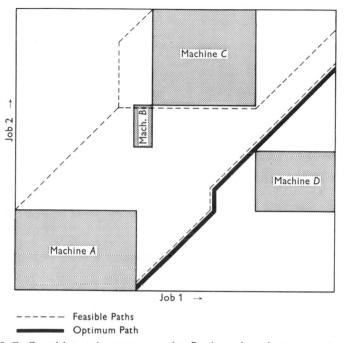

Figure 8-7. Feasible path sequences by Beckman's solution to the 2 job/4 machine problem.

paths are given in Figure 8-7. The optimum path gives a schedule with an accumulation time equal to $\sum$ (job 1 times) $+ \sum$ (job 2 times) $-$ diagonal length (from Table 8-7). This is: $16 + 14 - 10 = 20$, which is the same length as we achieved with Akers' solution, though this might not have been so. The actual path is a little different but the Gantt solution would of course be exactly the same.

8-6. PRIORITY DISPATCHING

The complexity of the job-shop scheduling problem is readily apparent when it is realized that the approaches just presented will lead to optimization only in very simple job-shop cases. One approach in scheduling more complex and realistic systems is the use of *priority dispatching*. With priority dispatching, one or more decision rules are utilized to determine *schedule priorities* for jobs in the system. For example, when we discussed Brook's algorithm for limited resource allocation, jobs were scheduled with priority based on the longest total time controlled through the network. Another rule we considered scheduled jobs according to the longest resource-time combination controlled through the network.

One of the advantages for a priority rule scheduling technique is that it is easy to administer, say on the shop floor. This advantage still holds even though priority dispatching is heuristic in nature and therefore no guarantee of optimality is either made or expected. In a study made by Conway[5] it was stipulated that the rule "shortest operation first" should be considered for job-shop applications because of ease of administration and its favorable effects on:

1. Minimum total completion time.
2. Mean total completion time.
3. Mean number of jobs in the system.
4. Mean waiting time.
5. Minimum total due-date slippage.

These characteristics are, of course, just a few of the possible criteria of effectiveness, several of which were given in the previous section.

Fendley[8] utilized priority dispatch concepts to good advantage in scheduling non-deterministic activities in interacting *multi-projects*. A simple example given in this study for a simple project, of which a job-shop sequence may be a special case, will help demonstrate the difficulty in deciding upon a specific priority rule to utilize in all situations.

Consider the project network given in Figure 8–8. Assuming that the

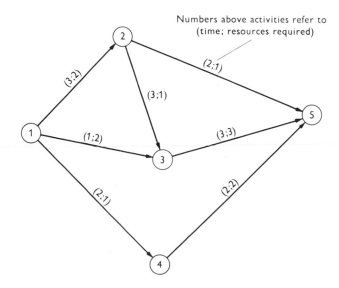

Figure 8–8. Example project network.

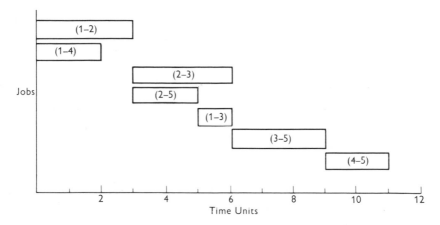

Figure 8–9. Priority rule (LPTC) schedule.

resource requirements, possibly skilled technicians, are the same for each job within the project and that three technicians are available for the project, as given in Figure 8–8. Then the Brook's algorithm schedule (Chapter 6) using as a priority rule the longest path to completion through the network (LPTC rule) would be as given in Figure 8–9. This schedule is for eleven days overall, two days longer than the *critical path method* solution with resources neglected.

The shortest operation rule (SOF rule) suggested by Conway as being desirable because of ease of implementation realizes the schedule shown in Figure 8–10. Of course this rule comes into play

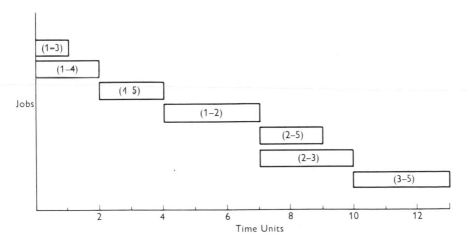

Figure 8–10. Priority rule (SOF) schedule.

only when several activities are legally competing for the same resource. At time period two- activities 1-2 and 4-5 legally qualify for scheduling. Activity 4-5 is scheduled first as it has the shortest duration. The overall schedule realized by the SOF rule is thirteen time units, two longer than the previous eleven.

Finally, another common scheduling rule is first-come first-served (FCFS). For a specific project, those activities whose predecessor jobs are completed first will be scheduled first, as resources become available. Applying the FCFS priority rule to the example network achieves the schedule represented in Figure 8–11. The FCFS schedule also gives eleven time units in length overall, as was the LTPC approach. How then do we choose between the two identical-time schedules? One common approach is to evaluate the utilization of the resource throughout the schedule. This can be seen in a *resource profile* diagram as given in Figure 8–12. The profile for the LPTC schedule seems to be smoother than that for FCFS, thus possibly denoting a better balance of resource. In other words, less moving of resources from one project to another would probably be realized with the LPTC schedule in this example. One way to quantify the profile smoothness is by computing a smoothness factor, S.F.:

$$\text{S.F.} = \sum_{i=1}^{R} (i)^2 (t_i)$$

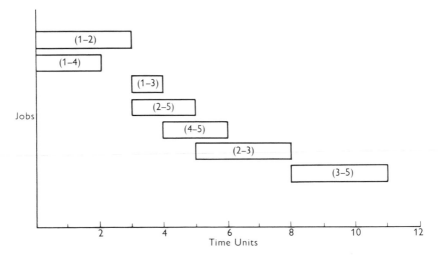

Figure 8–11. Priority rule (FCFS) schedule.

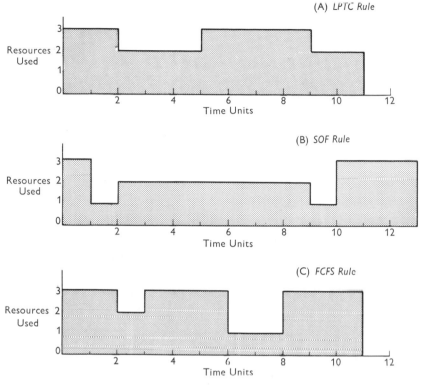

Figure 8–12. Resource profiles.

where $i = 1, 2, \ldots, R$ are the possible values of resource used in any time period.

t_i = the number of time units that resource level i is utilized for in the schedule.

For example, consider the resource profile for priority rule LPTC. There are six time units where three resource units were utilized, and five where two were needed. The smoothness factor would then be

$$\text{S.F.} = (3)^2(6) + (2)^2(5) + (1)^2(0) = 74.$$

Similarly, S.F. for the SOF and FCFS schedules are 66 and 78 respectively. For schedules of the same time length, the smaller the smoothing factor, then, the better is the resource balance. This, for the two eleven-day schedules, was achieved by the LPTC rule.

8–7. EXPERIMENTATION

Now the question arises as to how to evaluate priority rules for a particular situation. One successful approach is through project or job-shop digital computer simulation, assuming naturally that activity times are not deterministic. Each priority rule is replicated several times with systems similar to the ones expected in the facility which will utilize the priority dispatching approach. The simulation run results are then checked against measures of optimality and the best dispatch rule chosen.

Fendley considered several rules in his multi-project research, of which a few were:

1. *SOF*: *Shortest Operation First*—Priority is given to the shortest operation of those waiting. Priority ties were broken by use of the FIFO rule.
2. *FIFO*: *First In, First Out*.
3. *MAR*: *Most Available Resources*—Priority is given to that activity which requires the largest amount of available resources.
4. *MSA*: *Most Succeeding Activities*—Priority is given to that operation which controls the largest accumulated time of succeeding activities.
5. *MSF*: *Minimum Slack First*—Priority is given to that activity with minimum-slack-from-due-date, where the due date is assumed to be the PERT-calculated expected completion time.
6. *MCA*: *Most Critical Activities*—Priority is given to that operation which precedes the largest accumulation of critical activity times.

Eight mock projects were formulated by Fendley, each having up to twenty operations. Each activity was assumed to require 0, 1, 2, or 3 units of any or all of three scarce resources. Availabilities of six or twelve resource units for each of the three scarce resources was assumed. A beta probability distribution was assumed to be descriptive of each activity's performance time. It should be remembered that this distribution with simplification assumptions was utilized in PERT analysis. Two major conclusions resulted from the study:

1. The minimum-slack-first (MSF) priority rule, when used with realistic due dates, appeared to be the most desirable of those rules tested, especially if the primary objective is the avoidance of project slippage.
2. Realistic due dates may be set by analysis of resource load on the facility to determine the amount of slippage that must occur to perform all projects with fixed resources.

As Fendley suggests in his paper, the conclusions were based on *experimental* results from specific cases and their extrapolation must be directed by the situation.

REFERENCES CITED

1. AKERS, S. B., "A Graphical Approach to Production Scheduling Problems," *Operations Research*, Vol. 4, April 1956.
2. BAKSHI, M. S. and ARORA, S. R., "The Sequencing Problem," *Management Science*, Vol. 16, No. 4, December 1969.
3. BECKMAN, R. R., "Sequencing of Two Jobs on M Machines," Unpublished Master of Science Report, Industrial Engineering Department, Tempe, 1964.
4. CHURCHMAN, C. W., ACKOFF, R. L., and ARNOFF, E. L., *Introduction to Operations Research*, John Wiley and Sons, New York, N.Y., 1957.
5. CONWAY, R. W., "An Experimental Investigation of Priority Assignment in a Job Shop." Memorandum RM-3789-PR, The Rand Corporation, February, 1964.
6. CONWAY, R. W. MAXWELL, W. L., and MILLER, L. W., *Theory of Scheduling*, Addison-Wesley Publishing Company, Reading, Mass., 1967.
7. EILON, S., *Elements of Production Planning and Control*, The Macmillan Company, New York, N.Y., 1962.
8. FENDLEY, L. G., "The Development of a Complete Multi-Project Scheduling System Using a Forecasting and Sequencing Technique," Unpublished Ph.D. Dissertation. Arizona State University, May, 1967.
9. JOHNSON, S. M., "Optimal Two- and Three-Stage Production Schedules with Set-up Time included," *Naval Research Logistics Quarterly*, Vol. 1, No. 1, 1 March 1954.
10. SPINNER, A. H., "Sequencing Theory—Development to Date," *Naval Research Logistics Quarterly*, Office of Naval Research, Vol. 15, No. 2, June 1968.
11. SZWARC, W., "On Some Sequencing Problems," *Naval Research Logistics Quarterly*, Office of Naval Research, Vol. 15, No. 2, June 1968.

FURTHER READING

BROWN, R. G., "Simulations to Explore Alternative Sequencing Rules," *Naval Research Logistics Quarterly*, Office of Naval Research, Vol. 15, No. 2, June 1968.
ELMAGHRABY, S. E., "The Machine Sequencing Problem—Review and Extensions," *Naval Research Logistics Quarterly*, Office of Naval Research, Vol. 15, No. 2, June 1968.
MUTH, JOHN F., and THOMPSON, G. R., Editors, *Industrial Scheduling*, Prentice-Hall, Inc., Englewood Cliffs, N.J., 1963.

PROBLEMS

1. Consider the 2 job/3 machine sequencing problem given in Table 8–1. If the jobs can be scheduled through work centers in *any* sequence would this

change the schedule from fixing the sequences for both jobs as 1-2-3, assuming the objective is to minimize overall time in the shop?

2. Solve the same 2 job/3 machine problem given in Problem 1 by Akers' graphical method; assume the fixed sequence of 1-2-3 for both jobs.

3. Six jobs are required to go through two machines in sequence A-B. The following job/machine times are given

Job (i)	Machine A_i	B_i
1	10	5
2	6	9
3	9	8
4	15	12
5	14	18
6	6	10

What sequence of jobs will minimize overall production time? Give a Gantt chart representation of the optimum schedule.

4. Six jobs are required to go through three machines in sequence A-B-C. The following job/machine times are given:

Job (i)	Machine A_i	B_i	C_i
1	10	8	19
2	4	5	25
3	18	10	18
4	12	4	23
5	16	18	30
6	7	5	19

What sequence of jobs will minimize overall production time? Give a Gantt chart representation of the optimum schedule.

5. Consider the 3 job/3 machine data given in Table 8–2. Use Johnson's technique to schedule the 3 jobs in an attempt to minimize the overall time. Why does it not work? (Or does it?)

6. Consider the project network given in Figure 8–8. A new management consultant suggests that a priority dispatch rule LOF (Longest Operation First) be used to schedule the activities. Show whether or not LOF is satisfactory as contrasted with the three priority dispatch rules discussed in the text.

7. Evaluate the resource smoothness for your LOF schedule in Problem 6 by drawing the resource profile and computing the smoothness factor, S.F.

8. Suggest a priority dispatch rule of your own for scheduling the network of Figure 8–8, justifying its development. Also, use your rule to schedule the network and evaluate the resource smoothness.

III

CONTROL

9

Inventory Control

First come, first served.
BEAUMONT AND FLETCHER

9–I. CONCEPTS OF CONTROL

Now we are ready to start the third part of this text, that covering *control* concepts. This follows nicely from the first two parts, those of *planning* and *analysis*, as control will be the process whereby planned and analyzed systems will be made to conform to the specifications resulting from planning and analysis.

This initial control chapter will introduce the topic of inventory control. As with forecasting, which somewhat bridged the gap between planning and analysis, so does inventory control perform the same service between analysis and control. Forecasting could have been interpreted to fall into either the planning or analysis sections. Similarly, inventory control could fall into either the analysis or control sections.

Mostly, though, inventory control probably falls in the *control* area. From the production point of view, the prime functions of inventory control are:

1. To insure that the production function is not hampered due to lack of required items or, for that matter, a surplus of items. The production function is assumed to be developed in such a fashion that prior objectives will be satisfied with conditions optimized according to some specified criteria.

2. To insure that the procedures developed for obtaining and storing required inventory items will be such that a minimum cost is expended

on the inventory function, commensurate again with satisfying system objectives.

9–2. GENERAL CONSIDERATIONS OF INVENTORY CONTROL

The American Production and Inventory Control Society[1] has defined "inventory control" as

The technique of maintaining stock-keeping items at desired levels, whether they be raw materials, work-in-process, or finished products.

The determination of desired levels and maintaining inventory at these levels is the heart of the inventory control problem. The definition is clearly aimed at the control of *production* inventory. Equally applicable is the determination of desired levels and maintaining these levels for a purely department store type of activity. This is implied in the definition, though, with either the raw materials or finished product category of stock item.

The scope of inventory control covers all facets of the production or business operation. Not only is it applicable to department stores and production facilities, it is equally germane to such operations as supermarkets, warehousing, service station operations, and a myriad of others. From this point of view it is *systems* oriented, in that the solution approaches are certainly applicable to a large variety of different operations.

Probably inventory control should cover primarily:

A. Raw stock inventory levels.
B. Batch production of component items.
C. In-process inventory analysis.
D. Final product inventory.

Items A and B are the topics that have applicability for the material covered in this chapter. Item A can be treated as an *economic order quantity* problem where some quantity is ordered for each inventory item at an appropriate time such that inventory holding costs and ordering costs are minimized. Item B is a very similar problem except that instead of instantaneous receipt of an entire order as with the economic order quantity problem, items are produced at a finite rate in batches for consumption in the same facility. In this latter case, consumption is at a much *lower* rate than production.

Item C, which will not be covered in this material, refers to the specialized *production* problem where connecting production operations are *buffered* by in-process inventory banks. The overall product has to be produced through a sequence of these operations, say as in the manufacture of an automobile. If a panel stamping machine is one operation in the sequence, it is obvious that the multi-million dollar line should not be shut down if just the panel stamping operation fails. So, an inventory level of panels is maintained within the process sequence for such a contingency. The size of the inventory level would be dependent on both the production rate and the *probability* of operation failure.

The fourth category of inventory control, that of final product inventory required for customer satisfaction, is based on *forecasting analysis*. Item D then dictates production rates required which will have a significant bearing on the first three inventory categories, items A through C.

Inventory is a *cost* to the operation. It requires capital that is not working for the operation, except that it does allow the operation to work efficiently and allows customer satisfaction, without which the operation would not exist. The importance of inventory analysis and control is apparent to almost everyone. Magee and Boodman[5] state:

Inventory accumulation and depletion have long been recognized as a major contributing factor to fluctuations in business activity. Indeed, the unwitting and tardily recognized build-up of excess stocks is often recognized as a major cause of the 1920–21 depression. Four of the major business downturns in the post-World War II period to 1961 have been attributed to inventory fluctuations.

An idealistic yet ideal situation would be to have sufficient inventory on hand at all times to just match the demand at any given instant in time, with only one order charge for all time, an obvious impossibility. Forecasts of demand are subject to error because of the inherent uncertainty of customer whims and economic conditions. As mentioned several times already, operating systems are *dynamic* not static, thus requiring dynamic and not static policies.

Because of the dollar aspects of inventory, inventory planning can assist in *effective budgeting*. This point is well made by Stockton:[7]

Inventories are an asset in the firm and, as such, appear in dollar form on the balance sheet. From a financial standpoint, inventories represent a capital investment and must, therefore, compete with other asset forms for the firm's limited capital funds.

In some plants as much as 75 percent of the sale's dollar is spent for inventory, so it is important that material costs be closely controlled.

The investment in inventories is usually one of the largest items on the balance sheet (after plant and equipment). Having good knowledge of these costs through inventory analysis and control goes a long way to developing an effective budget. In this regard, *inventory management* rather than inventory control may be the tough problem. The percentage of cost to invest in inventory is one of the more difficult management decisions.

Most of the material in this chapter will be concerned with determining order quantities or batch production levels. However, many reasons exist for holding inventories higher than dictated by some optimized model. Typical would be:

A. Buying in larger quantities may sometimes result in overall inventory cost reduction due to *quantity discounts*. One large airplane manufacturer uses a small computer to evaluate the benefit of price breaks in relationship to the entire inventory cost picture.

B. Predicted price increases or labor increases, necessitating later price increases, can suggest benefits in buying inventory now at a reduced price. Again, the overall inventory cost picture should be evaluated.

C. Projected strikes indicating difficulty in inventory procurement would certainly dictate inventory stockpiling to be desirable. The automobile manufacturers' relationship with the steel industry is a frequent case in point.

Most of the disadvantages in having too large inventory levels accrue from the increased costs that result. A few would include:

A. Interest on investment in inventory. (This represents lost potential capital profit.)
B. Storage or space charges.
C. Taxes and insurance.
D. Physical deterioration and its prevention.
E. Obsolescence.

Many more could be included. It is necessary that close control be exercised over inventory so that procurement and holding costs are the lowest possible consistent with availability of material, space, and capital. As Magee and Boodman[5] point out:

... costs, and the balancing of opposing costs, lie at the heart of all production and inventory control problems. The cost elements essential to a production or inventory problem are characteristically not those reported in summary accounting records.

The main purpose of this chapter is to define, determine, and balance these opposing costs. This latter purpose will be accomplished through the development of graphical and mathematical models of the inventory system, which will then be optimized by unit inventory cost minimization.

Very basically, there are two categories of unit inventory cost:

A. Unit costs which tend to decrease as the size of the order increases. Primarily these would be the *unit cost* of physically ordering the inventory or the unit cost of setting up for a batch of items.

B. Costs which tend to increase as the size of the order increases. These include physical *storage costs* for warehouse depreciation charges and storage operating costs. Also included would be *carrying charges* including *interest* on inventory investment which is interpreted as a lost potential profit.

Inventory storage costs such as rent, heat, light, and janitor service may be computed by allocating all the costs of renting and operating storerooms to the items in *proportion* to the space occupied. The storage costs increase with respect to the time inventory is held in storage and so dimensions for unit storage costs are usually dollars/unit of inventory per unit of time. If several different products are stored in the same basic storage space then charges are usually calculated on the basis of the *average* amount of inventory held over an order or batch consumption time. If only one product is stored in a facility then all charges associated with that facility will be assigned as storage costs for the item. Unit costs are then based on the *maximum* quantity of inventory expected in the facility.

Carrying charges are usually based on the *average inventory* during a batch-use cycle. Such items as taxes, insurance and interest charges on capital investment in inventory are typical of these carrying charges. Usually, the interest charge would be based on the *return* achieved on the firm's assets. This may well be in the 15-to-25-percent range.

The total cost of carrying inventory is a function of the number of times the items are purchased as an order or produced as a batch, and the actual quantities purchased. For example, suppose an item is purchased for stock and the usage is $2,000 per year. One order might be placed for $2,000 or 12 orders for $167 each, the latter scattered at equal intervals through the year. The average inventory in the first case, assuming uniform depletion, is $1,000 while only $83.50 in the second. The order costs for the second case would be considerably higher than for the first. It is the *sum* of these costs that has to be minimized. In case one thinks that the cost of purchasing is trivial, these are frequently costed in the $30 to $50 per order range. Thus, the futility of ordering just one box of paper clips at a time is seen.

Several methods are available for costing inventory on the balance sheet. Ideally, if items in inventory were used immediately upon receipt of the item then each item could be priced at its input value. However, the realistic case has inventory in storage for varying lengths of time, with input prices of inventory relative to the time certain lots were received. Two familiar methods for pricing inventory, knowing that individual prices are not constant, are the FIFO and LIFO techniques, the former of which triggered the introductory chapter quotation.

FIFO, or first-in first-out, prices items on the basis of the *oldest lot* currently in storage, until that particular lot is exhausted. A lot is defined as one order quantity. Items withdrawn after exhaustion of this lot are then priced on the basis of the next oldest lot, and so on. LIFO, standing for last-in first-out, is the inverse of the FIFO system. With LIFO, outgoing items are priced according to the cost of the *latest lots* received until an amount of inventory corresponding to that lot is released. Subsequent items are then priced according to the next most recent lot until that is completely released.

The justification for FIFO and LIFO is mentioned by MacNiece:[4]

A. FIFO is applicable when manufacturing costs must reflect actual sequences of price fluctuations for raw materials. It certainly is applicable for *perishable* items which physically have to be routed first-in first-out to prevent spoilage.

B. LIFO permits stock to be carried on the books at old prices, so that inventory values do not change greatly from one accounting period to the next. Current fluctuations in the price of raw materials are more realistically reflected in the current cost of sales.

From a tax point of view, either method is valid as long as it is used *consistently*.

As with a large number of scientific management philosophies, the inventory control quantified approach can be traced back to the early 1900's. The most interesting historical treatment is presented in Fairfield Raymond's classic text, *Quantity and Economy in Manufacture.*[6] To the modern proponent of management science, the publication date of 1931 should be of interest.

Of significant interest in Raymond's historical sequence is:

> 1912: G. D. Babcock developed a cubic equation for economic lot sizes. This was apparently not published. According to H. M. Benning,[2] the cubic equation approach was simplified by D. B. Carter.

1925: Ford W. Harris at Westinghouse developed the so-called economic lot size formula. It is with Harris' work that most of today's inventory control optimization had its inception.

For the historian, Raymond cites some thirty-eight references which referred to, or applied, economic order quantities *prior to 1931*.

Finally, in these general introductory remarks prior to examining some approaches to quantitative inventory control, comment should be made regarding *inventory information*. Large quantities of inventory items require a complex information structure to keep track of the inventory. Input/output records for example can get horrendous. Physically tagging items for control can become a headache. We will not attack this problem *per se*, but in Chapter 12 we will give an overview of the *entire system* information picture, with possible approaches to handling the entire system information problem automatically.

Now we are ready to introduce the topic of modeling for inventory control. Initially, in Section 9–3, we will look at a way to simplify this problem for systems that have large numbers of different inventory items. Then we will slide into the optimization approach to finding the required order or production quantity levels, and procedures for maintaining them.

9–3. INVENTORY GROUPING—PARETO'S LAW

Now we will be concerned with modeling inventory systems so that costs of the system will be optimized commensurate with maintaining inventory objectives. The result of this optimization will be the development of inventory policies. A typical policy might tell us how much of a particular item to order at a specified time. The "time" could either be in terms of traditional calendar time or in terms of the current inventory level of the particular item. With multi-item inventory systems such as in department stores, the United States Air Force, mail-order catalog systems, and so on, it might be that when several different policies occur the actual cost of *policy implementation* may make the overall inventory system far from optimum. This is yet another case of sub-system optimization not necessarily forming an optimized aggregate system. One way to cut down on the implementation costs of inventory control is with the so-called ABC method.

There are many situations where a large percentage of cost is contributed by a small percentage of items. In the manufacture of an airplane, for example, even though there are hundreds of components, one of which would be rivets, probably some 70 or 80 percent of the total component cost comes from probably 15 or 20 percent of the actual number of items. The same relationship holds for family budget expenditures. One only has to look at the automobile and house mortgage payment to test the expected validity of this latter statement. A large proportion of the world's wealth will be found to be in the hands of a small proportion of its population. These types of relationship were widely publicized by *Vilfredo Pareto* (1848–1923), an Italian economist and sociologist, whose empirically derived *Pareto's Law* covered the distribution of incomes.

The same relationship frequently exists with items held in inventory. A relatively small percentage of the items will contribute to a disproportionate percentage of the cost. Controlling closely the inventory holding costs of these high-cost items will clearly lead to effective control of a large percentage of the overall inventory costs. Clerical costs will at the same time be reduced.

9–4. THE ABC CLASSIFICATION SYSTEM

The common inventory control method for handling this is the ABC method where inventory is classified into high-value (A class), medium value (B class), and low-value (C class) items. The classification does not have to follow the three-class approach, but this is by far the most common approach. The actual percentage of total items held in each class is quite arbitrary, but typical is a breakdown by Magee and Boodman:[5]

Class A: The top 5 to 10 percent of the items, which accounts for the *highest dollar* inventory investment.

Class B: The middle 20 to 30 percent of items, which accounts for a *moderate* share of the inventory.

Class C: The large remaining group of stock-keeping items, which accounts for a *small fraction* of total cost.

The major difference in policy for these items is that investment should be held down for class A items; therefore an optimized policy which minimizes costs should be held quite stringently. Class C items should be overstocked to insure non-runout with little control required. The middle group is a little hazy as far as policy is concerned. Possibly manipulating policies a little to allow blanket policies to cover several

Table 9-1

List of Inventory Items and Annual Investment Costs

Item Identification	(I) Annual Usage	(II) Item Investment Cost	(I) x (II) Annual Investment
A-15	50	$ 3.00	$ 150.00
A-34	1000	1.05	1,050.00
A-21	475	2.00	950.00
B-7	10	10.00	100.00
B-15	2600	0.50	1,300.00
B-28	600	5.00	3,000.00
B-81	1000	0.25	250.00
CD-84	2000	11.00	22,000.00
CD-91	3000	0.10	300.00
G-4	100	0.40	40.00
G-15	600	0.10	60.00
G-25	440	2.50	1,100.00
H-10	2000	0.25	500.00
			$30,800.00

items is one approach for class B items. However, this may be feasible for class A items and this could be a reason for an AB method rather than ABC.

The technique should be quite clear but a little example might clarify it somewhat. Consider the list of inventory items given in Table 9–1, with their estimated annual usage and unit investment cost (purchase cost). Obviously, this is a very limited number of inventory items and except for academic reasons would not warrant ABC analysis.

If the annual investments are ranked in an increasing sequence with accumulated annual investment also calculated, we get the data in Table 9–2, which now will dictate ABC classification. Clearly, unit CD-84 stands by itself and should constitute class A. It's a little hard to say about class B, but items A-21, A-34, G-25, B-15, and B-28 are quite high in value compared to the remaining items. The resultant class items and dollar percentages are given in Table 9 3. Performing tight control procedures on item CD-84 would control 71.4 percent of the total inventory investment while physically controlling only 7.6 percent of the inventory items. If only an AB method were used, class A and B items would be optimized as far as inventory policy goes, with class C items being overstocked for protection but little control.

The overall ABC philosophy is rather important. It shows how a large complex problem of multi-inventory policies can be simplified,

Table 9-2

Cumulative Inventory Annual Investment

Item Identification	Annual Investment	Cumulative Annual Investment
G-4	$ 40.00	$ 40.00
G-15	60.00	100.00
B-7	100.00	200.00
A-15	150.00	350.00
B-81	250.00	600.00
CD-91	300.00	900.00
H-10	500.00	1,400.00
A-21	950.00	2,350.00
A-34	1,050.00	3,400.00
G-25	1,100.00	4,500.00
B-15	1,300.00	5,800.00
B-28	3,000.00	8,800.00
CD-84	22,000.00	30,800.00

Table 9-3

Inventory Item Classification by the ABC Method

	Items	Class Annual Investment	Percentage of Total Items (13)	Percentage of Total Investment ($30,000)
Class A:	CD-84	$22,000.00	7.6%	71.4%
Class B:	B-28; B-15; G-25; A-34; A-21	7,400.00	38.5	24.1
Class C:	H-10; CD-91; B-81; A-15; B-7; G-15; G-4	1,400.00	53.9	4.5

while at the same time favoring the *overall* objective of minimizing costs—both operational and inventory costs. This same philosophy can be extended into many fields.

9-5. MODELING FOR INVENTORY ANALYSIS—GRAPHICAL

When determining optimum order quantities, order points, or order times, it is helpful to *graphically* portray the patterns of inventory fluctuation before developing the mathematical inventory models which will themselves lead to the optimized policy. Logically, the graphical representations will be a plot of inventory levels versus time, showing the depletion and accretion characteristics that are inherent in a dynamic inventory situation. First, only *deterministic* inventory cases will be considered. Later we will present cases where stochastic variation is realized to occur.

The basic and most simple inventory model is where items are ordered from an external vendor at some constant order quantity, Q. It is assumed that each order will arrive where needed at exactly that time when the previous order completely depletes. Also, it is assumed that depletion of stock is at some constant linear rate. This model, commonly called the economic order quantity model, has as its real-world application such cases as department store ordering or factory raw-material acquisition. The major problem of course is that neither delivery nor consumption of an order rarely would ever conform to the deterministic assumptions, though on the average the stochastic variations may balance whereby early delivery effects, for example, counteract late delivery variation, so that the deterministic case may be a reasonably good approximation. Some uncertainty cases will be considered in Chapter 10.

The graphical representation of the economic order quantity (EOQ) model is given in Figure 9–1. The figure should be self-explanatory, but some definition of terms is in order:

Order Quantity, Q: The number of units of one particular stock item

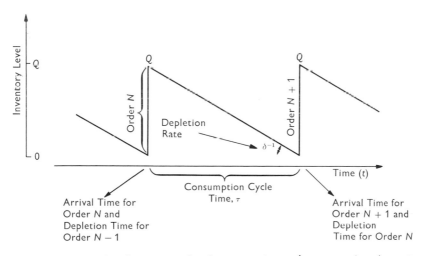

Figure 9–1. Graphical portrayal of economic order quantity inventory patterns with respect to time.

ordered at one time. The *optimum* order quantity determined through later mathematical modeling will be symbolized by Q'. The optimization of Q will be based on the criterion of minimum total inventory costs per consumption cycle, τ.

Consumption Cycle, τ: The time elapsing between receipt of adjacent orders. It can also be defined as the expected time for depletion of one order of size Q units.

Depletion Rate, δ: The rate, in terms of units per unit time, at which the particular item of inventory is depleted. The unit time may be in terms of hours, days, years, etc. The mathematical definition of depletion rate from Figure 9–1 is

$$\delta = \frac{Q}{\tau} \qquad (9\text{--}1)$$

An objective of inventory control can now be stated as follows: Knowing the expected depletion rate from prior forecasting and analysis, and knowing the various component costs of inventory, what order quantity Q' will minimize the total inventory cost during the cycle time τ?

Many ramifications of the basic EOQ model can now be made which will evolve a more realistic picture. For example, knowing that it is quite possible for order $(N - 1)$ to be exhausted some time prior to order (N) arriving would lead to the conclusion that it should be advantageous to have a number of extra units on hand to act as a safety buffer. Occasionally, order $(N - 1)$ might arrive *before* order (N) is depleted. In the long run, the number of extra safety items, now to be called *safety stock*, will average to some constant value ξ. The addition of safety stock to the minimal EOQ model is shown in Figure 9–2. Obviously, more inventory is held during the cycle period τ, with an increased inventory cost. However, this should be offset by elimination of runout conditions created with the model of Figure 9–1 when depletion of order $(N - 1)$ occurs before the arrival of order (N).

Another concept that can be brought out with the graphical EOQ model is that of *reorder time* and *reorder level*. These are depicted in Figure 9–3.

Reorder Time: This is the time period at which an order has to physically be initiated in order for receipt of the order to be as desired. Calling this desired receipt time, or arrival time, t_a, and knowing an expected vendor lead time, t_1, it follows that the reorder time, t_r,

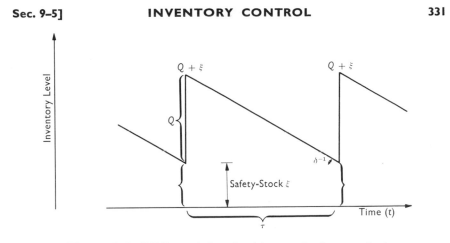

Figure 9–2. EOQ model with addition of safety-stock, ξ.

would be

$$t_r = t_u - t_1 \tag{9–2}$$

The anticipated time interval between adjacent t_r values will be the cycle time, τ, when it is assumed that a constant demand and lead time is realistic.

Reorder Level: With a constant depletion rate of inventory, δ,

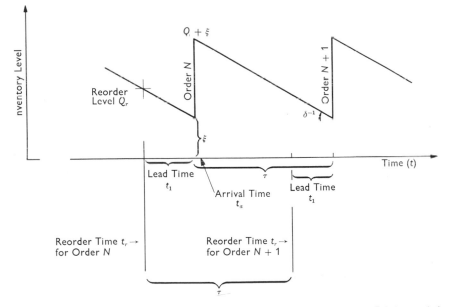

Figure 9–3. Concept of reorder points in conjunction with the EOQ model.

and with an assumed constant lead time, t_1, it follows that order (N) could be ordered when order $(N - 1)$ reaches a reorder level Q_r equal to

$$Q_r = \xi + (\delta)(t_1) \qquad (9\text{–}3)$$

This, of course, assumes that order (N) has a desired arrival time which corresponds to that time when inventory recedes to a level equal to that of the safety stock, ξ.

9–6. ORDER POLICIES

One possible policy is to reorder a particular item when the inventory dips to a level Q_r. The order quantity would be Q' such that the expected inventory level upon receipt of the order is $Q' + \xi$. A common way to represent this policy is to call it a $(Q_r, Q' + \xi)$ policy. Frequently in the literature it is called an (s, S) policy.

The $(Q_r, Q' + \xi)$ policy is typical of possibly the original quantitative inventory control policy, the two-bin system. Here, the units of a particular inventory item are stored in two bins. Possibly one holds (Q_r) units and the sum of the two holds $(Q' + \xi)$ units. Items are drawn from the bin *not* holding Q_r units. When it is empty, an order is made that will replenish both bins. While waiting for order receipts, units are drawn from the Q_r bin. This situation is frequently seen in book and record departments. A red tag near the bottom of the stack indicates reorder. The remaining items constitute Q_r which provide a supply until the new order arrives.

If the $(Q_r, Q' + \xi)$ policy is observed, it should be apparent that ordering may not be accomplished on a strictly cyclic basis, τ time units apart. This would be due to *uncertainty* in demand, a topic to be discussed later. Frequently, cyclic ordering is desired. When this is utilized, the orders are made at reorder times t_r. However, usually only sufficient items to bring the expected level of inventory at time t_a to $Q' + \xi$ are ordered. Now the reorder quantity, Q, is considered a variable, and $[Q' + \xi + (\delta)(t_1) - Q_{\text{current}}]$ units are ordered at t_r. This will be classified as a $(t_r, Q' + \xi)$ policy. In the literature this is frequently classified as the (t, S) policy. A variant of the $(t_r, Q' + \xi)$ policy is that replenishment is only made if the inventory level at time t_r is equal to or less than some specified Q_r value. If current inventory Q is greater than Q_r, then no action is considered for another τ time units. This policy will be classified as a $(t_r, Q_r, Q' + \xi)$ policy.

9–7. BATCH INVENTORY

The EOQ model assumes that all units in a particular order arrive simultaneously and instantaneously at time t_a. The arrival *rate* then may be considered to be infinite. If items are *produced* in a facility for use or sale, then this arrival rate would probably not be infinite, though if sufficient items for a year's use are produced in a single day, then the arrival rate might well be approximated as with the EOQ model. If that time for producing the order is significant then this changes the graphical portrayal. Now we have to consider the arrival picture and the depletion situation and sum the two, as is depicted in Figure 9–4.

Some things should be obvious from the diagram but will be mentioned while discussing the graphical result of the batching model.

A. $\alpha \geqslant \delta$: The arrival rate has to be equal to or greater than the depletion rate or we cannot have continuous depletion. Of course, if the model were such that the depletion was not continuous, this would not be mandatory. Further, if α equals δ, there is no fluctuation of inventory and so no inventory control problem exists as such. Usually, in a production system, batched items, such as horn rings for an automobile, can be produced at a much greater rate than they are consumed in the production facility.

B. $t_\alpha = 0$; $\alpha = \infty$: If the time for producing a *batch* of units is zero, or approaches zero, the arrival rate is infinite. When this occurs, the batch model reverts to the EOQ model. The batch model is really a general inventory model, with the EOQ model being a special case.

C. $\xi =$ Safety Stock: Because $\alpha > \delta$, it follows that a safety stock is forced. However, this is only a realistic usable safety stock if the items are immediately usable in consumption as soon as they are produced. The physical storage space for at least ξ units all the time is of course correct, unless the produced items are stored on something like an overhead conveyor in some process such as drying or curing.

D. $\xi = f(Q)$: It follows that the batching safety stock is dependent on the size of Q required. This can be shown as follows, using trigonometric relationships from Figure 9–4.

1. $\delta = \dfrac{Q}{\tau}$

2. $\alpha = \dfrac{Q}{t_\alpha}$

3. So, $Q = \delta\tau = \alpha t_\alpha$

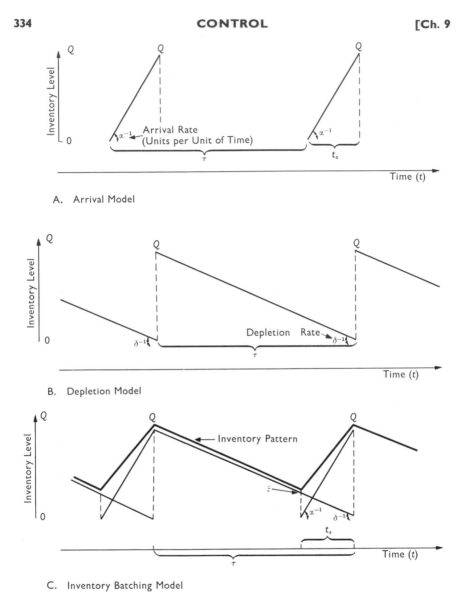

A. Arrival Model

B. Depletion Model

C. Inventory Batching Model

Figure 9–4. Basic batching graphical model.

But the arrival rate, α, and depletion rate, δ, are constants, so t_α/τ is a constant.

$$\delta = \frac{Q}{\tau} = \frac{\xi}{t_\alpha}$$

and

$$\xi = (Q)\left(\frac{t_\alpha}{\tau}\right) \tag{9–4}$$

But we just saw that t_α/τ is a constant, so

$$\xi = f(Q)$$

Variants of the batching model can be made by adjusting the time at which items are produced with relationship to the consumption (depletion) pattern. In Figure 9–4, the position for the arrival model in the combined model was predicated on minimizing overall inventory while insuring that batch $(N + 1)$ would *all* be available when batch (N) was depleted. If no safety stock were desired and if an item produced is immediately usable then the batching model could be as shown in Figure 9–5. Addition of safety stock, ξ, would allow for uncertainty in either consumption or production.

The maximum value of inventory for which to provide storage, Q_M, is seen to be less than the quantity produced each cycle. It can be shown that Q_M is a function of Q using trigonometric relationships from Figure 9–5:

1. $\delta = \dfrac{Q_M}{\tau - t_\alpha}$

2. $\delta = \dfrac{Q}{(\tau)}$

So,

$$Q_M = Q \cdot \left[\frac{(\tau - t_\alpha)}{(\tau)} \right] = Q \cdot \left[1 - \frac{t_\alpha}{\tau} \right] \tag{9–5}$$

But earlier, t_α/τ was shown to be a constant, as used in Equation 9–4,

so $\left[1 - \dfrac{t_\alpha}{\tau} \right]$ has to be a constant, and $Q_M = f(Q)$. As t_α becomes small

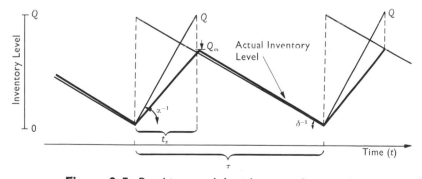

Figure 9–5. Batching model with zero safety stock.

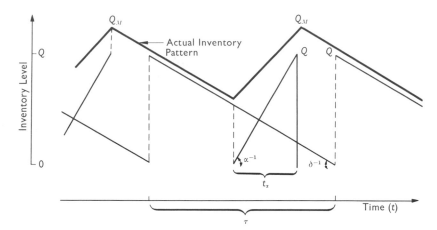

Figure 9–6. Inventory pattern resulting from batch (*N*) being completely produced prior to batch (*N* — 1)'s depletion.

with respect to τ, then Q_M approaches Q and we get the original EOQ model again.

Another adjustment for positioning the arrival model in Figure 9–4 is to position it such that the batch is completed *prior* to the consumption of the previous batch. This will result in overall increased inventory as pictured in Figure 9–6 and so is not deemed a very practical case, except when the new batch is not usable until the entire batch is completed, and a safety stock of the prior batch is required.

Many other changes in the pictorial models, both for the economic-order-quantity model as well as the batching model, could be suggested. Once the basic ideas of drawing the model have been firmed, any situation can be so described. It is felt that the models of Figures 9–1, 9–2, and 9–5 are the basic ones on which most other cases can be built. It is these three that will further be treated mathematically in the next section.

9–8. MODELING FOR INVENTORY ANALYSIS —MATHEMATICAL

The objective of the mathematical analysis will be to find that order quantity, Q', which minimizes inventory unit costs, with inventory patterns as represented graphically earlier. Since the model is cost oriented we will first define the cost components before combining them as the cost model to be minimized.

S: Cost of ordering or manufacturing one order or batch of parts. Dimensionally, S will have units of dollars per batch.

I: Interest charges per unit of inventory per unit of time. Interest costs are a function of both how many units are held in inventory and for how long. Thus, the dimensions for I will be dollars/product unit/time unit. Since interest is a function of how much capital is invested in the product that is not realizing any profit, it follows that

$$I = (i)(C)$$

where $i =$ interest rate per unit of time

$C =$ unit capital invested in dollars/unit

H: Storage charge for holding an inventory item, typically a warehousing cost. As with I, H has dimensions of dollars/product unit/time unit.

Z: Total unit inventory cost to be minimized. This will be the appropriate sum of order costs, interest charges, and storage costs.

Typically, interest charges are based on the *average* number of units on hand during the time in which inventory is being evaluated. This time would be the cycle time, τ, in our case. The average quantity should make intuitive sense. If the quantity is constant over τ, interest charges should certainly be based on that quantity. But, if the quantity decreases uniformly from Q to zero, initially interest charges would be based on Q, but at the end of the evaluation period would be based on zero units. A happy medium is to base overall interest charges on the average inventory.

Two standard ploys are used for charging storage or holding costs. If only one product is being stored in a particular section of the facility, storage charges should always be based on the maximum quantity expected in storage. When several products are stored in the same area, charges would usually be based on *average* inventory expected for the product on the theory that the other products would be charged for the remainder of the storage time. If it is known that a particular product will tie up a specified storage space for a certain percentage of time, storage charges would be based on that particular percentage, rather than average inventory.

The total unit cost, Z, is formed from the sum of the individual unit costs. For example, if Q units are ordered at an order cost equal to S, the unit order cost is S/Q. If interest and storage charges are both based on average inventory, the interest and storage cost per unit during the cycle time, τ, would be

$$\frac{(I + H)(\tau)(\text{Average Inventory})}{Q}$$

The division by Q is to give a cost per unit based on an evaluation period which is the order or batch time. Therefore, the cost model when storage charges are based on average inventory (several products in the same storage area) is

$$Z = \frac{S}{Q} + \frac{(I + H)(\tau)(\text{Average Inventory})}{Q} \qquad (9\text{--}6)$$

In all the models developed in the previous material, we had

$$\tau = \frac{Q}{\delta}$$

where δ is the depletion rate of inventory. So now Equation 9–6 can be rewritten

$$Z = \frac{S}{Q} + \frac{(I + H)(Q)(\text{Average Inventory})}{Q\delta}$$

and

$$Z = \frac{S}{Q} + \frac{(I + H)(\text{Average Inventory})}{\delta} \qquad (9\text{--}7)$$

If only one product is being considered for the storage area, with unused storage area lying empty when inventory is depleted, storage charges are based on *maximum* inventory, not average. This would result in the following equation:

$$Z = \frac{S}{Q} + \frac{(I)(\text{Average Inventory})}{\delta} + \frac{(H)(\text{Maximum Inventory})}{\delta} \qquad (9\text{--}8)$$

Remember, these two equations only hold if $\tau = \dfrac{Q}{\delta}$, which itself only holds if inventory has a *continuous* linear consumption rate. A variation of this continuous depletion will be indicated following this section. First, we will apply the models of Equations 9–7 and 9–8 to three of the graphical situations given earlier in Section 9-5.

1. *Economic Order Quantity—No Safety Stock:* This initial model was given pictorially in Figure 9–1. The main reason for the pictorial presentation of the dynamic inventory patterns is to enable the determination of the average inventory for insertion into the mathematical models. For the EOQ model this average inventory is simply

$Q/2$, since it has a maximum of Q, a minimum of zero, and is linear in between. Assuming multi-products in storage, Equation 9–7 is applicable, so inserting $Q/2$ for average inventory we get

$$Z = \frac{S}{Q} + \frac{(I + H)(Q)^*}{2\delta} \tag{9–9}$$

To find that Q which minimizes Z we need to take the first derivative of Z with respect to Q, set this derivative to zero, and solve for Q, assuming the second derivative is positive. Taking the first two derivatives, we get

$$\frac{dZ}{dQ} = -\frac{S}{Q^2} + \frac{(I + H)}{2\delta} \tag{9–10}$$

$$\frac{d^2Z}{dQ^2} = \frac{2S}{Q^3}$$

which is positive since S and Q are both positive. Setting Equation 9–10 to zero and solving for Q we get

$$\frac{S}{Q^2} = \frac{(I + H)}{2\delta} \tag{9–11}$$

and

$$Q' = \sqrt{\frac{2\delta S}{I + H}} \tag{9–12}$$

where Q' is the order quantity which minimizes unit inventory costs.

One point of interest arises if we multiply Equation 9–11 by Q on both sides of the equation, which does not then affect the equality:

$$\left[\frac{S}{Q^2}\right]Q = \frac{(I + H)}{2\delta}Q$$

or

$$\frac{S}{Q} = \frac{(I + H)Q}{2\delta}$$

Now looking back at Equation 9–9, the original mathematical model, we see that the optimum Q occurs at that point where the ordering cost component of the model equals the interest and storage costs. This indicates that the problem could, if necessary, be solved graphically as

---

* If purchase cost, C, is required in Z, then C is simply added to the other two terms in Equation 9–9. C of course falls out when the derivative of Z is taken with respect to Q, and Q' stays the same. In all analysis in this text we will assume inventory holding charges only are of interest, not holding costs plus original investment.

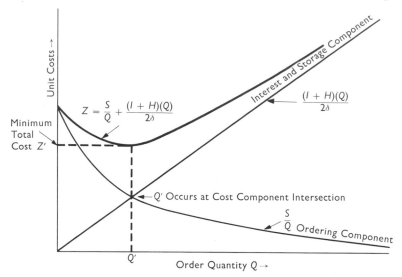

Figure 9–7. Graphical portrayal of EOQ mathematical solution.

shown in Figure 9–7. A numerical example will be given after Q' is determined for that case where only one product is stored in the facility.

This latter case would require Equation 9–8. Since we are still considering only the EOQ model without safety stock, the average inventory is still $Q/2$. Maximum inventory, from Figure 9–1 is, of course, Q. So Equation 9–8 can now be written

$$Z = \frac{S}{Q} + \frac{(I)(Q)}{2\delta} + \frac{(H)(Q)}{\delta}$$

Or, simplifying:

$$Z = \frac{S}{Q} + \frac{(I + 2H)Q}{2\delta} \qquad (9\text{–}13)$$

Taking the first two derivatives of Z with respect to Q we get

$$\frac{dZ}{dQ} = -\frac{S}{Q^2} + \frac{(I + 2H)}{2\delta} \qquad (9\text{–}14)$$

$$\frac{d^2Z}{dQ^2} = \frac{2S}{Q^3}$$

which is positive since S and Q are both positive. Setting Equation

9–14 to zero and solving, we get

$$\frac{S}{Q^2} = \frac{(I + 2H)}{2\delta}$$

and

$$Q' = \sqrt{\frac{2\delta S}{(I + 2H)}} \qquad (9\text{–}15)$$

Which differs from Equation 9–12 only in the denominator, which difference is caused by the change in the storage charge assumption.

This is the last time that we will utilize the concept of single-product unique storage, which resulted in Equation 9–15. In future discussion, only multi-product common storage will be considered whereby storage charges are based on *average* inventory.

EOQ Example. The following data on a product are obtained from the accounting and industrial engineering departments:

$$\delta = 500 \text{ units per month}$$
$$S = \$30 \text{ per batch}$$
$$I = \$2.40/\text{product} \cdot \text{year}$$
$$H = \$0.55/\text{product} \cdot \text{month}$$

Needless to say, all time units have to be consistent, so I is changed to $\$2.40/12 = \$0.20/\text{product} \cdot \text{month}$.

The optimum order quantity is found from Equation 9–12:

$$Q' = \sqrt{\frac{2\delta S}{I + H}} = \sqrt{\frac{(2)(500)(30)}{(0.20 + 0.55)}}$$

$$Q' = \sqrt{\frac{30,000}{0.75}} = 200 \text{ units}$$

This tells us several things. Since cycle time, τ, equals Q/δ, the optimum τ' is $\frac{200}{500}$, or 0.4 months.

For simplicity, two weeks might be set as the ordering cycle time. Also, the minimum unit cost, Z', is found by Equation 9–9, the original model:

$$Z' = \frac{S}{Q'} + \frac{(I + H)(Q')}{2\delta}$$

$$Z' = \frac{30}{200} + \frac{(0.75)(200)}{1,000} = 0.15 + 0.15 = \$0.30/\text{unit}$$

The fact that the two cost components have the same value should not be surprising, as this was shown to be the case in Figure 9–7 for Q'.

Therefore, Z' could easily have been found by

$$Z' = \frac{2S}{Q'}$$

Another interesting concept has been suggested by Eilon.[3] Since the total cost curve Z is usually quite flat around Q', a quite large range about Q' will result in a very slight increase in Z from Z'. If management stipulates an allowable Z, some small percentage above Z', then an allowable Q range can be determined.

For example, consider Equation 9–9:

$$Z = \frac{S}{Q} + \frac{(I + H)(Q)}{2\delta}$$

Multiplying both sides of the equation by Q and rearranging we get

$$\frac{(I + H)}{2\delta} Q^2 - (Z)(Q) + S = 0$$

Using the quadratic formula to solve for Q, we get

$$Q_{\text{allow}} = \frac{Z \pm \sqrt{(Z)^2 - \dfrac{4S(I + H)}{2\delta}}\;^*}{\dfrac{(I + H)}{\delta}} \qquad (9\text{–}16)$$

The two solutions for Q give the upper and lower boundaries of the allowable range, Q_U to Q_L.

Consider the data just utilized in determining an EOQ order point. Z' was found to be \$0.30/unit. Suppose management stipulates that an allowable Z may lie no more than 10 percent above Z'. Thus, an allowable Z is:

$$Z = (Z')(1.10) = \$0.33/\text{unit}$$

Using this value of Z in Equation 9–16 in conjunction with the original data, we get

$$Q_{\text{allow}} = \frac{0.33 \pm \sqrt{(0.33)^2 - \dfrac{(4)(30)(0.75)}{1000}}}{\dfrac{0.75}{500}}$$

---

* If purchase cost was included in the original equation for Z, then Z will be replaced in both cases in Equation 9-16 by $(Z - C)$, where C is the purchase cost. It is doubtful whether purchase cost should be included in an allowable deviation from inventory holding costs, other than inventory charges I.

and

$$Q_{\text{allow}} = 129 \text{ to } 311$$

Since Q' was originally found to be 200, the allowable range represents an upper limit over 50 percent greater than Q' and a lower limit showing almost a 40 percent reduction—quite a large increase contrasted to the 10 percent allowable Z change. The range certainly would allow a cycle time of two weeks to be employed. The graphical concept of the production range is given in Figure 9–8. Another interesting point by Eilon indicates that another criterion of optimality could be the *maximization* of order profit. Even though this is interesting it is not too realistic. A fixed annual demand is implied when the depletion rate δ is fixed. The maximum overall profit assuming fixed sales price has to then occur when overall costs are minimum, which is at the minimum unit costs just evaluated.

2. *Economic Order Quantity—With Safety Stock:* Now let's find Q' for the EOQ model with safety stock ξ, as depicted in Figure 9–2. The basic model of Equation 9–7 is still applicable since τ still equals Q/δ:

$$Z = \frac{S}{Q} + \frac{(I + H)(\text{Average Inventory})}{\delta}$$

The average inventory during τ from Figure 9–2 would be the same as for the original EOQ model, $Q/2$, except that a constant ξ units are

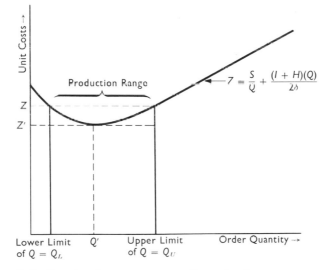

Figure 9–8. Graphical presentation of production range concept.

added. Therefore, the average inventory is $\frac{Q}{2} + \xi$ and the model becomes

$$Z = \frac{S}{Q} + \frac{(I + H)\left(\frac{Q}{2} + \xi\right)}{\delta} \tag{9-17}$$

Since ξ is a constant, it follows that it falls out when the derivative is taken and Q' is the same for this model as for the EOQ model without safety stock. Of course, Z' will increase by a factor of $(I + H)(\xi)/\delta$.

If ξ were a percentage of Q, say $0.20(Q)$, then Equation 9–17 would be

$$Z = \frac{S}{Q} + \frac{(I + H)(0.7Q)}{\delta}$$

and

$$\frac{dZ}{dQ} = 0 = -\frac{S}{Q^2} + \frac{(0.7)(I + H)}{\delta}$$

and

$$Q' = \sqrt{\frac{S\delta}{(0.7)(I + H)}}$$

3. *Economic Order Quantity—Batching:* Now let's consider the batching model, Figure 9–5, without safety stock. The Equation 9–7 model is still applicable as $\tau = Q/\delta$:

$$Z = \frac{S}{Q} + \frac{(I + H)(\text{Average Inventory})}{\delta} \tag{9-18}$$

The average inventory during τ is obviously, from Figure 9–5, $Q_M/2$. We found in Equation 9–5 that

$$Q_M = Q\left[1 - \frac{t_\alpha}{\tau}\right] \tag{9-19}$$

where t_α equals that time for producing a batch of inventory. It was also shown in Section 9–7 that

$$\frac{t_\alpha}{\tau} = \frac{\delta}{\alpha}$$

where α is the inventory arrival (production) rate

So, Equation 9–19 may be written

$$Q_M = Q\left[1 - \frac{\delta}{\alpha}\right]$$

And knowing $Q_M/2$ is the average inventory, Equation 9–18 becomes

$$Z = \frac{S}{Q} + \frac{(I + H)\left(1 - \frac{\delta}{\alpha}\right)Q}{2\delta} \qquad (9\text{–}20)$$

Taking the first derivative of Z with respect to Q:

$$\frac{dZ}{dQ} = \frac{-S}{Q^2} + \frac{(I + H)\left(1 - \frac{\delta}{\alpha}\right)}{2\delta}$$

and

$$Q' = \sqrt{\frac{2\delta S}{(I + H)\left(1 - \frac{\delta}{\alpha}\right)}} \qquad (9\text{–}21)$$

If the arrival rate, α, approaches infinity as with the EOQ model, then δ/α approaches zero, and Equation 9–21 reduces to the EOQ result found in Equation 9–12.

It should be noted that the production range equation would not be exactly the same as previously found in Equation 9–16. The production range would be found by multiplying Equation 9–20 through by Q and solving the resultant quadratic equation for the two roots of Q that form the allowable production range boundary.

9–9. UNUSUAL CASES

As a wrap-up of the deterministic modeling procedure, we will consider two unusual inventory patterns. The values of Q', Z', and τ' will be determined initially. The arrival and depletion models are given in Figure 9–9, prior to assimilation in Figure 9–10. The usage of the batch item is considered to be continuous but the arrival is in three segments. If t_a is considered to be the time for production of the complete batch, then half the batch is produced in the first third of t_a. Nothing is produced in the second third of t_a, and the remaining half batch is produced in the last third of t_a. A realistic case might be a limitation on the time applicable in a machining center for any *one* product.

The combined inventory model given in Figure 9–10 is predicated on completing batch (N) at exactly the depletion time for batch $(N - 1)$, thus allowing for a safety stock. Using Figures 9–9 and 9–10,

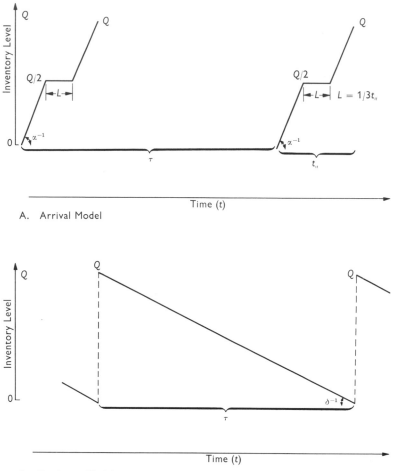

A. Arrival Model

B. Depletion Model

Figure 9–9. Inventory arrival and depletion characteristics for deterministic example.

the following relationships hold; they will aid in determining the average inventory during τ:

1. $\delta = \dfrac{Q_1}{t_a}$

2. $\alpha = \dfrac{Q/2}{\frac{1}{3}t_a}$

3. so: $t_a = \dfrac{3}{2}\dfrac{Q}{\alpha}$ (9–22)

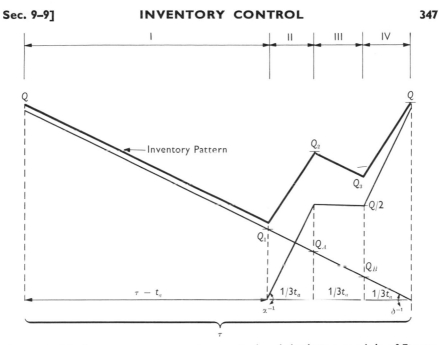

Figure 9–10. Inventory pattern when arrival and depletion models of Figure 9–9 combined.

4. and $Q_1 = \dfrac{3}{2}\dfrac{Q\delta}{\alpha}$ $\qquad\qquad$ (9–23)

5. $\delta = \dfrac{Q_B}{\frac{1}{3}t_a}$, so, with Equation 9–22:

6. $Q_B = \dfrac{1}{2}\dfrac{Q\delta}{\alpha}$ $\qquad\qquad$ (9–24)

7. But $Q_A = 2Q_B$;

$\quad$ so, $Q_A = \dfrac{Q\delta}{\alpha}$ $\qquad\qquad$ (9–25)

8. $Q_2 = Q/2 + Q_A$, from Figure 9–10

9. So, $Q_2 = Q\left[\dfrac{\alpha + 2\delta}{2\alpha}\right]$ $\qquad\qquad$ (9–26)

10. $Q_3 = Q/2 + Q_B$, from Figure 9–10

11. So, $Q_3 = Q\left[\dfrac{\alpha + \delta}{2\alpha}\right]$ $\qquad\qquad$ (9–27)

There are three breakpoints in the *inventory* pattern in Figure 9–10 giving four basic segments, labelled I, II, III, and IV. The average inventory, $\bar{Q}_i$, within these segments is:

Segment I

$$\bar{Q}_I = \frac{Q + Q_1}{2} \qquad \left\{Note: \ Q_1 + \frac{(Q - Q_1)}{2} = \frac{Q + Q_1}{2}\right\}$$

Using Equation 9–23, this is

$$\bar{Q}_I = Q \left[\frac{3\delta + 2\alpha}{4\alpha}\right] \tag{9–28}$$

Segment II

$$\bar{Q}_{II} = \frac{Q_1 + Q_2}{2}$$

Using Equations 9–23 and 9–26, we get

$$\bar{Q}_{II} = Q \left[\frac{\alpha + 5\delta}{4\alpha}\right] \tag{9–29}$$

Segment III

$$\bar{Q}_{III} = \frac{Q_2 + Q_3}{2}$$

Substituting Equations 9–26 and 9–27 gives

$$\bar{Q}_{III} = Q \left[\frac{2\alpha + 3\delta}{4\alpha}\right] \tag{9–30}$$

Segment IV

$$\bar{Q}_{IV} = \frac{Q_3 + Q}{2}$$

Using Equation 9–27 realizes

$$\bar{Q}_{IV} = Q \left[\frac{3\alpha + \delta}{4\alpha}\right] \tag{9–31}$$

The overall average inventory is found by taking a weighted sum of , $\bar{Q}_I \, \bar{Q}_{II}$, $\bar{Q}_{III}$, and $\bar{Q}_{IV}$, where each is weighted by the percentage of τ for which it is valid. $\bar{Q}_{II}$, $\bar{Q}_{III}$, and $\bar{Q}_{IV}$ are then each weighted by

$$\frac{\frac{1}{3}t_a}{\tau} \tag{9–32}$$

From Figure 9–10, we get

1. $\delta = \dfrac{Q}{\tau}$ and $\alpha = \dfrac{3}{2}\dfrac{Q}{t_a}$

2. So, $Q - \delta\tau - \dfrac{2\alpha t_a}{3}$

3. And $t_a = \dfrac{3\delta\tau}{2\alpha}$ \hfill (9–33)

Substituting in Equation 9–32 gives

4. Weight for $\bar{Q}_{\text{II}}$, $\bar{Q}_{\text{III}}$, $\bar{Q}_{\text{IV}}$ is:

$$\frac{1}{2}\frac{\delta}{\alpha} \tag{9–34}$$

The weight for segment I is, using Equation 9–33:

$$\frac{\tau - t_a}{\tau} = 1 - \frac{3}{2}\frac{\delta}{\alpha} \tag{9–35}$$

The overall weighted average inventory is now

$$(\bar{Q}_{\text{I}})\left(1 - \frac{3}{2}\frac{\delta}{\alpha}\right) + (\bar{Q}_{\text{II}} + \bar{Q}_{\text{III}} + \bar{Q}_{\text{IV}})\left(\frac{1}{2}\frac{\delta}{\alpha}\right)$$

And, substituting Equations 9–28 through 9–31 for $\bar{Q}_{\text{I}}$, $\bar{Q}_{\text{II}}$, $\bar{Q}_{\text{III}}$, $\bar{Q}_{\text{IV}}$ and simplifying gives the average inventory of

$$\bar{Q} = Q\left[\frac{3\delta + 2\alpha}{4\alpha}\right] \tag{9–36}$$

Using the original basic cost per unit model of Equation 9–6:

$$Z = \frac{S}{Q} + \frac{(I + H)(\text{Average Inventory})(\tau)}{Q}$$

And substituting Equation 9–36 for average inventory and Q/δ for τ, we get

$$Z = \frac{S}{Q} + (I + H)Q\left[\frac{3\delta + 2\alpha}{4\alpha\delta}\right] \tag{9–37}$$

Taking the derivative of Z with respect to Q and setting to zero gives

$$\frac{dZ}{dQ} = \frac{-S}{Q^2} + (I + H)\left[\frac{3\delta + 2\alpha}{4\alpha\delta}\right] = 0$$

and

$$Q' = \sqrt{\frac{4\alpha\delta S}{(I + H)(3\delta + 2\alpha)}} \tag{9--38}$$

Assume: $\alpha = 40$ units/month

$\delta = 10$ units/month

$(I + H) = \$1.10/\text{unit·month}$

$S = \$400/\text{batch}$

By Equation 9–38:

$$Q' = \sqrt{\frac{(4)(40)(10)(400)}{(1.10)(30 + 80)}} = 73 \text{ Units/batch}$$

Since

$$\tau' = \frac{Q'}{\delta} = \frac{73 \text{ units/batch}}{10 \text{ units/month}}$$

there should be about 7.3 months between batches. The unit inventory cost is

$$\frac{2S}{Q'} = \frac{(2)(400)}{73}$$

or $10.96/unit.

In all of the models thus far, the assumption has been made that consumption is continuous with

$$\tau = \frac{Q}{\delta}$$

This equation, of course, does not hold if consumption is discontinuous. For this case, the problem attack is exactly as presented. For example, consider the modified EOQ situation given in Figure 9–11. Assuming both (I) and (H) based on *average* inventory, the model of Equation 9–6 holds:

$$Z = \frac{S}{Q} + \frac{(I + H)(\text{Average Inventory})(\tau)}{Q}$$

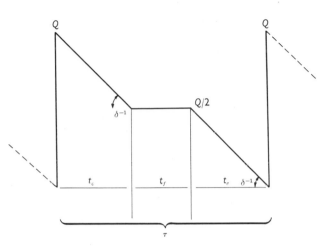

Cycle time $\tau = 2t_c + t_f$
Where t_f is a *constant* delay time

Figure 9–11. Variant of EOQ model to allow discontinuous consumption.

Trigonometrically, it can be seen that

1. $\delta = \dfrac{Q}{2t_c}$

2. And, $\tau = 2t_c + t_f$

3. Therefore, $t_c = \dfrac{\tau - t_f}{2}$

4. Which gives: $\delta = \dfrac{Q}{\tau - t_f}$

5. Finally, $\tau - \dfrac{Q}{\delta} + t_f$

Since t_f is a constant, this relationship for τ is substituted directly into the model:

$$Z = \frac{S}{Q} + \frac{(I + H)(\text{Average Inventory})}{\delta}$$

$$+ \frac{(I + H)(\text{Average Inventory})(t_f)}{Q} \qquad (9\text{–}39)$$

The optimization process now continues as before, finding the average inventory in terms of Q and then determining Z' and Q'.

In summary, determination of a deterministic batch or order size would be as accomplished with the example problem:

A. Determine *arrival* or production pattern.

B. Determine *depletion* pattern.

C. Assimilate to determine *inventory* pattern.

D. Determine *average* inventory by segmentation or integration.

E. Determine cost per unit model in terms of average, and order or batch quantities.

F. Take derivative of cost model with respect to Q, set to zero, and solve for Q'.

G. If Z' can be increased, then an allowable range around Q' may be found giving scheduling flexibility.

This concludes the deterministic inventory considerations. Chapter 10 will consider a few stochastic variations.

REFERENCES CITED

1. *APICS Dictionary of Production and Inventory Control Terms*, American Production and Inventory Control Society, Chicago, Illinois, 1966.
2. BENNING, H. M., "The Determination of the Economic Size of Production Orders," Course XV, Thesis No. 3, Massachusetts Institute of Technology, Cambridge, Mass., 1924.
3. EILON, S., *Elements of Production Planning and Control*, The Macmillan Company, New York, 1962.
4. MACNIECE, E. H., *Production Forecasting, Planning and Control*, John Wiley and Sons, New York, 1961.
5. MAGEE, J., and D. M. BOODMAN, *Production Planning and Inventory Control*. McGraw-Hill Book Co., New York, 1967.
6. RAYMOND, FAIRFIELD E., *Quantity and Economy in Manufacture*. McGraw-Hill Book Co., Inc., New York, 1931.
7. STOCKTON, R. S., *Basic Inventory Systems: Concepts and Analysis*, Allyn and Bacon, Boston, Mass., 1965.

FURTHER READING

ARROW, K. J., S. KARLIN, and H. SCARF, *Studies in the Mathematical Theory of Inventory and Production*. Stanford University Press, Stanford, Calif., 1958.
NADDOR, E., *Inventory Systems*. John Wiley and Sons, Inc., New York, 1966.
STARR, MARTIN K., and D. W. MILLER, *Inventory Control: Theory and Practice*. Prentice-Hall, Inc., Englewood Cliffs, N.J., 1962.

PROBLEMS

1. Consider the inventory data given in the accompanying table.
  A. Suggest, with appropriate calculations, item classification into an ABC system.
  B. Do these data seem to follow Pareto's Law?
  C. What differentiation would you recommend, as far as inventory *policy* is concerned, for Class B and C items?

Item	Units/Year Demand	Unit Cost	Item	Units/Year Demand	Unit Cost
XB-5	3,850	$ 2.20	LE-45	375	$ 1.80
XH-14	96	4.80	EY-6	15,000	0.002
ZA-5	567	0.85	MX-15	180	2.60
AB-24	128	1.37	PO-1	760	0.15
YA-12	3,862	2.95	AY-16	2,000	0.01
CD-4	51	126.50	ZX-5	280	0.18
X-9	589	6.42	UR-10	19,000	0.016
AH-15	5,869	0.88	XE-4	15	38.40
C-12	850	64.53	FG-15	105	6.50
DF-10	2,569	3.59	ZM-12	8,500	0.10
XE-41	500	0.15	AA-81	200	0.001
YA-16	25,000	0.006	DB-81	50,000	0.0001
AA-4	865	0.05	XYM-1	680	0.21
BX-12	9,050	1.84	AY-3	100	0.50
AE-5	186	58.50	ZA-5	1,400	0.15
GK-10	365	1.80	XOP-15	28,000	0.002
MN-1	14,800	0.001	MBA-10	15	3.85
ZD-15	1,654	0.38	ZO-4	45	5.20
LM-6	12	1,080.00	BOK-117	750	0.30
AN-54	500	0.36	LP-5	10,000	0.002
GX-9	85	0.86	XR-77	960	0.10
LY-4	3,500	0.0015	DAB-12	85,000	0.0003

2. Consider your Class A items from Problem 1. Determine a *cyclic* ordering schedule for these items only, based on an EOQ formulation. Demand for each product is assumed linear through the year. Cost of making an order is $31 per order. Interest charges are set at 20% per year. Storage costs have been determined at $0.30/unit month, and random storage is in effect allowing storage charges to be based on *average* inventory held. Management allows a 3% increase in unit holding costs above Z' to be acceptable. In addition to finding a reasonable ordering schedule, what would the inventory holding costs actually be for the schedule?

3. How does your ordering schedule inventory holding costs from Problem 2 compare with the optimum costs based on Z'? What happens to these costs if each Class A item is ordered only once per year?

4. A certain product purchased for internal consumption is to be ordered so that delivery occurs 3 days before the expected runout of the previous order. Demand is considered deterministic and is linear. Derive the economic-order-quantity formula for this problem, using the symbols given in the text. Do it for both cases: one where storage charges are based on average inventory and the second for the situation with storage costs based on maximum inventory.

5. In conjunction with the batching quantity Q' formula given in Equation 9–21, the following data are given:

> Setup costs: $800 per batch
> Batch production rate: 3000 items/day
> Batch depletion rate: 500 items/day
> Storage costs: $2 per piece per year
> Investment per unit: $40
> Interest rate: 20% per year
> Working days per year: 260

Find Q', τ', and Z'. *Note:* Interest charges and storage charges can obviously be based as well on a per-working-day base as on any other consistent time base.

6. If the cost per unit, Z', from Problem 5 is allowed to increase to $3Z'$, what is the effect on the batch quantity range? Display graphically the cost functions and the production range.

7. A production facility has the following peculiar production/consumption cycle:

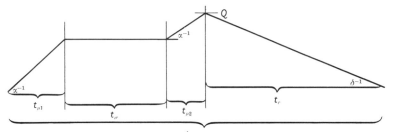

$$\text{cycle time} = \tau$$

Given: $t_w = 2t_{p1}$ $I = $ interest charges; $/unit · unit time

$t_e = 4t_{p1}$ $H = $ storage costs; $/unit · unit time

$t_{p1} = 2t_{p2}$ $\alpha = $ arrival rate

                      $\delta = $ depletion rate

                      $S = $ setup charges; $/batch

Derive the formula for the batch quantity, Q', that minimizes unit inventory costs, assuming storage charges based on maximum inventory.

8. The following data are available for Problem 8 setup:

> $\alpha = 200$ units/day $H = $2/unit/month$
>
> $I = $3/unit/month$ $S = $500/batch$

Find Z', τ', and Q', knowing there are 22 working days a month.

10

Inventory Control Under Uncertainty

He is no wise man that will quit a certainty for an uncertainty.

SAMUEL JOHNSON

10-1. PROBABILISTIC INVENTORY MODELING

The analysis presented in the previous chapter was predicated on deterministic conditions. Usually this assumption is not valid, though frequently deterministic assumptions yield reasonable approximations to the stochastic case. Basically, the probabilistic characteristics inherent in the economic order quantity (EOQ) model are caused by:

A. The vendor of a particular item may not always deliver the items at exactly the required date due to uncertainty in his own operation.

B. Runout of the particular item will not be exactly on a specified date, therefore creating the possibility of running out of the item for a certain length of time. Conversely, the possibility of creating inventory levels higher than desired is also a possibility if delivery is consistently made prior to a desired due date.

Needless to say, if an analysis of stochastic conditions is to be made, then historical data are required regarding delivery dates as contrasted to order dates for particular vendors. The traditional problem in performing analyses in industry is lack of applicable data. It is quite a simple matter to record delivery dates in relation to order dates on

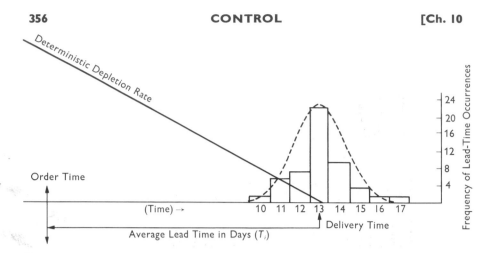

Figure 10–1. Histogram of historical lead-time data—stochastic vendor effects with deterministic depletion.

order cards for each item. These are updated each time an item is ordered and each time an order is delivered.

Initially, we will consider only *vendor lead-time* uncertainty, as depicted in Figure 10–1. The lead time will be defined as the time from order initiation to order delivery. The lead-time histogram is plotted from fifty values obtained from historical files, and given in Table 10–1. The dotted line, of course, approximates the shape of the probability distribution which will be assumed to be normal in Figure 10–1. The cumulative area, working from the left of the distribution to a particular lead time represents the probability of delivery being within that lead-time value.

Table 10-1

Historical Vendor Lead-Time Data

Lead Time (T_i) in Days	Frequency (f_i) of Occurrence of Lead Time (T_i)
10	1
11	6
12	7
13	22
14	9
15	3
16	1
17	1
	50

Normally, a lead time would be set so that the receipt of the order would be within the lead time at some specified probability, say 98 percent. Assuming a normal distribution for the data of Figure 10-1, the standard deviation of lead time, σ_T, is found by

$$\sigma_T = \sqrt{\frac{\sum\limits_{i=1}^{N}(T_i - \bar{T})^2 f_i}{\sum\limits_{i=1}^{N} f_i}}$$

where $\bar{T}$ is the lead-time average equal to

$$\frac{\sum\limits_{i=1}^{N} f_i T_i}{\sum\limits_{i=1}^{N} f_i}$$

and N is the number of histogram classes.

The required calculations, given in Table 10-2, evolve

$$\bar{T} = 13$$
$$\sigma_T = 1.3$$

If a probability of 98 percent were stipulated for receipt of an order within a lead time, then this lead time would be computed as follows: Number of standard deviations above $\bar{T}$ for 98 percent is

$$Z = 2.05$$

Table 10-2

Calculation of $\bar{T}$ and σ_T for Vendor Lead Times

T_i	f_i	$T_i f_i$	$(I_i - \bar{T})^2$	$f_i(T_i - \bar{T})^2$
10	1	10	9	9
11	6	66	4	24
12	7	84	1	7
13	22	286	0	0
14	9	126	1	9
15	3	45	4	12
16	1	16	9	9
17	1	17	16	16
	50	650		86

$$\bar{T} = \frac{650}{50} = 13$$

$$\sigma_T = \sqrt{\frac{86}{50}} = 1.3$$

from Appendix Table A–1. Since

$$Z = \frac{T_i - \bar{T}}{\sigma_T}$$

$$2.05 = \frac{T_i - 13}{1.3}$$

and

$$T_i = 16 \text{ days (rounded off)}$$

So, if the demand curve is purely deterministic then the next order should be made 16 days *prior* to the known runout of the current order in order to insure receipt before runout with a probability of 98 percent.

This problem becomes more complex when demand characteristics are stochastic as well as the delivery lead-time conditions. With the problem just considered, that with a known and fixed demand but with a variable lead time, once the lead time has been determined, a quantity would be ordered equal to some economic order quantity calculated as discussed in our deterministic analysis. With a varying demand pattern and varying lead time this might not be true.

A typical situation is as depicted in Figure 10–2. The three points *A*, *B*, and *C* denote average and worst-case stock conditions. If demand is average and if the lead-time is average, a safety stock around point *A* would be realized. But, if conditions continue "average" then this safety stock will grow in size as that would be the amount each cycle left from the *previous order* when the new order arrives.

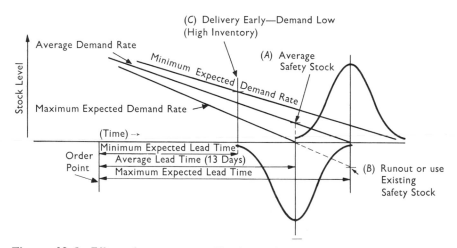

Figure 10–2. Effect of uncertainty of both supply and demand in the inventory model.

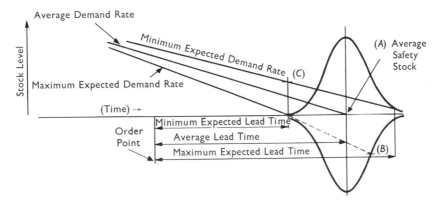

Figure 10–3. Effect of shifting demand depletion/lead-time relationship.

Note that previous order is mentioned, not previous inventory level. If lead times tend to maximum and demand to maximum, then runout conditions will occur and get worse and worse.

A solution might be to have an order/demand relationship as given in Figure 10–3. The expected average safety stock, or remainder of the previous order, is zero. So, if a true safety stock were initially set and if demand and lead times were both normally distributed, then it would be expected that the true average safety stock would hover around the initial value in inventory. A safety stock is desired in order to protect against high demand/maximum lead-time combinations.

10–2. INVENTORY POLICIES UNDER UNCERTAINTY

Three possible ordering policies were introduced in Section 9–6 and will be reconsidered here as they are most applicable to the situation that is uncertain.

A. *Policy* $(Q_r, Q' + \xi)$: Here, a reorder quantity is pre-determined, say Q_r. A Q' value is determined possibly using conventional EOQ formulas and based on an average demand rate. A desired safety stock, ξ, is considered to protect against emergency conditions. When current inventory depletes to a level Q_r, an order is made equal to (Q') on the assumption that current inventory will deplete to ξ by the time the new order arrives. Thus, expected inventory on arrival of the order is $(Q' + \xi)$. What should this Q_r value be? Logically, it should be a function of lead time and demand rate, possibly (average demand rate) multiplied by (average lead time). Some authors suggest (maximum demand rate) (maximum lead time) for Q_r to protect against drastic conditions, and then lowering Q_r when inventories start to build.

B. *Policy* $(t_r, Q + \xi)$: An obvious disadvantage for $(Q_r, Q' + \xi)$ is that a continuous monitoring of inventory is required in order to catch the inventory level at Q_r. The reorder is not cyclic from a time viewpoint. The $(t_r, Q' + \xi)$ policy evaluates the inventory level each time cycle, t_r. The time cycle could be based on the cycle τ from the earlier deterministic EOQ computations. For protection, τ might be based on

$$\tau = \frac{Q'}{\text{Maximum Expected Demand Rate}}$$

where Q' is that order quantity which minimizes unit inventory costs.

At each t_r period, sufficient units are ordered so that upon delivery, an expected $Q' + \xi$ units total will be on hand. The order quantity is not necessarily Q' now, it will vary. Using the concept of Q_r from the policy $(Q_r, Q' + \xi)$, if Q units are on hand at t_r, then the quantity ordered is $[Q' - (Q - \xi)]$. One problem now is that if Q is close to Q', when demand is low, small quantities will be ordered. Also, if demand is high, possible runout could be realized if Q is very low. The third policy, $(t_r, Q_r, Q' + \xi)$ guards against the first problem. Inventory is checked every t_r cycle, but an order is made only if Q is equal to or less than Q_r. The same interpretation is made for $(Q' + \xi)$ as was made with the two previous policies.

10–3. CONTINUOUS AND STOCHASTIC INVENTORY MODELS

It should be apparent that most of the models looked at so far could have been evaluated using integration of the inventory level curve over the cycle period being evaluated in order to determine average expected costs. It is beyond the scope of this text to present continuous probability functions as applied to inventory analysis, but it is of interest to see how to *develop* the continuous model so that analysis may be made by the interested reader. The subsequent section covering Monte Carlo simulation will show how such techniques may be simply applied to the stochastic inventory problem by those not well versed in probability theory.

As an example of applying integrals to inventory models, consider the original deterministic EOQ model with safety stock given previously in Figure 9–2. With symbols defined in that earlier section we have

$$\delta = \frac{Q}{\tau} ; \qquad \tau = \frac{Q}{\delta}$$

The inventory level curve depletes from a maximum of $(Q + \xi)$ units at a rate $(\delta)(t)$ giving the equation

$$(Q + \xi) - (\delta)(t) = I$$

Integrating this from $t = 0$ to $t = \tau$ realizes

$$\int_0^{Q/\delta} [(Q + \xi) - (\delta)(t)]\, dt,$$

knowing that $\tau = Q/\delta$. This results in

$$\left(\frac{Q}{2} + \xi\right)\left(\frac{Q}{\delta}\right)$$

which is the expected average inventory multiplied by τ. The cost model can now be set up as a function of the average inventory and cycle time in the same fashion as was used earlier.

Now, what if demand is not a deterministic function, but is a random variable X behaving according to some probability distribution function? It is found that the cost function has to be developed for two different conditions, according to the state of the demand at the end of the cycle period τ. If we order to some quantity S such that at the end of the cycle period we expect the cumulative inventory to be S, then two possible conditions of the random variable X relative to S could occur:

A. $X \leq S$, indicating that no runout has occurred. This is the same assumption utilized in the earlier deterministic models, except that now there is no assurance of the value of X, the demand in τ. This condition is pictured in Figure 10–4. The concept of S is of course the same as used in the inventory policies presented earlier to assist in handling the problems of inventory under uncertainty. The objective of this model will be to determine that value of S to which inventory should be ordered so as to minimize expected costs.

B. $X \geq S$ is the second condition of X relative to S, showing that a runout of stock has been realized. Some cost per unit would have to be found for *runout* cost in this case, instead of the usual *holding* cost considered. Traditionally, this has been one of the hardest

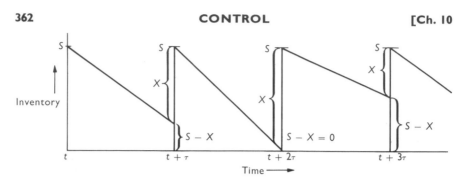

Figure 10–4. Inventory patterns showing no runout.

features of inventory control to quantify. It entails the determination of a *customer dissatisfaction* value. The runout possibility is graphically given in Figure 10–5.

There are three *average inventory* patterns to be considered:

A. *Inventory on Hand.* For both cases, $X \leq S$ and $X \geq S$, there will be inventory on hand during τ. When $X \leq S$, we see from Figure 10–4 that this will be

$$\frac{S + (S - X)}{2} = \frac{2S - X}{2} \tag{10–1}$$

For $X \geq S$, inventory is on hand only during t_H, giving an average inventory of

$$\frac{\left(\dfrac{S}{2}\right)(t_H) + (0)(t_R)}{\tau} \tag{10–2}$$

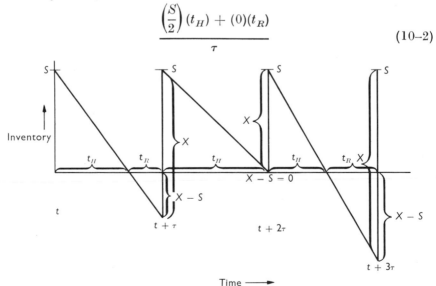

Figure 10–5. Inventory patterns showing runout.

Trigonometrically it can be seen that

$$\frac{t_H}{\tau} = \frac{S}{X} ; \qquad t_H = \frac{S\tau}{X} .$$

Substituting this relationship for t_H into Equation 10–2 results in an average inventory of

$$\frac{S^2}{2X} \qquad (10\text{–}3)$$

If H is the holding cost per unit then the expected cost of inventory on hand for both cases of X related to S would be, remembering that X is a random variable:

$$H \int_{X=0}^{S} \left(\frac{2S - X}{2} \right) f(x) \, dx + H \int_{X=S}^{\infty} \left(\frac{S^2}{2X} \right) f(x) dx \qquad (10\text{–}4)$$

The limits should be self-evident. The first integral represents the expected cost when $X \leq S$; thus X is only considered up to S. Similarly, the second integral is for $X \geq S$ and the limits of integration are set from S to infinity.

B. *Inventory Shortage.* The average inventory shortage during τ is found from Figure 10–5 to be

$$\frac{\dfrac{(X - S)}{2}(t_R) + (0)(t_H)}{\tau} \qquad (10\text{–}5)$$

where

$$\frac{t_R}{\tau} = \frac{(X - S)}{X} ; \qquad t_R = \frac{(X - S)(\tau)}{X}$$

Substituting in Equation 10–5 gives

$$\frac{(X - S)^2}{2X} \qquad (10\text{–}6)$$

Shortage can only occur if $X \geq S$, so if R is defined as the runout charge per unit the expected runout cost per period would be

$$R \int_{X=S}^{\infty} \frac{(X - S)^2}{2X} f(x) \, dx \qquad (10\text{–}7)$$

The total cost equation to be minimized is a combination of Equations 10–4 and 10–7

$$Z = H \int_{X=0}^{S} \left(\frac{2S - X}{2} \right) f(x) \, dx + H \int_{X=S}^{\infty} \left(\frac{S^2}{2X} \right) f(x) \, dx$$

$$+ \int_{X=S}^{\infty} \frac{(X - S)^2}{2X} f(x) \, dx \quad (10\text{–}8)$$

In order to minimize the total cost, the derivative of Z has to be taken with respect to S. This resultant equation is set equal to 0 and solved for S. If the limits of integration are *constants* then it is possible to take partial derivatives with respect to S of the equations being integrated, and then the integration is handled. If the limits are *variables*, then the Leibnitz rule of integration is usually applied.* Naddor[4] applied this rule to the problem at hand and found

$$\int_{0}^{S} f(x) \, dx + \int_{S}^{\infty} \frac{S}{X} f(x) \, dx = \frac{R}{R + H} \quad (10\text{–}9)$$

Unfortunately, this can be a difficult problem except for certain distributions, such as $f(x)$ being exponential, for example. If $f(x)$ is assumed uniform, with $f(x) = 1/(\beta - \alpha)$, then Equation 10–9 would have to be completely re-derived using integration limits of α to S for $X \leq S$, and S to β for $X \geq S$. This will result in an equation which includes the natural log of S and other forms of S and which has to be solved for S. This is rather difficult to solve analytically.

The development of a stochastic inventory model is certainly mathematically interesting but it can have limited application based on tenuous assumptions. One possible way out of this problem is to utilize Monte Carlo simulation.

10–4. MONTE CARLO SIMULATION

One approach to probabilistic discrete systems is with the use of random numbers. Historical data are taken, say demand and supply data for the inventory system. Each possible class in the cumulative histograms of each set of data is assigned a set of random numbers, each of which has an equal likelihood of being drawn, corresponding to the frequency for which the items represented by the histogram are

---

* For example, see *Introduction to Operations Research* by F. S. Hillier and G. J. Lieberman, Holden-Day, Inc., 1968., page 607.

expected to occur. A simulation time scale is then set and events made to occur and accumulate according to the random numbers drawn. The overall process is classified as Monte Carlo simulation. An inventory example should clarify this, but first a few points on the random number drawing and histogram representation will be given.

Suppose data are gathered from some process and formed into a histogram as shown in Figure 10–6, where one thousand historical observations of whether A, B, C, or D occurred are plotted. Item A occurred 5 percent of the time. If 100 equally-likely-to-occur random numbers, say 00 to 99, represent percent of occurrence, then numbers 00 to 04 could represent Item A. Similarly, numbers 05 through 24 would stand for Item B, 25 to 89 for Item C and, finally, 90 through 99 for Item D. Note that the random numbers are assigned according to *cumulative* item frequency. Now, if random numbers are drawn in sequence, they will indicate a possible ordering for which A, B, C, and D could occur. Also, their frequency of occurrence in the long run will approximate their historical pattern. With several distributions interacting together on a system, similar histogram/random number arrangements allow all interacting effects to be examined.

A typical table of random digits is given in Appendix B. Any combination of digits will allow a random drawing. For example, with percentages running from 1 to 100 where we require random numbers 00 through 99, using the first two digits of each number will allow this.

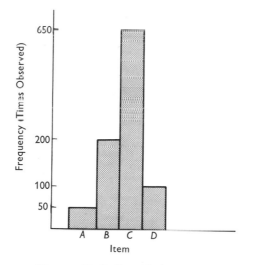

Figure 10–6. Sample histogram.

Table 10–3

100 Random Number Drawings and Item Equivalence Corresponding to the Histogram of Figure 10-6

Random Number	Item	Random Number	Item	Random Number	Item	Random Number	Item
36	C	98	D	23	B	94	D
34	C	47	C	12	B	25	C
25	C	34	C	50	C	95	D
50	C	24	B	89	C	07	B
47	C	86	C	70	C	64	C
36	C	40	C	28	C	07	B
23	B	49	C	37	C	05	B
50	C	91	D	82	C	03	A
41	C	72	C	90	D	04	A
15	B	37	C	28	C	68	C
34	C	34	C	86	C	89	C
17	B	96	D	40	C	19	B
74	C	70	C	25	C	34	C
68	C	05	B	32	C	46	C
78	C	96	D	86	C	90	D
89	C	99	D	06	B	43	C
30	C	40	C	90	D	24	B
38	C	62	C	25	C	42	C
10	B	03	A	94	D	48	C
05	B	83	C	08	B	94	D
10	B	85	C	76	C	05	B
30	C	58	C	77	C	98	D
39	C	92	D	08	B	35	C
13	B	80	C	94	D	73	C
14	B	05	B	05	B	37	C

Item A: Random numbers 00–04

Item B: Random numbers 05–24

Item C: Random numbers 25–89

Item D: Random numbers 90–99

Accuracy to a tenth of a percent would have required 1,000 random numbers, with sequences of three digits being drawn for each percent. One hundred drawings of two-digit random numbers are given in Table 10–3 with the item, A, B, C, or D, which corresponds to that number. The top row indicates the first four random numbers and item pairs in the table. For example, the first five random numbers drawn from a random number table were 36, 98, 23, 94, and 34.

Counting occurrences in Table 10–3 shows:

A:	3 times;	3%
B:	23 times;	23%
C:	59 times;	59%
D:	15 times;	15%

This does not check *exactly* with the histogram in Figure 10–6, but it is a reasonable approximation. As *more* data are taken, the results should more and more closely approximate the histogram. Ergo, one moral in simulation is: the more runs, the better.

As an example of applying Monte Carlo simulation to inventory analysis, consider that a company has a particular inventory item for which they would like to test three inventory policies. Both vendor lead time and demand rates have historically proved to be probabilistic, as shown in Table 10–4. The vendor data are based on an analysis of the delivery patterns for several items and also on the vendor's own evaluation of his delivery capabilities. The demand data were culled from the last 300 days of operation.

In order to be able to apply Monte Carlo sampling to the data, both delivery and demand *cumulative* frequency distributions on a percentage basis are plotted from the Table 10–4 data, and depicted in Figure 10–7.

Now we are ready to assign random numbers to correspond to the

Table 10–4

Historical Delivery and Demand Data

A. Vendor Lead-Time Distribution

Days Required for Delivery	Frequency of Occurrence
1	1
2	6
3	21
4	12
5	8
6	2
	50

B. Demand Distribution

Demand per Day	Frequency of Occurrence
7	9
8	30
9	45
10	180
11	36
	300

A.   Cumulative Days Required for Delivery

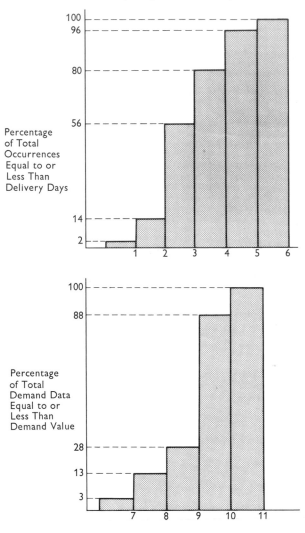

B.   Cumulative Daily Demand

Figure 10–7. Cumulative percentages for delivery and demand data given in Table 10–4.

Table 10–5

**Random Number Assignment Corresponding to Percentage Values
Given in Figure 10-7**

Days Required for Delivery	1	2	3	4	5	6
Random Numbers (Inclusive)	00–01	02–13	14–55	56–79	80–95	96–99

Demand per Day	7	8	9	10	11
Random Numbers (Inclusive)	00–02	03–12	13–27	28–87	88–99

percentage values given in Figure 10–7, so that demand and delivery sampling can begin, to allow simulation of the inventory patterns under proposed policies. The logical assignment will use random numbers 00 through 99 to represent the 100 percentage possibilities. For example, consider just the cumulative histogram for delivery days, Figure 10–7A. Random numbers 00 and 01 will indicate a delivery length of one day. Numbers 02 through 13 will trigger a length of 2 days, and so on. The random number assignment for delivery and demand conditions is summarized in Table 10–5.

Now a daily pattern of inventory may be evaluated, based on each specific policy, drawing a random number for *each* day and assigning the corresponding demand for that day. When the particular policy indicates an order is to be made, then a random number is drawn and the delivery time corresponding to that random number is used. We will evaluate three policies, each for a sixty-day period, in this manner.

Using our inventory analysis symbols, the three policies under consideration are:

1. $(Q_r, Q' + \xi)$: When inventory gets to some level Q_r, order such that the expected *total* inventory on delivery is $Q' + \xi$. Q' is the economic order quantity, and ξ is a safety stock.

2. $(t_r, 100)$: Treat the system as though it is deterministic. On a cyclic basis, t_r, order 100 units. Q' has been determined, by the way, to be 100 for all policies.

3. $(t_r, Q' + \xi)$: On a cyclic basis, t_r, order sufficient items such that the expected total inventory on delivery will be $Q' + \xi$.

| Day | Demand Random Number | Demand | Starting Inventory | Policy (Q_r, $Q^l + \xi$) | | | | Ending Inventory |
				Order S=Start R=Receipt	Delivery Random Number	Delivery Time	Order/Receipt Size	
1	50	10	130					120
2	56	10	120					110
3	36	10	110					100
4	27	9	100					91
5	79	10	91					81
6	61	10	81					71
7	38	10	71					61
8	57	10	61					51
9	56	10	51	S	73	4	160−51=109	41
10	67	10	41					31
11	02	7	31					24
12	62	10	24					14
13	01	7	14	R			109	109+14−7=116
14	96	11	116					105
15	20	9	105					96
16	87	10	96					86
17	49	10	86					76
18	37	10	76					66
19	85	10	66					56
20	55	10	56	S	98	6	160−56=104	46
21	07	8	46					38
22	21	9	38					29
23	73	10	29					19
24	07	8	19					11
25	25	9	11					2
26	46	10	2	R			104	104+2−10=96
27	83	10	96					86
28	01	7	86					79
29	26	9	79					70
30	14	9	70					61
31	35	10	61					51
32	36	10	51	S	59	4	160−51=109	41
33	04	8	41					33
34	21	9	33					24
35	80	10	24					14
36	07	8	14	R			109	109+14−8=115
37	22	9	115					106
38	86	10	106					96
39	56	10	96					86
40	15	9	86					77
41	93	11	77					66
42	38	10	66					56
43	37	10	56	S	24	3	160−56=104	46
44	41	10	46					36
45	69	10	36					26
46	09	8	26	R			104	104+26−8=122
47	73	10	122					112
48	79	10	112					102
49	16	9	102					93
50	86	10	93					83
51	18	9	83					74
52	19	9	74					65
53	48	10	65					55
54	13	9	46	S	92	5	160−55=105	46
55	02	7	55					39
56	10	8	39					31
57	60	10	31					21
58	10	8	21					13
59	06	8	13	R			105	105+13−8=110
60	54	10	110					100

10-6

Simulation for Three Policies

	Policy (t_r, 100)						Policy (t_r, $Q' + \xi$)				
Starting Inventory	Order S=Start R=Receipt	Delivery Random Number	Delivery Time	Order/Receipt Size	Ending Inventory	Starting Inventory	Order S=Start R=Receipt	Delivery Random Number	Delivery Time	Order/Receipt Size	Ending Inventory
100					90	130					120
90					80	120					110
80					70	110					100
70					61	100					91
61					51	91					81
51					41	81					71
41	S	73	4	100	31	71	S	73	4	160-71=89	61
31					21	61					51
21					11	51					41
11					01	41					31
01	R			100	94	31	R			89	113
94					84	113					103
84					77	103					96
77					66	96					85
66					57	85					76
57					47	76					66
47	S	98	6	100	37	66	S	98	6	160-66=94	56
37					27	56					46
27					17	46					36
17					7	36					26
7					-1	26					18
-1					-10	18					9
-10	R			100	97	9	R			94	93
97					89	93					85
89					80	85					76
80					70	76					66
70	S	59	4	100	60	66	S	59	4	160-66=94	56
60					53	56					69
53					44	69					60
44					35	60					51
35	R			100	125	51	R			94	135
125					115	135					125
115					107	125					117
107					98	117					108
98					88	108					98
88					80	98					90
80	S	24	3	100	71	90	S	24	3	160-90=70	81
71					61	81					71
61					51	71					61
51	R			100	142	61	R			70	122
142					131	122					111
131					121	111					101
121					111	101					91
111					101	91					81
101					91	81					71
91					83	71					63
82	S	92	5	100	73	63	S	92	5	160-63=97	53
73					63	53					43
63					54	43					34
54					44	34					24
44					35	24					15
35	R			100	166	15	R			97	103
126					116	103					93
116					107	93					84
107					100	84					77
100					92	77					69
92	S	08	2	100	82	69	S	08	2	160-69=91	59
82					74	59					51
74	R			100	166	51	R			91	134
166					156	134					124

After the sixty-day simulation a cost analysis will be run on each policy result to help evaluate which to utilize in the future, assuming the same patterns will continue. To test the policies, prior analysis reveals the following to be acceptable:

1. $Q' = 100$ units
2. S = order cost = \$50 per order
3. $\xi = 30$ units of safety stock
4. $Q_r = 60$ units
5. $t_r = 10$-day cycle
6. Carrying charges $(I + H) = \$0.10$ per unit-day

We will assume with all three policies that initial stock at the beginning of day one is $Q' + \xi$, or 130 units. Also, runout is rather traumatic as it is estimated from past experience that only one-third of sales that cannot be immediately satisfied can be delayed for delivery until the next order is received. In other words, two-thirds of runout is considered lost sales. Accounting has come up with a cost of \$10 for each lost sale which includes a badwill estimate in addition to the unit profit of the item involved. The simulation policies will simply subtract from the next order received one-third of runout sales on the assumption these will be sold immediately upon receipt of the order.

Monte Carlo simulations for the three policies finding cumulative inventory levels with respect to time are given in Table 10–6. A few pertinent comments concerning the immediate results will be given before a cost analysis is considered. The random number sequence of 50, 56, 36, . . . , given under the demand random number column, was taken sequentially from a random number table. The demands corresponding to each random number were found directly from Table 10–5.

Plans $(Q_r, Q' + \xi)$ and $(t_r, Q' + \xi)$ had a starting inventory at day one of 130, equal to Q' plus safety stock ξ of 30. Policy $(t_r, 100)$ being deterministic *without* safety stock was initialized at 100 units. The ending inventory for any day which did not have an order receipt is calculated by

$$\text{Ending Inventory} = \text{Starting Inventory} - \text{Demand}$$

The first order for policy $(Q_r, Q' + \xi)$ is required on day 9. This is the first day at which beginning inventory is *below* the Q_r level of 60. If a fully automatic procedure in the physical system realized inventory dropped below 60 in day 8, then ordering could have been triggered at that time. We will assume inventory review is made at the beginning of every day. The delivery times corresponding to the random numbers given in Table 10–5, were then used. For both $(Q' + \xi)$ policies, the order quantity was calculated by

$$\text{Order} = 160 - \text{Day's Starting Inventory}$$

This was predicated on the assumption that 130 units, $Q' + \xi$, would be desired upon receipt of the order. The average vendor lead time was assumed to be three days and the average demand to be ten units, so demand in a lead time was estimated to be 30 units, which when added to $Q' + \xi$ gives 160 units. Actually, the average of the historical lead times given in Figure 10–7A is closer to 3.5 days. If 35 units had been used as the demand in a lead time, then inventory might not have had the *slight* tendency to decrease as found with the $(Q_r, Q + \xi)$ plan. The ending inventories for those days in which an order was received, should have averaged about 120, assuming a demand in these days of 10 units. The ending inventories for days in which a $(Q_r, Q' + \xi)$ was implemented were found to be 116, 96, 115, 122, and 110 for an average of 112 units.

The policies using t_r rather than Q_r ordered items every ten days. The *first* order was made on the *seventh* day of the simulation on the assumption that an average vendor lead time of three days was prevalent. Simulating these policies was accomplished, of course, in the same manner as for $(Q', Q + \xi)$.

One overall conclusion that can be made prior to running a cost analysis is the fallacy of using deterministic criteria for variable situations. Relying on just an order quantity of 100 was dangerous since runout occurred on days 21 and 22. Then paradoxically, on both t_r systems, inventory climbed drastically. This was due to ordering just plain too often. Trying to offset the climb with $(Q' + \xi)$ in the third policy rather than (100) helped, but inventories still averaged rather high.

The costs for the three policies were evaluated by

$$\text{Total Cost} = [\text{Total Inventory Units}][I + H]$$

$$+ [\text{Number of Orders}][\text{Order Cost}] + [\text{Lost Orders}][10].$$

Summing the total inventory for the 60 days of course gives the same result as *average inventory* used in the model analysis. The "lost orders" factor is only applicable to the second policy. A total of ten units were not on hand when needed but on the initial assumptions made, only seven of these will be assumed *lost sales*.

The policy costs were then found to be:

1. $(Q_r, Q' + \xi)$:
   $(3,902)(0.10) + (5)(50.00) + 0 = \$640.20$
2. $(t_r, 100)$:
   $(4,306)(0.10) + (6)(50.00) + (7)(10.00) = \$800.60$
3. $(t_r, Q' + \xi)$:
   $(4,358)(0.10) + (6)(50.00) + 0 = \$753.80$

Because of the relatively small amount of days evaluated in the simulation the results have to be considered somewhat inconclusive. Probably, though, it would be quite safe to decide that, if these are the only three policies possible, then $(Q_r, Q' + \xi)$ should be implemented.

10-5. COMPUTER SIMULATION

The Monte Carlo inventory simulation, when performed by hand, has some shortcomings that can be overcome with the digital computer. The primary problem has to be one of time required for the simulation. If several hundred days' operation were to be simulated with possible replication, then hand-simulation for the simple problem given would be somewhat prohibitive. In addition, the statistics calculated within the simulation were somewhat naive. We could have maintained average daily inventories, cumulative cost data, and so on. Also, it would have been much more logical to have the computer test a variety of policies and policy parameters to try to find an optimum combination. The policy $(Q_r, Q' + \xi)$ was found to be the best of the three policies looked at, but Q_r and ξ were pre-determined. Varying them in combinations while repeating the simulation would have been much more realistic. The number of runs required would logically require some form of automatic computation in order to be feasible.

With time-oriented dynamic systems, as commonly encountered in this text, two approaches to the simulation may be taken. First, the computer could have tackled the problem as attacked by our Monte Carlo simulation, accumulating statistics at *every unique time point*, in that case every day. If a rocket shot were being simulated, with discrete time periods in the order of seconds and with unusual occurrences happening infrequently, this may be very inefficient. A better way would be to utilize a *next event* approach where, using probability distributions as before, the length of time to the *next change* in current operating conditions is determined. Time is incremented to this "next-change" time and intermediate statistics accumulated according to the intermediate static conditions. For the inventory Monte Carlo problem these "next-event" times might have been receipt of an order, or current order runout. Intermediate demand could have been estimated by demand between order receipts multiplied by expected daily demand. This latter figure would have been found from the demand probability characteristics. We will classify time-oriented simulations as $(T \to T)$ simulations, and $(E \to E)$ will represent event-oriented situations. A short example should clarify their approaches.

Consider the inventory control policy, $(t_r, 100)$, just evaluated. For simplicity the expected demand per day is assumed to be ten units, so the only variability will be in the delivery lead time. The time-oriented simulation, $(T \to T)$, will be exactly as just accomplished, except that each day's demand will be assumed a constant ten units. Table 10–7 gives the result of a forty-day simulation. No demands are indicated since the daily demand is a constant ten units. Also, for simplicity only, it is assumed that runout sales will be *lost* sales. So on day 23, none of the twenty items will be assumed to be back-ordered, and beginning inventory is assumed to be zero. A flow chart for this simulation is given in Figure 10–8. Delivery lead-times were found by sampling the delivery distribution given earlier in Table 10–5.

The event-oriented simulation, $(E \to E)$, is much easier to apply for this very simple example. First, equations have to be developed which allow the next-event time, t_R, to be calculated, and also which permit the determination of inventory characteristics at this next-event time.

The value of t_R is a function of the cycle time, t_r: the number of cycles transpired, and the initial order day. It turns out for our example that t_R can be found by:

$$t_R = 7 + (K-1)(t_r) + LT_k$$

where K is the number of the current cycle; $K = 1, 2, \ldots$
      LT_k is the current sampling of order lead time
      t_r is the cycle time, or 10 days

Thus, the sequence of orders is received on the following days:

$K = 1;$ $t_R = 7 + 0 + LT_1 = 7 + 0 + 4 = \text{day } 11$

$K = 2;$ $t_R = 7 + (1)(10) + LT_2 = 7 + 10 + 6 = \text{day } 23$

$K = 3;$ $t_R = 7 + (2)(10) + LT_3 = 7 + 20 + 4 = \text{day } 31$

$K = 4;$ $t_R = 7 + (3)(10) + LT_4 = 7 + 30 + 3 = \text{day } 40$

Table 10-7

Example of Time-Oriented ($T \to T$) Simulation of (t_r,100) Inventory Policy

Day	Starting Inventory	Order; S=Start R=Receipt	Delivery Lead-Time Random Number	Lead Time	Ending Inventory
1	100				90
2	90				80
3	80				70
4	70				60
5	60				50
6	50				40
7	40	S	73	4	30
8	30				20
9	20				10
10	10				0
11	0	R			90
12	90				80
13	80				70
14	70				60
15	60				50
16	50				40
17	40	S	98	6	30
18	30				20
19	20				10
20	10				0
21	0				-10
22	0				-20
23	0	R			90
24	90				80
25	80				70
26	70				60
27	60	S	59	4	50
28	50				40
29	40				30
30	30				20
31	20	R			110
32	110				100
33	100				90
34	90				80
35	80				70
36	70				60
37	60	S	24	3	50
38	50				40
39	40				30
40	30	R			120

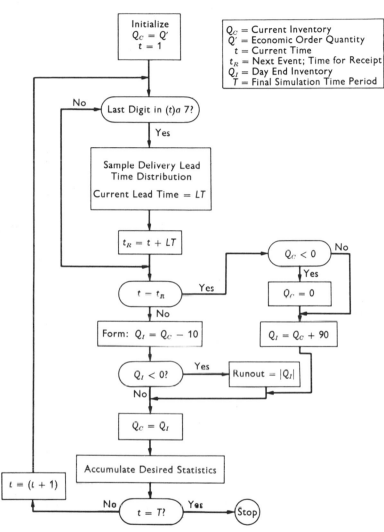

Figure 10–8. Flow chart of inventory ($T \rightarrow T$) simulation.

The LT_K values were found by sampling the delivery distributions as before.

The inventory levels at the *beginning* of day t_R can be found by

$$Q_D = Q_{C_{t_{R-1}}} - (t_R - t_{R-1} - 1)(10)$$

where $Q_{C_{t_{R-1}}}$ is the inventory at the end of the previous t_R day.

$(t_R - t_{R-1} - 1)(10)$ is the demand during the current cycle.

The first value of t_R is day 1, with an ending inventory level of 90 units. The second t_R was day 11. Therefore, the inventory level at the *beginning* of day 11 would be

$$90 - (11 - 1 - 1)(10) = 0$$

This particular calculation tells us the *runout* condition by day t_R. The inventory at the *end* of t_R, knowing a demand of 10 occurs during the day and knowing 100 units are delivered is

$$Q_{C_{t_R}} = Q_D + 90$$

The inventory levels can now be found at the various t_R periods:

$t_R = 1$; $\quad Q_{C_1} = 90$

$t_R = 11$; $\quad Q_D = 90 - (11 - 1 - 1)(10) = 0$

$\qquad\qquad Q_{C_{11}} = 0 + 90 = 90$

$t_R = 23$; $\quad Q_D = 90 - (23 - 11 - 1)(10) = -20$

$\qquad\qquad$ Runout of 20 items total

$\qquad\qquad Q_{C_{23}} = 0 + 90 = 90$

$t_R = 31$; $\quad Q_D = 90 - (31 - 23 - 1)(10) = 20$

$\qquad\qquad Q_{C_{31}} = 20 + 90 = 110$

$t_R = 40$; $\quad Q_D = 110 - (40 - 31 - 1)(10) = 30$

$\qquad\qquad Q_{C_{40}} = 30 + 90 = 120$

And, of course, these values equal those found with the $(T \rightarrow T)$ simulation given in Table 10–7. A flow chart giving the procedure for the $(E \rightarrow E)$ simulation is given in Figure 10–9.

The advantages of the event-oriented simulation should be clear by now. However, it is not so rosy if many events are possible, such as in a machine shop being simulated in order to determine how many setup men or repairmen are required. Events would be required for each machine failing, being repaired, waiting for repair or setup men, and so on. Keeping track of the *next* event by hand would be extremely cumbersome. Also, if *profiles with respect to time*, say of inventory patterns or utilization of repairmen, were required, then the advantages of time-oriented simulation are obvious. In both cases, the use of the digital computer in conjunction with available *simulation languages* can be of much benefit.

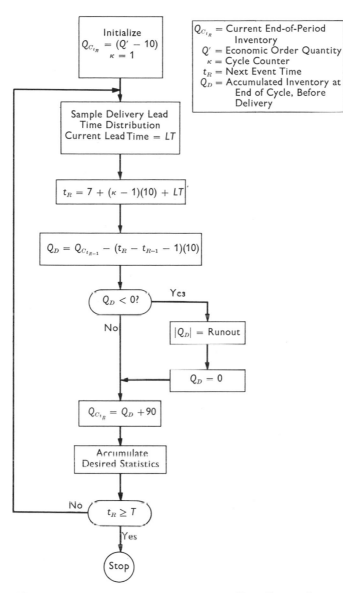

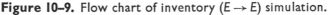

Figure 10–9. Flow chart of inventory ($E \rightarrow E$) simulation.

10–6. AVAILABLE SIMULATION LANGUAGES

A digital computer simulation may be programmed in an acceptable digital computer language, the most common being FORTRAN. This is the manner in which early digital computer simulations were approached. Now there are available several *simulation languages* that can eliminate a large amount of the effort expended when programming the system from scratch is required. Some languages are quite general while others are highly specialized, being geared to specific problems such as production control environments.

According to Pritsker,[5] *all* simulation languages have three things in common: providing concepts and statements for

1. Representing the state of a system at a single point in time.
2. Moving a system from state to state.
3. Performing relevant chores such as data generation and data analysis.

Typical of such languages would be GPSS, GASP, and PROSIM. *Many* others exist, but these three will give an idea of typical language capabilities.

GPSS

The General Purpose Simulation System was developed by Geoffrey Gordon of the IBM New York Scientific Center. The language is rather *problem oriented*, somewhat toward queuing problems. Typically, these include problems where objects move through a variety of processing stages. Even though lack of generality is implied through problem orientation, many problems can be formulated in this manner. Production flow problems, inventory analysis and so on are typical applications. According to Gordon,[1] GPSS had as an objective to be applicable for users with little or no programming ability. This eliminates some flexibility whereby the user could make extensive additions with his own subroutines. This is not to imply that additions cannot be made; they are not necessarily simple to add. A more flexible language is GASP, but it requires a more comprehensive programming knowledge.

GASP

A General Activity Simulation Program was developed originally by P. J. Kiviat for the United States Steel Corporation.[2] GASP II was developed at Arizona State University under the direction of A. A. B. Pritsker, and stemmed from Kiviat's original work. The prime advantages of GASP are that it is FORTRAN-based and modular, fitting on most machines that have FORTRAN capability. Because of the FORTRAN orientation, it is easily modified and extended. Basically, GASP II is a group of FORTRAN subroutines that assist in conducting a simulation study. Typical are routines to keep track of time, remove and insert file data, and which generate data for specific probability distributions. The language SIMSCRIPT is another which falls into the "general" application category of GASP.

PROSIM[3]

The *PRO*duction system *SIM*ulator was developed at Auburn University under the direction of Joe Mize and is an example of a digital computer simulation approach for highly specialized problems. PROSIM was designed to be a production control *teaching simulator*, whereby student teams are given a production problem for which they have to design a control system. The student has to make production decisions which are implemented by the simulator which then provides such items as forecast results, status of the system, idle time within the system, inventory status and total manufacturing costs. One prime advantage for PROSIM is that it provides a unique method for demonstrating the interactive effects discussed in Chapter 1 of this text. Another typical specialized simulation program is DYNAMO (*DYNA*mic *MO*dels) developed for Industrial Dynamics models.

The analyst planning to use digital computer simulation would be well advised to check possible simulation languages available for his machine to possibly eliminate some of the toil and strain inherent in developing one-of-a-kind programs each time he simulates.

REFERENCES CITED

1. GORDON, GEOFFREY. *System Simulation.* Prentice-Hall, Inc., Englewood Cliffs, N.J., 1969.
2. KIVIAT, P. J. *GASP—A General Activity Simulation Program.* Applied Research Laboratory, United States Steel Corporation, Monroeville, Pennsylvania, 1963.
3. MIZE, J. H., B. E. HERRING, M. S. CHUN, and C. L. COOK. *PROSIM V Instructor's Manual.* Auburn University, Project THEMIS Technical Report No. AU-T-5, Contract DAAH01-68-C-0296, Army Missile Command, Huntsville, Alabama, November, 1969.
4. NADDOR, E., *Inventory Systems.* John Wiley and Sons, Inc., New York, N.Y., 1966.
5. PRITSKER, A. A. B., and P. J. KIVIAT. *Simulation with GASP II: A FORTRAN Based Simulation Language.* Printice-Hall, Inc., Englewood Cliffs, N.J., 1969.

FURTHER READING

HADLEY, G., and T. M. WHITIN, *Analysis of Inventory Systems.* Prentice-Hall Inc., Englewood Cliffs, N.J., 1963.

PROBLEMS

1. A set of time-series data has been relatively constant about an average of 100 units per day. At any time period (day), there is a possibility of a *process mean* change according to the following distribution:

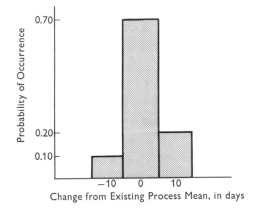

Change from Existing Process Mean, in days

Also, for each day the following variability *about* the existing mean exists:

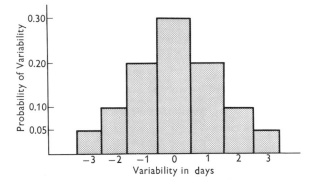

Variability in days

Simulate 50 days' demand data according to these characteristics. Test single exponential smoothing as a forecast procedure using a lead-time of 4 days and finding error terms for the last 30 days of data. Try α values of 0.3 and 0.1. Which alpha appears best? Any intuitive reasoning for your result?

Now test the two alpha values with the same forecasting specifications for demand data you generate with *no process mean* variability, only variability around the existing mean of 100 days. Evaluate the best alpha value and discuss fully your findings.

2. Extend the Monte Carlo simulation for evaluating inventory policies in Table 10–6 an additional sixty days. Does the same cost relationship between the policies continue?

3. Justify, if possible, the values of Q', ξ, Q_r, and t_r for the inventory problem attacked by Monte Carlo simulation in Section 10–4.

4. Consider product C-12 only in the Chapter 9, Problem 1 data. The vendor for this item is sure to deliver within 10 days plus or minus 2. The demand, 850 units per year, is constant. The plant works 7 days a week, 52 weeks a year. Suggest the inventory ordering policy $(t_r, Q' + \xi)$, including specifying a safety stock ξ.

11

Adaptivity in Control

The world's a scene of changes, and to be constant, in Nature were inconstancy.

ABRAHAM COWLEY

We must cut our coat according to our cloth, and adapt ourselves to changing circumstances.

DEAN W. R. INGE

11-1. NEED FOR ADAPTIVE CONTROL

The techniques we have looked at under the major topics of forecasting, scheduling, and inventory control were designed under the constraint of some current estimates of environmental conditions. *Forecasting*, for example, is probably optimized over a certain length of time, usually a *historic* period. The assumption that just because a set of parameters was found adequate for this segment of time by no means should indicate that it will be adequate for all future time. Environmental conditions are rarely static, they are dynamic. Therefore, cognizance should be taken of the fact that environmental conditions are notoriously changeable, with the result that specific techniques designed with systems analysis should preferably be designed to be adaptable to these changing conditions.

An adaptive control procedure should test some characteristic or characteristics of the technique being used to determine if the parameters of that technique are really performing as desired. In general,

384

some allowable *error condition* is the characteristic being monitored. If the error condition goes beyond allowable limits then the technique parameters should be adjusted in some logical manner.

In forecasting, this error term would be some deviation measure of predicted versus actual value. A variety of measures could be found in *scheduling*. We might wish to control lateness of order deliveries or have some specified maximum value for the time any job should be in the production facility. In *inventory control*, we might wish to measure and control deviations below a specified safety stock, or control inventory above an acceptable average inventory level. The two approaches we will look at as adaptive control procedures are both applicable to these control situations.

Two prime objectives should be prevalent for the *control* function:

1. Control is necessary to insure that planned and analyzed procedures are maintained within the system. Since occurrences are generally stochastic in nature, the planned and analyzed procedures should allow satisfaction of system goals and objectives within some agreeable tolerance; perhaps a 95 percent to 99 percent satisfaction level
2. Control should allow the procedures to be modified or changed according to significant environmental changes. This adaptive control concept should, if at all possible, be *self*-adapting, improving the procedures when the satisfaction level is not met by changing procedure parameters or even possibly procedural models.

This chapter will delve a little into the characteristics required for control by looking at two basic topics with the view to giving the reader an insight into potential ways for maintaining or improving response characteristics of those procedures designed to satisfy systems objectives. These topics will be: (1) control chart theory and (2) evolutionary operations (EVOP).

11-2. CONTROL CHART THEORY AND EVOLUTIONARY OPERATION

The first of the topics, taken from the traditional topic of quality control, is that of control chart theory. Here we find a technique that will allow us to measure the *current* status of forecasting, scheduling, or possibly inventory control as regards the ability to measure up to some performance criterion. The rather simple control chart approach is one which would dictate procedure changes only when such changes are required, rather than allowing continuous changes. A dynamic adaptive situation could certainly be designed whereby a new set of parameters is developed immediately upon the performance criterion deviating from some optimum setting. This would undoubtedly result in settings or procedures being changed almost constantly with a corresponding increase in "analyst cost" and result in a very *noisy* overall response for the system. The control chart approach allows a *damping* of the continuous adjustment, balancing an increase in error costs with a corresponding result of system stability. One fallacy with the control chart approach is that it is primarily a *one-variable* control device. As will be seen in quality control, this variable is usually some measurement characteristic. When the control chart indicates a multi-variable process is out of control then judgment has to be made regarding how to get that process back in control. The second topic of this chapter, that of evolutionary operations, will attempt to define the contribution of *each* variable to a process change.

Evolutionary operation is a statistical technique developed by G. E. P. Box[1] and had as its original philosophy operating a process with what Box called a "built-in" procedure to increase productivity. Box stipulated that the basic philosophy of evolutionary operation is that it is nearly always inefficient to run an industrial process to produce product alone. A process, continuing Box's theme, should be run so as to generate product *plus information on how to improve the product.*

Using this philosophy, it will be shown how a simple response surface analysis of forecasting parameter effects will allow the parameters to be chosen dynamically, with an objective being to continually improve (decrease) the forecast errors. This same approach could then be used in dynamically improving (or adapting) scheduling or inventory procedures.

11–3. CONTROL CHARTS

In quality control inspection, parts are sampled from a process being controlled and some required characteristic is measured. These characteristics are plotted on the control chart as they are measured and compared to limits on the chart which are designed statistically to indicate whether or not there is something wrong with the *process*. This same philosophy can be used as an adaptive control tool. First, a cursory look at the mechanics of control charting will be given. For those who wish to go deeper there are many suitable introductory quality control texts, some of which are listed at the end of the chapter.

The prime objective for control charts is to aid in the distinguishing of random fluctuations from assignable cause conditions. Whatever the task, there is inherently some random variation in the result of that task over which we would have no control.

For example, if we were tossing pennies in a ring after much practice we might be able to get ten out of ten in the ring. However, the location of the pennies *within* the ring would partly be due to random happenings. These would include how the penny landed, the hardness of the particular surface it hit, the regularity of the surface, and so on. Therefore, we would not expect all the pennies to land one on top of the other. The ring is made big enough to handle some of these random actuations that are bound to occur even with the most experienced penny-tossers. Now what happens if a right-handed operator hurts his right hand and has to throw left-handed? In all probability quite a few coins would fall outside the ring. These "errors" would not be due to random variations but are a function of the assignable cause created by switching the throwing hand. If we saw two rings such as given in Figure 11–1, each with pennies thrown by an expert, and assuming the ring is of sufficient diameter, we could say with a large degree of confidence that the variation in penny position in ring A is due to random fluctuations, but the variation in ring B is due to assignable cause.

Such is the purpose of the control chart. If we have an industrial process where a part dimension is being measured against a set of specifications we would expect the dimensions from part to part to vary by some minute amount due to random causes. Knowing that a variable set of data has to come from a distribution with some mean, $\bar{X}$, and standard deviation, σ, we also know from statistical theory that some 90 percent of all the data should lie between $+3\sigma$ limits around the mean, whatever the distribution of the data and assuming no shift in the distribution.

Where the data are physical measured dimensions, it is usually assumed that the individual measurements, X_i, come from a bell-shaped normal distribution where

$$\sigma_X = \sqrt{\sum_{i=1}^{N} \frac{(X_i - \bar{X})^2}{N}} \tag{11-1}$$

$\bar{X}$ is the average of the X_i values:

$$\bar{X} = \frac{\sum_{i=1}^{N} X_i}{N}$$

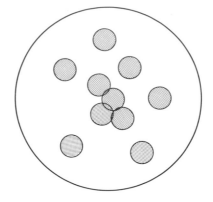

A.   Variation in Penny Locations Due to *Random* Causes

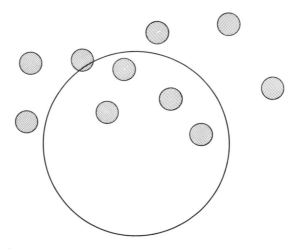

B.   Variation in Penny Location Due to *Assignable* Causes

Figure II–I. Variation in tossing pennies into a ring.

and σ_X is the standard deviation of the X values. Since measurement variation should be around the mean of the measurement, control limits can be set by

$$\text{Upper Limit:} \quad \text{UL} = \bar{X} + 3\sigma_X$$
$$\text{Lower Limit:} \quad \text{LL} = \bar{X} - 3\sigma_X \tag{11-2}$$

The control chart would now be drawn as shown in Figure 11–2.

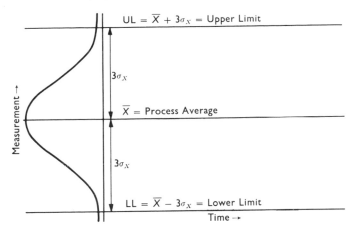

Figure 11-2. General measurement control chart based on three standard deviation limits.

We assume the following:

1. Control limits are based on standard deviations calculated from data that are in control, and

2. The data come from a normal distribution, and using the normal distribution values given in Table A-2, we know that in the long run 99.74 percent of the part dimensions should fall within the control limits if $\bar{X}$ and σ_X do not change, and if random fluctuations only are present. Thus, measurements falling outside the control limits pretty well indicate a change in the process distribution created by an assignable cause. As an example, Figure 11-3 shows a control chart with points drifting gradually out of limits. Such a situation might be indicative of tool or die wear.

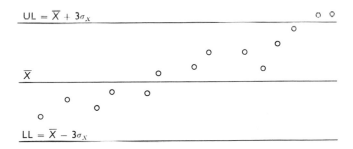

Figure 11-3. Control chart with measurement data giving trend of process change.

If only random deviations are present in the measurement it would be expected that a measurement would have an equal probability of lying above or below the center line, $\bar{X}$. The compound probability of the first five points all lying *below* the center line would be $(0.5)^5$ due to independence of the measurements. This turns out to be a probability of about 3 in 100. The probability of the last nine measurements being *above* the centerline is $(0.5)^9$ if only random causes are present, giving a value of about 2 chances in a thousand. Neither probability is very high. This shows that even if a point does *not* lie outside the control limits, assignable causes can be predicted if an unusually large sequence of observations lies above or below the centerline.

There is no magic to the 3 standard deviation limits. It has been found empirically that these provide a good *cost balance* between looking for an assignable cause when it is not there and in not looking for one when it is present—two standard statistical errors. These two errors are frequently classed as shown in Table 11–1. If control limits are set at one standard deviation away from the centerline, the type I error will predominate. The process may have a large number of parts outside the limits but which still fall within the random curve category if they are within three standard deviation limits. Even so, only the one standard deviation limit would be plotted and an assignable cause would be assumed when one or two points fall outside the limits. Conversely, if limits are set at five standard deviations then virtually no points would ever fall outside the limits due to random variation. Unfortunately, though, the type II error would be reasonable as assignable cause variations might be present that would not be caught by the 5σ limits. These situations are graphically demonstrated in Figure 11–4.

As mentioned earlier, the 3σ limits have been found to balance the

Table 11-1

Two Possible Statistical Errors Inherent in Actions of Uncertainty

Assumption	Actual Condition	
	True	False
True	Correct	Type II error
False	Type I error	Correct

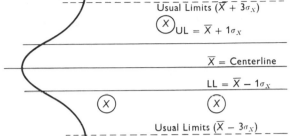

A. Example of Points Falling *Outside* σ_X Limits Indicating Assignable Cause,
   Which Probably is Non-Existent (Type I error)

$$\text{Usual Limits } (\overline{X} + 3\sigma_X)$$

$$UL = \overline{X} + 1\sigma_X$$

$$\overline{X} = \text{Centerline}$$

$$LL = \overline{X} - 1\sigma_X$$

$$\text{Usual Limits } (\overline{X} - 3\sigma_X)$$

B. Example of Points Falling *Inside* $5\sigma_X$ Limits Indicating Random Variation,
   When Assignable Cause Present (Type II error)

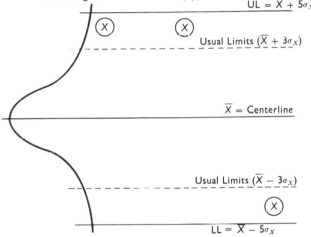

$$UL = \overline{X} + 5\sigma_X$$

$$\text{Usual Limits } (\overline{X} + 3\sigma_X)$$

$$\overline{X} = \text{Centerline}$$

$$\text{Usual Limits } (\overline{X} - 3\sigma_X)$$

$$LL = \overline{X} - 5\sigma_X$$

Figure 11–4. Examples of control chart errors.

two error costs pretty well. In certain other countries, 2σ limits have been the most utilized. In fact, if a control chart is planned for use with individual X values, frequently a 2σ limit system is used if the data points are available only at infrequent intervals. This would force more "assignable causes" to be checked but if one truly is available then the probability that it would be found is high, thus alleviating the problem of an assignable cause being present for long periods of time.

11–4. THE $\overline{X}$ CHART

We have so far only talked about control charts where individual measurements are plotted. These will generally have $\overline{X} \pm 3\sigma_X$

limits. Usually, *averages* of data *samples* are plotted on what is commonly called an $\bar{X}$ chart or average X chart. The $\bar{X}$ values have the advantage of being more representative of the process than are single X values. Also, it can be shown that true process changes are found faster with an $\bar{X}$ chart, in the long run, than with an X chart. A most important advantage for the $\bar{X}$ chart is that if the measurements are independent items, as is usually assumed, then by applying the *central limit theorem* (Appendix D) it will be seen that $\bar{X}$ values tend to be normally distributed even if the X values are not. Further, large amounts of X_i data can be condensed with an $\bar{X}$ chart.

The control limits for an $\bar{X}$ chart are found in exactly the same manner as for an X chart, except that $\bar{X}_j$ values are used instead of X_i's:

$$UL = \bar{X} + 3\sigma_{\bar{X}}$$
$$LL = \bar{X} - 3\sigma_{\bar{X}}$$
(11–3)

where $\sigma_{\bar{X}}$ is standard deviation of *average values* found in each sample.

The fact that similar results will be obtained with both X and $\bar{X}$ charts can better be shown with an example. Consider the data given in Table 11–2. These might represent 35 coded measurement values. The individual readings are grouped so that 7 samples of 5 measurements each are available for an $\bar{X}$ chart. The control limits for the X and $\bar{X}$ charts are:

X Chart

$$\bar{X} = \frac{\sum\limits_{i=1}^{35} X_i}{35} = \frac{280}{35} = 8.0$$

$$\sigma_X = \sqrt{\frac{\sum\limits_{i=1}^{35} (X_i - \bar{X})^2}{35}} = \sqrt{\frac{126}{35}} = \sqrt{3.6} = 1.9$$

Limits by Equation 11–2 are

$$UL = \bar{X} + 3\sigma_X = (8.0) + (3)(1.9) = 13.7$$
$$LL = \bar{X} - 3\sigma_X = (8.0) - (3)(1.9) = 2.3$$

X̄ Chart

$$\sigma_{\bar{X}} = \sqrt{\frac{\sum\limits_{j=1}^{7} (\bar{X}_j - \bar{X})^2}{7}} = \sqrt{\frac{5.28}{7}} = 0.87$$

Table 11–2

Example Data with Sample Means

	X_1	X_2	X_3	X_4	X_5	$\sum\limits_{i=1}^{5} x_i$	$\overline{X_j}$
A	8	8	10	8	7	41	8.2
B	12	8	5	11	9	45	9.0
C	8	5	6	8	5	32	6.4
D	4	10	11	12	6	43	8.6
E	9	7	8	7	8	39	7.8
F	8	9	9	8	10	44	8.8
G	7	8	6	7	8	36	7.2
						280	

Limits by Equation 11–3 are

$$UL = \bar{X} + 3\sigma_{\bar{x}} = (8.0) + (3)(0.87) = 10.6$$
$$LL = \bar{X} - 3\sigma_{\bar{x}} = (8.0) - (3)(0.87) - 5.4$$

As expected, the limits for *averages* are quite a bit tighter than those for individual readings. Plots of the control charts, X and $\bar{X}$, are given in Figure 11–5. By chance alone we would expect 68.3 percent

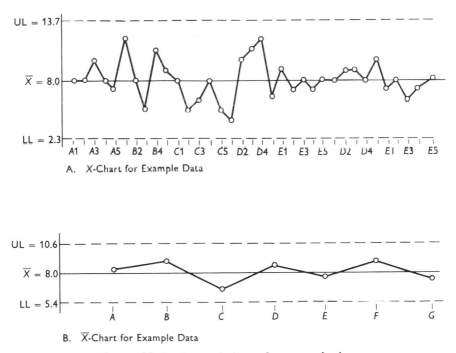

A. X-Chart for Example Data

B. $\overline{X}$-Chart for Example Data

Figure 11–5. Control charts for example data.

of the readings to fall within 1σ limits, about 6.1 to 9.9 on the X-chart. We have 21 out of 35, or exactly 60 percent. The 2σ limits, 11.8 to 4.2 on the X-chart, have 32 points within, for about 91 percent. The expectancy with the normal distribution is about 95.4 percent. The data seem *reasonably* normally distributed and in control. A chi-square test would be used if normality determination is imperative. We will assume it is safe to continue the limits, plotting new measurements to *insure* control continuance. Table 11–3 gives additional measurement data which now have a gradual shift in process mean. These new values for X and $\bar{X}$ are plotted on their respective control charts in Figure 11–6, using the original control limits developed when the process exhibited excellent control.

The $\bar{X}$-chart is the first to get a point out of control limits, on sample K. So, twenty individual points were needed before this happened. For the X-chart, the first point out was the twenty-fourth so *theoretically* the $\bar{X}$-chart was the first to exhibit out-of-control conditions.

In actual practice, though, we would realize with the X-chart pretty fast that something was wrong due to the run of points sequentially on or above the centerline. Action is generally taken when ten follow this pattern with a probability of about $(0.5)^{10}$, or one in a thousand. Also, if one point does fall above or below a control limit, it is not by itself indicative of problems. By chance alone a point can fall above or below the 3σ control limits about 0.26 percent of the time. This indicates that all the data should be considered when determining if a process is out-of-control, not just the out-of-limit data points.

Once an assignable cause is found then it should be removed as should all pertinent data affected by that cause. Once this is done, limits should be re-calculated.

Table 11–3

Additional Example Data with Process Shift

	X_1	X_2	X_3	X_4	X_5	$\sum\limits_{i=1}^{5} x_i$	$\overline{X_j}$
H	8	9	8	9	10	44	8.8
I	10	9	10	9	11	49	9.8
J	11	8	9	11	13	52	10.4
K	12	11	13	12	13	61	12.2
L	12	13	13	14	16	68	13.6

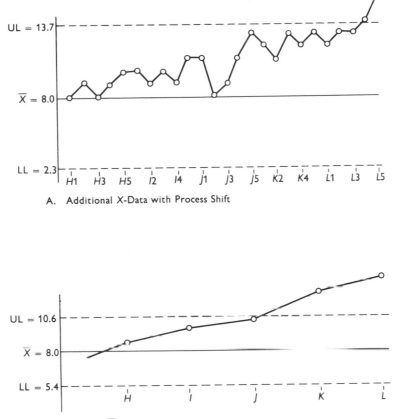

A. Additional X-Data with Process Shift

B. Additional $\bar{X}$-Data with Process Shift

Figure 11–6. Data indicating process shifts.

11–5. VARIABILITY CHART

The concept of the X-chart is the only one suggested if some control chart adaptive procedure is considered. Limits would be set tightly if considerable cost is attained when the process goes out of control, and relatively loosely if this cost is slight. A rule of thumb would be 2σ or 3σ limits in general. For *quality control* inspection procedures a variability chart, say *standard deviation* chart, is frequently plotted with the $\bar{X}$-chart (not with the X-chart for obvious reasons). While the process is exhibiting control, say with a good operator and good tool conditions, the standard deviation for each sample, say σ_{X_j}, is determined. The variability chart would then be like an X-chart with the individual readings being the σ_{X_j} values. The limits would be:

Centerline:
$$\frac{\sum\limits_{j=1}^{m} \sigma_{X_j}}{m} = \overline{\sigma_X}$$

UL:
$$\overline{\sigma_X} + 3\sigma_{\sigma_X}$$

LL:
$$\overline{\sigma_X} - 3\sigma_{\sigma_X}$$

$$(11\text{--}4)$$

For the original data given in Table 11–2, the various σ_{X_j} values are:

Sample A:
$$\sigma_{X_A} = \sqrt{\frac{4.00}{5}} = 0.90$$

Sample B:
$$\sigma_{X_B} = \sqrt{\frac{30.00}{5}} = 2.45$$

Sample C:
$$\sigma_{X_C} = \sqrt{\frac{9.20}{5}} = 1.36$$

Sample D:
$$\sigma_{X_D} = \sqrt{\frac{47.20}{5}} = 3.07$$

Sample E:
$$\sigma_{X_E} = \sqrt{\frac{2.80}{5}} = 0.75$$

Sample F:
$$\sigma_{X_F} = \sqrt{\frac{2.80}{5}} = 0.75$$

Sample G:
$$\sigma_{X_G} = \sqrt{\frac{2.80}{5}} = 0.75$$

The centerline for the standard deviation, σ, chart would be

$$\overline{\sigma_X} = \frac{0.90 + 2.45 + 1.36 + 3.07 + 0.75 + 0.75 + 0.75}{7}$$

$$\overline{\sigma_X} = 1.44$$

The value of σ_{σ_X} is the standard deviation of the seven σ_{X_j} values and turns out to be

$$\sigma_{\sigma_X} = 0.872$$

And the σ-chart control limits by Equation 11–4:

UL: $\qquad\qquad \overline{\sigma_X} + 3\sigma_{\sigma_X} = 1.44 + (3)(0.872) = 4.06$

LL: $\qquad\qquad \overline{\sigma_X} - 3\sigma_{\sigma_X} = 1.44 - 2.62 = 0$

(Obviously σ_{X_j} can never be <0.)

The plot of the σ-chart is given in Figure 11–7, with the σ_{X_j} values for all samples A through L. Even after the process shift the variability seems in control, though having five points in a row above the center-line might indicate some peculiarity in the process.

What is the worth of the σ-chart in conjunction with the $\bar{X}$-chart? In general, the σ-chart will show whether process *variability* is in control and in general the $\bar{X}$-chart shows whether the process *level* is in control. Thus, in a machining operation for example, it is possible for the $\bar{X}$-chart to show tool malfunctions such as wear or incorrect setting. The σ-chart could indicate variability in operator performance. Usually, no attempt should be made in quality control to get $\bar{X}$ limits until the variability chart shows control.

Finally, in a quality control vein, the objective of control charts is to insure that specifications for a product are met. Specifications should *never be within* $\bar{X} \pm 3\sigma_X$, otherwise points may fall outside such specifications by chance alone. If the process is such that the specifications are too tight then either the process or design has to be changed, or you can expect a large amount of points *not* to meet specifications.

For example, consider the limits and specifications shown in Figure 11–8.

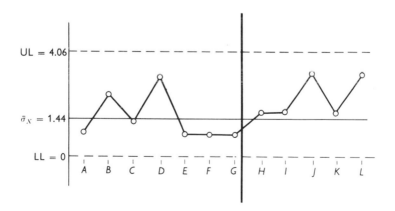

Figure 11–7. Variability σ-chart from example data.

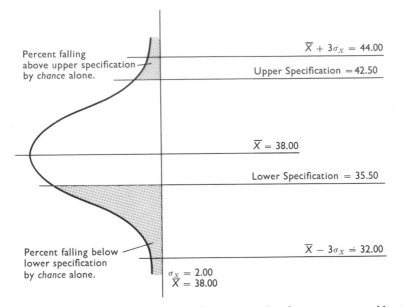

Figure II–8. Incorrect setting of specifications with relation to control limits.

The number of standard deviations at which the *upper* specification is above the centerline is

$$Z_U = \frac{42.50 - 38.00}{\sigma_X} = 2.25$$

The number below $\bar{X}$ at which the lower specification lies is

$$Z_L = \frac{35.50 - 38.00}{\sigma_X} = -1.25$$

Using normal distribution Table A–2 given in Appendix A we find that the percentage of points expected to fall out of the specifications by chance alone are

1. Percentage above upper specification; $Z_U = +2.25$; percentage $= 1.22\%$
2. Percentage below lower specification; $Z_L = -1.25$; percentage $= 10.56\%$

If 11.78 percent not meeting specifications is allowable then the process is all right, assuming control is shown with the $\bar{X}$-chart. Usually 11.78 percent out of limits would be exorbitant.

11–6. FURTHER STATISTICAL CONSIDERATIONS

In using control charts as an *adaptive* tool one would normally plot a continuous stream of *error terms* on a chart which has limits set at allowable error values. For example, forecasting refrigerator sales might have an allowable 0–5 percent error characteristic. Forecast errors would then be plotted for each forecast period when the true demand is known. When an error exceeds allowable limits then the forecast model is re-evaluated. In exponential smoothing this might mean that the exponential smoothing constant α is increased to allow process changes to be monitored more closely. When the forecast starts being 'in control'' this α value might be lowered. During satisfactory forecasting periods, the control limits could be calculated from the error-term standard deviation.

In scheduling, the error term may refer to time slippage. Limits would then be set on both sides of a due date. If production is completed too early this possibly could mean excessive inventory charges due to having to hold finished items prior to shipping. Certainly some upper value would be desirable regarding slippage of due-dates. Once schedules start falling outside the allowable band then production processes or scheduling techniques, such as resource allocation procedures, should be checked and revised if necessary.

An inventory article was developed by Eilon[3] where adaptive limits were used in *inventory control*. Usually a control chart approach can be considered in an inventory situation where the *lower limit* corresponds to a safety stock to guard against runouts, and an upper limit is set to which the stock is replenished at certain intervals. The Eilon procedure computed adaptive control limits based on a forecasting procedure that took account of seasonal fluctuations and trends.

When we discuss evolutionary control we will find that variable limits will be set on the differences between current conditions and average past conditions. The standard deviation estimates used in the limits are calculated from range values, thus simplifying greatly the calculation. Since this approach is a traditional quality control device it might be worthwhile to introduce it at this point.

It should be intuitive that there should be some relationship, if a sample of n items are taken, between the standard deviation of the items within that sample and the range (maximum-minimum) of values within that sample. Also, it would seem logical that the number of items n in that sample would have a bearing on the relationship.

Table 11-4

**Range to Standard Deviation
Conversion Constants, d_2**

Sample Size n	Constant d_2
2	1.128
3	1.693
4	2.059
5	2.326
6	2.534
7	2.704
8	2.847
9	2.970
10	3.078
11	3.173
12	3.258
13	3.336
14	3.407
15	3.472

Source: From *Engineering Statistics and Quality Control*, by I. W. Burr, Copyright © 1953, used with permission of McGraw–Hill Book Company.

A sample of two would not be too safe, for example, in estimating the standard deviation as the range is just the difference between these two readings.

Well, it can statistically be shown that a relationship does exist between the range, R, and standard deviation, σ, and tables of relating constants, commonly called d_2, have been developed. The relationship is

$$\text{Estimated } \sigma = \frac{R}{d_2} \qquad (11\text{–}5)$$

Values of d_2 for samples of size 2 through 15 are given in Table 11–4. d_2, for $n = 5$, is 2.326.

If we used this procedure to calculate σ_{X_j} for the eight samples originally given in Table 11–2 we would get estimates as shown in Table 11–5. As expected, the estimates of σ are not exactly the same as the calculated values, but they are reasonable and control limits certainly could be based on them. This is the same procedure that will be utilized with EVOP later in this chapter.

Table 11-5

Estimates of Sample Standard Deviations from Their Range

Sample	X_1	X_2	X_3	X_4	X_5	Range (R) (Max-Min)	Estimated σ: $R/2.326$	Calculated σ
A	8	8	10	8	7	3	1.29	0.90
B	12	8	5	11	9	7	3.00	2.45
C	8	5	6	8	5	3	1.29	1.36
D	4	10	11	12	6	8	3.44	3.07
E	9	7	8	7	8	2	0.86	0.75
F	8	9	9	8	10	2	0.86	0.75
G	7	8	6	7	8	2	0.86	0.75

11–7. USING CONTROL CHARTS FOR ADAPTIVE FORECASTING

As just indicated, control charts have their paramount benefit with single-variable processes. One example of this in forecasting is the use of exponential smoothing in polynomial fitting. This section will present a short example of single exponential smoothing with control limits applied, to attempt to adapt the smoothing constant, α, to changing process conditions. The actual exponential smoothing forecast is based on material presented in Chapter 4 where

$$\hat{Y}(t) = (\alpha)(Y(t)) + (1 - \alpha)(\hat{Y}(t - 1))$$

where $\hat{Y}(t)$ is current smoothed average

$Y(t)$ is current demand

$0 < \alpha < 1$ is a smoothing constant

With an assumption of noisy but relatively constant demand data, from any current time period T a prediction τ periods ahead is made by $\hat{Y}(t)$.

Table 11–6 gives a set of time-series data, $Y(t)$, that has two distinct process changes. Starting with the conventional α of 0.1, the first five pieces of data are used to stabilize $\hat{Y}(t)$ in Table 11–7. $\hat{Y}(5)$ is 15.0 which is also seen to be $\overline{Y}(5)$ if the first five pieces of data are averaged. Data at times 6 through 12, also in Table 11–7, are used to calculate forecast errors assuming forecasts are made with a τ value of 1. These seven error values, which are

$$\text{Error} = [Y(t) - \hat{Y}(t - 1)]^2$$

Table 11-6

Time-Series Data Used in Forecasting
Control Chart Example

t	Y(t)	
1	15	
2	14	
3	17	
4	15	
5	14	
6	15	
7	15	
8	16	
9	15	
10	13	
11	16	
12	14	
13	17	
14	19	First Process Shift
15	21	
16	22	
17	21	
18	22	
19	21	
20	22	
21	24	Second Process Shift
22	26	
23	25	
24	25	
25	25	

Table 11-7

Setting Forecast Error Limits at $2\sigma_e$

	(I)				(II) Prediction from	Error:	
t	Y(t)	$\alpha Y(t)$	$\beta\hat{Y}(t-1)$	$\hat{Y}(t)$	$\hat{Y}(t-1)$	$(I-II)^2$	
1	15	1.5	—	15			
2	14	1.4	13.5	14.9			Initialize $\hat{Y}(t)$
3	17	1.7	13.4	15.1			
4	15	1.5	13.6	15.1			
5	14	1.4	13.6	15.0			
6	15	1.5	13.5	15.0	15.0	0	
7	15	1.5	13.5	15.0	15.0	0	
8	16	1.6	13.5	15.1	15.0	1.00	Find
9	15	1.5	13.6	15.1	15.1	0.01	Errors
10	13	1.3	13.6	14.9	15.1	4.41	for
11	16	1.6	13.0	14.6	14.9	1.21	Control
12	14	1.4	13.1	14.5	14.6	0.36	Limits

are then used to determine control limits for future errors, an analysis of which will dictate whether to adjust the α value.

Limits were set on the errors at $2\sigma_e$ where

$$\sigma_e = \text{standard deviation of the forecast errors, } e_t$$

where

$$e_{(t)} = [Y(t) - \hat{Y}(t-1)]^2$$

$$\sigma_e = \sqrt{\frac{\sum_{t=6}^{12}(e_{(t)} - \bar{e}_{(t)})^2}{7}} = 1.5, \text{ approximately}$$

Since the mean of forecast errors squared is one, limits are

$$1 + (2)(1.5) = 0 \text{ to } 4 \text{ (based on } 2\sigma_e \text{ limits)*}$$

Table 11–8 gives the forecasting results using $\alpha = 0.1$ when *no* adaptive control of α is effected. This table is just a continuation then of Table 11–7. If the error terms are averaged, it will be found that the average forecast error, $[Y(t) - \hat{Y}(t-1)]^2$, is about 26.40.

Table 11–9 gives an example of forecasting using adaptive control. If the error at any time period exceeds 4, then the α value is raised

Table 11–8

Forecasting with $\alpha=1$, Using Data from Table 11–6 — No Adaptive Control

	(I)					(II) Prediction from	Error
t	$Y(t)$	α	$\alpha Y(t)$	$\beta\hat{Y}(t-1)$	$\hat{Y}(t)$	$(t-1)$	$(I-II)^2$
13	17	0.1	1.7	13.1	14.8	14.5	6.25
14	19	0.1	1.9	13.3	15.2	14.8	17.64
15	21	0.1	2.1	13.6	15.7	15.2	33.64
16	22	0.1	2.2	14.1	16.3	15.7	39.69
17	21	0.1	2.1	14.7	16.8	16.3	22.09
18	22	0.1	2.2	15.1	17.3	16.8	27.04
19	21	0.1	2.1	15.6	17.7	17.3	13.69
20	22	0.1	2.2	15.9	18.1	17.7	18.49
21	24	0.1	2.4	16.3	18.7	18.1	34.81
22	26	0.1	2.6	16.8	19.4	18.7	53.29
23	25	0.1	2.5	17.5	20.0	19.4	31.36
24	25	0.1	2.5	18.0	20.5	20.0	25.00
25	25	0.1	2.5	—	—	20.5	20.25

* Limits can be set on any multiple of σ_e. Two σ_e limits allow a more rapid response of α than, say $3\sigma_e$ limits.

Table 11–9

Forecasting with $\alpha=1$, Using Data from Table 11–6 —
With Adaptive Control

	(I)				(II) Prediction from	Error
t	$Y(t)$	α	$\alpha\hat{Y}(t)$	$\beta\hat{Y}(t-1)$	$\hat{Y}(t)$	$(t-1)$	$(I-II)^2$
13	17	0.2†	3.4	11.6	15.0	14.5	6.25*
14	19	0.3†	5.7	10.5	16.2	15.0	16.00*
15	21	0.4†	8.4	9.7	18.1	16.2	23.04*
16	22	0.5†	11.0	9.1	20.1	18.1	15.21*
17	21	0.4†	8.4	12.1	20.5	20.1	0.81
18	22	0.3†	6.6	14.4	21.0	20.5	2.25
19	21	0.2†	4.2	16.8	21.0	21.0	0.00
20	22	0.1†	2.2	18.9	21.1	21.0	1.00
21	24	0.2†	4.8	16.9	21.7	21.1	8.41*
22	26	0.3†	7.8	15.2	23.0	21.7	18.49*
23	25	0.2†	5.0	18.4	23.4	23.0	4.00
24	25	0.1†	2.5	21.1	23.6	23.4	2.56
25	25	0.1	–	–	–	23.6	1.96

*Error out of $2\sigma_e$ limit, or > 4.0

†Because error > 4.0, α increased by 0.1; (Max $\alpha = 0.9$)

‡Error $\leqslant 4.0$ but previous $\alpha > 0.1$, so α decreased by 0.1; (Min $\alpha = 0.1$)

by 0.1. This is a high change but good for an academic problem. In a realistic case with small process changes, 0.01 might be more feasible. Once the process reverts back within limits, then α is set down 0.1, to a lower limit of 0.1. A maximum level for α was set at 0.9, though this was not reached with the problem. The average (error)^2 if calculated, is about 7.65, or less than a third of that without adaptive control. Certainly the benefits are obvious for only just a little more work.

The error limits could have been set about the future demand value. In fact, one frequent measure of a forecast is whether it falls within

$$Y(t) \pm (P)Y(t)$$

where P is some acceptable fractional percent, such as 0.05.

11–8. EVOLUTIONARY OPERATIONS (EVOP)

In the introductory section of this chapter, EVOP was attributed to G. E. P. Box. In his original paper, Box[1] suggested that EVOP has an analogy with the *biological* evolutionary process. He stipulated that the advancement of living things is by:

1. Genetic variability due to various agencies such as mutation.
2. Natural selection.

The theory is that future species will be selected from those having the best attributes which vary due to mutation.

The improvement process with EVOP is basically the same; thus the semantic derivation of *evolutionary* operations. It is assumed that a process to be improved has inherent variability depending on parameter settings. Instead of running the process at one static set of conditions, the process is run experimentally at settings *around* the run point, as well as at the run point. The result of running once at all these points is classified as an EVOP cycle, and at the completion of each cycle the benefits accrued (yielded) for each setting are evaluated. If it is found that statistically one of the parameters, or a combination of parameters, results in an improved yield then a decision is made as to whether or not to shift the operating point. If this is done then a set of operating conditions is effected around the *new* point and EVOP starts another phase of operation.

This same procedure is now quite common in digital computer process control, though frequently the process is classified as *perturbation control*. The variables of the process are continually perturbed small incremental amounts. If the process shows improvement then those variable settings that resulted in the improvement are utilized and perturbation continues from that point. This process continues until no further improvements can be realized. This is a self-optimizing process. The perturbations have to be minute in order to prevent a traumatic *upset* of the process.

Similarly with EVOP: Only very small deviations of variable settings are permitted about the operating point. Therefore, in one *cycle* it is doubtful that significant effects will be realized. Several cycles (replications) are run, constituting a *phase*, before statistical effects, if any, are realized. Only then are operating point adjustments made.

Figure 11–9 pictorially represents one-, two-, and three-variable designs for a cement kiln control operation. Realistically, kiln control is dependent on more variables, but we will pretend that three distinct conditions are plausible. The objective is to try to improve cement production and so pounds of yield are measured against the operating conditions.

The one-variable design requires for each cycle just three fuel-rate settings. The setting ϕ represents the operating condition, and A

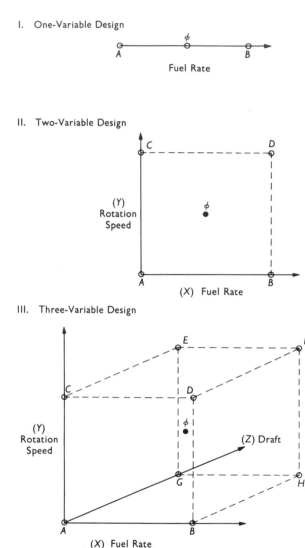

Figure 11–9. Possible designs for EVOP experimentation with up to three variables.

and B are settings at each side of the operating condition. The cement yields are checked at all three points and if A or B is found to give a significant increase, then ϕ is moved, possibly to A or B, and new A and B points are defined.

The two-variable design requires four settings for the two variables in addition to the operating condition. If points B and D give a significant yield versus A and C, then the fuel rate should be adjusted by moving ϕ to the right. Similarly for A and B versus C and D, except that rotation speed is significant.

The third design, that of three variables, would have eight operating conditions around the point ϕ, with each of the three variables having values just bounding the ϕ condition. We will examine the one- and two-variable situations in this and the next section. The reader wishing information regarding higher-order designs and analysis should consult Box and Draper.[2]

When the response is checked for the various parameter settings, say the three conditions found with the one-parameter design, a response-surface is formed as in Figure 11–10. This is defined by the *average* response for each condition, $\overline{Y}_i$. Because of inherent variability it is expected that differences between $\overline{Y}_i$ response surfaces for various cycles n and the current response surface conditions will be allowed for in the fashion of the control chart standard deviation limits. If, in our one-variable situation, the current $\overline{Y}_A$ and $\overline{Y}_B$ themselves have a difference greater than the response surface difference limits, it is assumed that there is a validity to saying one response is significantly

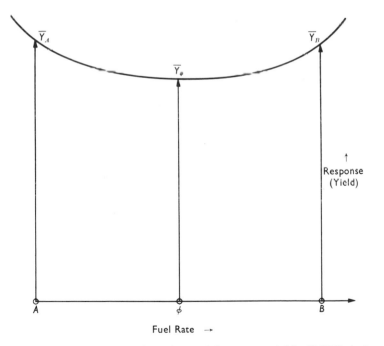

Figure 11–10. Response surface formed by one-variable EVOP design.

greater than the other. Therefore, one problem is to determine variable *effects* or response differences and another is to determine *allowable limits* on these differences. These variable effects will be called main effects.

One other factor should be presented before discussing further these two points. A change in mean (CIM) effect is also desirable, along with its allowable limits. CIM is simply, for each cycle:

$$\text{CIM} = \frac{\sum_{p=1}^{P} \bar{Y}_p}{p} - \bar{Y}_\phi \qquad (11\text{--}6)$$

where $p = 1$, P are the number of operating points analyzed each cycle. $P = 3$ for one variable; $P = 5$ for two variables, etc. CIM gives a measure of the difference between *average response* and $\bar{Y}_\phi$. The average response is usually called the *phase mean*. The phase mean gives an estimate of the average yield during an EVOP phase. Box gives two interpretations for CIM which are important when making the analysis:

1. Positive CIM indicates a near *minimum*.
2. Negative CIM indicates a near *maximum*.
3. CIM outside 2σ limits and with a value near the main effects might be indicative that a maximum or minimum is being closely approached.

For the single-variable design the only main effect is

$$[\bar{Y}_B - \bar{Y}_A], \text{ for each cycle} \qquad (11\text{--}7)$$

and CIM would be

$$\text{CIM} = 1/3(\bar{Y}_A + \bar{Y}_B + \bar{Y}_\phi) - \bar{Y}_\phi$$

These values are calculated *each* cycle and checked against main effect or CIM limits. The limits for the main effect and CIM are:*

Main Effect:
$$\pm (l)\sqrt{\frac{2}{n}}\,(s) \qquad (11\text{--}8)$$

CIM:
$$\pm (l)\sqrt{\frac{2}{3n}}\,(s) \qquad (11\text{--}9)$$

where (s) is the estimate of σ and (l) is the number of standard deviations

---

* Derivation of standard errors and a discussion of main effects can be found in many texts, typical of which is that by Hicks.[4]

Table 11–10

Values of $f_{k,n}$ Used in Calculating Effect Limits

Cycles (n)	Value of k		
	3	5	9
2	0.42	0.30	0.24
3	0.48	0.35	0.27
4	0.51	0.37	0.29
5	0.53	0.38	0.30
6	0.54	0.39	0.31
7	0.55	0.40	0.31
8	0.55	0.40	0.31
9	0.56	0.40	0.32
10	0.56	0.41	0.32

Source: Condensed from Table V, p. 222 in *Evolutionary Operation* by G. E. P. Box and N. R. Draper. Courtesy of John Wiley and Sons.

used in the limits. (l) is usually 3 in quality control work, but Box suggests a value of 2 for EVOP, which is the value we will utilize.

The calculation of (s) is accomplished using the standard quality control procedure discussed earlier in Section 11–6, utilizing the *range* of response surface *differences* for each cycle. For each operating point, p, a difference is calculated between the previous cycle's response *average* and the current response. The minimum of these values is subtracted from the maximum, which constitutes the *range* of differences. (s) is then found by

$$(s) = (\text{Range})(f_{k,n}) \qquad (11\text{–}10)$$

where $f_{(k,n)}$ is a factor dependent on the number of operating points, k, and the number of cycles, n. For a one-variable problem we will utilize $f_{3,n}$ values and for two variables, $f_{5,n}$. Values for $f_{3,n}$ and $f_{5,n}$ are given in Table 11–10. In addition, $f_{9,n}$ is given for the three-variable problems in case the reader gets involved at that level.

Two-Variable Effects and Limits

In a similar fashion, the effects and limits are calculated for the two-variable case. Once we get *above* the one-variable situation it is possible to get interaction effects between variables. If interaction occurs, it might be said that a significant effect was created in one variable *by another*. Therefore, before changing a particular variable found significant, it should first be determined if an interaction effect is present. If so, then a second variable would probably be the culprit in making the first effect significant. Changes of variable would be indicated by the particular differences evaluated in the interaction. If interaction is negligible then the original variable should be changed alone. The equations for finding effects and limits are, using the variable designations given in Figure 11–11:

Main Effects:

$$X \text{ Effect: } 1/2(\bar{Y}_B + \bar{Y}_D - \bar{Y}_A - \bar{Y}_C) \tag{11-11}$$

$$Y \text{ Effect: } 1/2(\bar{Y}_C + \bar{Y}_D - \bar{Y}_A - \bar{Y}_B) \tag{11-12}$$

$$\text{Interaction } (XY) \text{ Effect: } 1/2(\bar{Y}_C + \bar{Y}_B - \bar{Y}_D - \bar{Y}_A) \tag{11-13}$$

$$\text{CIM: } 1/5(\bar{Y}_\phi + \bar{Y}_A + \bar{Y}_B + \bar{Y}_C + \bar{Y}_D) - \bar{Y}_\phi \tag{11-14}$$

Limits:

$$\text{Effects and Interaction: } \pm \frac{2}{\sqrt{n}}(s) \tag{11-15}$$

$$\text{CIM: } \pm \frac{1.79}{\sqrt{n}}(s) \tag{11-16}$$

The EVOP procedure is now quite straightforward. Effects and

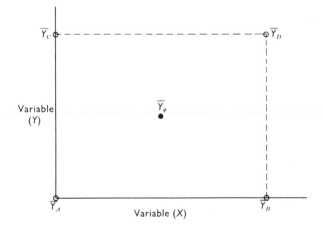

Figure 11–11. Response designations for the five operating points in a two-variable EVOP design.

limits are determined for each sequential cycle. If an effect is determined significant in a particular cycle then the operating conditions *might* be changed, depending on operator judgment. For example, suppose the X effect is found significant in the two-variable case with $\overline{Y}_B$ and $\overline{Y}_D$ being higher the $\overline{Y}_A$ and $\overline{Y}_C$, with response being *maximized*. The operating point X_ϕ would probably be changed to the value of X found at points B and D. New boundary points would then be set around the new X_ϕ and old Y_ϕ. This process will be illustrated in the next section with two examples, one for the single-variable case and the other for two variables.

11–9. EVOP APPLIED TO FORECASTING—EXAMPLES

These problems will deal with the application of EVOP to *time-series forecasting*. Specifically, to keep the problem within text bounds, two forecasting cases, in the fashion of Chapter 2, will be considered:

$$1. \ \hat{Y}_{(T+\tau)} = A_T \tag{11–17}$$

$$2. \ \hat{Y}_{(T+\tau)} = A_T + (B_T)(\tau) \tag{11–18}$$

where $\hat{Y}_{(T+\tau)}$ is the forecast for time period $(T + \tau)$ made at time period (T)

$A_{(T)}$ is zero-order term of a fitted polynomial

$B_{(T)}$ is first-order term of a fitted polynomial

Obviously, Equation 11–17 represents a *constant* forecasting model, where A_T represents an *average* of past demands. Equation 11–18 is a *linear* forecasting model which has a slope, $B_{(T)}$, and intercept, $A_{(T)}$, *occurring* at T. In Chapter 4 we discussed procedures for continually *updating* the various models as the data changes. EVOP will be used to first define a procedure for updating the model in Equation 11–17. This will be an example of a *one-variable design*. Lastly, a *two-variable design* approach will be utilized to update Equation 11–18, so that effects of both $A_{(T)}$ and $B_{(T)}$ can be observed.

It is not intended that this be an efficient method for updating the two models in an adaptive fashion, though as model complexity grows the EVOP approach becomes more reasonable. For example, third-order polynomial prediction with exponential smoothing requires a relatively complex equation but the forecast is dependent only on *one* smoothing constant, α. Judiciously finding an "optimum" value for α is another problem. Since there is only one variable this would still be a single-variable EVOP problem, as we will utilize for Equation 11–17.

The simplified EVOP approach follows the suggestion by Roberts[5] in his Self-Adaptive Forecasting Technique (SAFT). The response to be measured by the one-and-two-variable designs is that of average *forecast error squared*, the same criterion we used with control charts:

$$\bar{Y}_i = \sum_{t=1}^{n} \frac{(\hat{Y}_{(t+\tau)} - Y_{(t+\tau)})^2}{n} \qquad (8\text{--}19)$$

where $Y_{(t+\tau)}$ is the actual demand at period $(t + \tau)$ for the ith operating point

$\hat{Y}_{(t+\tau)}$ is the prediction for period $(t + \tau)$ at the ith operating point

n is the number of cycles in the current EVOP phase

Actually, since τ can be a variable we might possibly analyze the two models with two- and three-variable designs, adjusting τ as well as A and B. For simplicity we will assume a lead time of one time unit, so τ will be fixed at 1 in the problem.

The model in Equation 11–17 will now be updated according to the time-series demand data given in Table 11–11. This is relatively constant for five periods and then has a step increase. We will pretend we are at time period 4 with four pieces of historical demand data available. A logical value for $A_{(4)}$ to start with is the average of the first four pieces of data, or 11. In order to utilize EVOP, an $A_{(i)}$ value on each side of 11 would now be chosen. These would normally have small incremental differences from 11, say a difference of ± 0.1. For ease of example, we will utilize side values of 10 and 12, with a resultant one-variable design given in Figure 11–12.

Predicted values for any period of time with the constant model are the *actual values* of A_i. An initial EVOP cycle using these values is given in Table 11–12. Subsequent tables through 11–17 give remaining cycles. First of all a response term has to be calculated. Tabular formats conform to those suggested by Box and Draper.[2] The response

Table 11-11

Time-Series Data Set for Use with One-Variable EVOP Design in Adaptive Forecasting

Time Period (t)	1	2	3	4	5	6	7	8	9	10
Demand [$Y(t)$]	11	10	12	11	10	15	16	14	16	15

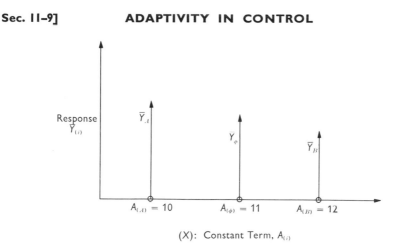

(X): Constant Term, $A_{(i)}$

Figure 11–12. One-variable EVOP design for example problem.

will be forecast error, which will be desirable for minimization. The error term is

$$\text{Forecast Error}_{(t)} = [A_i - Y_{(t)}]^2$$

which is the square of the forecast minus true demand difference. An *average* of these response values is maintained and the difference between the average and current response values constitutes the differences on which the (s) values, or standard deviation estimates, are calculated. Since this is the first cycle, no average (s) can be found. The effect calculations should be self-explanatory.

The second cycle, Table 11–13, allows the first (s) to be determined. The range of response differences (line 4) is $-5 - (-25)$ or 20. Since this is the second cycle, $n = 2$, $f_{3,2}$ is 0.42, from Table 11–10. (s) is then found by $(0.42)(20) = 8.40$. Effects and CIM are within limits so no change should be made. A positive CIM indicates a minimum response is realizable, but not yet found. A similar situation occurs for cycle 3.

Cycle 4, Table 11–15, gives our first phase completion. The A effect is out of the limits ± 7.45. A decision might be made to wait a cycle to see if the condition persists but we will assume a change should now be made. Since $\overline{Y}_B$ response is lower than $\overline{Y}_A$ and we wish to *minimize* response in this case, A_ϕ is set at the value resulting in $\overline{Y}_B$, or A_B. A new A_A and A_B are then set at values around A_ϕ. Thus the three values of 11, 12, and 13 for A_A, A_ϕ, and A_B.

We could start Phase 2, Cycle 1 (Table 11–16) in the same manner as Phase 1, Cycle 1, using no (s) value. We do, however, have a prior

Table 11-12

Single-Variable EVOP Worksheet; Phase 1, Cycle 1

1-Variable Design

Cycle $n = 1$; ($t = 5$)

Response: Forecast Error Squared

Project: 9-04-A

Phase: 1

Date: January 1, 19--

$A_A = 10$ $A_\phi = 11$ $A_B = 12$

Calculation of Averages

Operating Conditions	ϕ	A	B
Current Forecast (A_i)	11	10	12
Current Observation $[Y(t)]$	10	10	10
Current Error $= [A_i - Y(t)]^2$ #	1	0	4
(1) Previous Cycle Error Sum	–	–	–
(2) Previous Cycle Error Average	–	–	–
(3) Current Error #	1	0	4
(4) Differences (2) – (3)	–	–	–
(5) New Error Sum (1) + (3)	1	0	4
(6) New Error Average $\bar{Y}_i = (5/n)$	1	0	4

Calculation of Standard Deviation

Previous Sum(s) = –

Previous Average(s) = –

New(s) = Range $\times f_{3,n}{}^* = $ –

Range = –

New Sum(s) = –

New Average(s) = $\dfrac{\text{New Sum(s)}}{n-1}$ = –

Calculation of Effects

Phase Mean $= \frac{1}{3}(\bar{Y}_\phi + \bar{Y}_A + \bar{Y}_B) = 1.67$

A Effect $= (\bar{Y}_B - \bar{Y}_A) = 4.00$

(CIM) Change in Mean Effects = Phase Mean $- \bar{Y}_\phi = 0.67$

Calculation of 2 S.E. Limits

For Effects: $\pm 2 \sqrt{\dfrac{2}{n}} (s) = $ –

For CIM: $\pm 2 \sqrt{\dfrac{2}{3n}} (s) = $ –

$^*f_{3,n} = $ –; $n = $ –

Table 11-13

Single-Variable EVOP Worksheet, Phase 1, Cycle 2

1-Variable Design

$A_A = 10$ $A_\phi = 11$ $A_B = 12$

Project: 9-04-A
Phase: 1
Date: January 2, 19--

Cycle $n = 2$; $(t = 6)$
Response: Forecast Error Squared

Calculation of Averages

Operating Conditions	ϕ	A	B
Current Forecast (A_i)	11	10	12
Current Observation $[Y(t)]$	15	15	15
Current Error $= [A_i - Y(t)]^2$ #	16	25	9
(1) Previous Cycle Error Sum	1	0	4
(2) Previous Cycle Error Average	1	C	4
(3) Current Error #	16	25	9
(4) Differences (2) − (3)	-15	-25	-5
(5) New Error Sum (1) + (3)	17	25	13
(6) New Error Average $Y_i = (5/n)$	8.50	12.50	6.50

Calculation of Standard Deviation

Previous Sum(s) = -

Previous Average(s) = -

New(s) = Range $\times f_{3,n}$* = 8.40

Range = 20

New Sum(s) = 8.40

New Average(s) = $\dfrac{\text{New Sum(s)}}{n-1}$ = 8.40

Calculation of Effects

Phase Mean = $\frac{1}{3}(\bar{Y}_\phi + \bar{Y}_A + \bar{Y}_B)$ = 9.17

A Effect = $(\bar{Y}_B - \bar{Y}_A)$ = -6.00

(CIM) Change in Mean Effects = Phase Mean − $\bar{Y}_\phi$ = 0.67

Calculation of 2 S.E. Limits

For Effects: $\pm 2\sqrt{\frac{2}{n}}$ (s) = ± 16.80

For CIM: $\pm 2\sqrt{\frac{2}{3n}}$ (s) = ± 9.66

*$f_{3,n}$ = 0.42; $n = 2$

Table 11-14

Single-Variable EVOP Worksheet; Phase 1, Cycle 3

1-Variable Design

$A_A = 10 \quad A_\phi = 11 \quad A_B = 12$

Cycle n = 3; (t = 7)
Response: Forecast Error Squared

Project: 9-04-A
Phase: 1
Date: January 3, 19--

Calculation of Averages

Operating Conditions	ϕ	A	B
Current Forecast (A_i)	11	10	12
Current Observation $[Y(t)]$	16	16	16
Current Error $= [A_i - Y(t)]^2$ #	25	36	16
(1) Previous Cycle Error Sum	17	25	13
(2) Previous Cycle Error Average	8.50	12.50	6.50
(3) Current Error #	25.00	36.00	16.00
(4) Differences (2) – (3)	-16.50	-23.50	-9.50
(5) New Error Sum (1) + (3)	42.00	61.00	29.00
(6) New Error Average $Y_i = (5/n)$	14.00	20.33	9.67

Calculation of Standard Deviation

Previous Sum(s) = 8.40

Previous Average(s) = 8.40

New(s) = Range $\times f_{3,n}*$ = 6.72

Range = 14.00

New Sum(s) = 15.12

New Average(s) = $\dfrac{\text{New Sum(s)}}{n-1}$ = 7.56

Calculation of 2 S.E. Limits

For Effects: $\pm 2\sqrt{\dfrac{2}{n}}\,(s) = \pm 12.22$

For CIM: $\pm 2\sqrt{\dfrac{2}{3n}}\,(s) = \pm 7.11$

$*f_{3,n} = 0.48; \; n = 3$

Calculation of Effects

Phase Mean $= \dfrac{1}{3}(\bar{Y}_\phi + \bar{Y}_A + \bar{Y}_B) = 14.67$

A Effect $= (\bar{Y}_B - \bar{Y}_A) = -10.66$

(CIM) Change in Mean Effects = Phase Mean $- \bar{Y}_\phi = 0.67$

Table 11-15

Single-Variable EVOP Worksheet; Phase 1, Cycle 4

1-Variable Design

$A_A = 10$ $A_\phi = 11$ $A_B = 12$

Cycle $n = 4$; $(t = 8)$

Response: Forecast Error Squared

Project: 9-04-A
Phase: 1
Date: January 4, 19—

Calculation of Averages

Operating Conditions	ϕ	A	B
Current Forecast (A_j)	11	10	12
Current Observation $[Y(t)]$	14	14	14
Current Error $= [A_j - Y(t)]^2$ #	9	16	4
(1) Previous Cycle Error Sum	42.00	61.00	29.00
(2) Previous Cycle Error Average	14.00	20.33	9.67
(3) Current Error #	9.00	16.00	4.00
(4) Differences (2) − (3)	+5.00	+4.33	+5.67
(5) New Error Sum (1) + (3)	51.00	77.00	33.00
(6) New Error Average $Y_j = (5/n)$	12.75	19.25	8.25

Calculation of Standard Deviation

Previous Sum(s) = 15.12

Previous Average(s) = 7.56

New(s) = Range $\times f_{3,n}{}^* = 0.68$

Range = 1.33

New Sum(s) = 15.80

New Average(s) = $\dfrac{\text{New Sum(s)}}{n - 1}$ = 5.27

Calculation of Effects

Phase Mean $= \frac{1}{3}(\bar{Y}_\phi + \bar{Y}_A + \bar{Y}_B) = 13.42$

A Effect $= (\bar{Y}_B - \bar{Y}_A) = -11.00^{**}$

(CIM) Change in Mean Effects $=$ Phase Mean $- \bar{Y}_\phi = 0.67$

**A effect out-of-limits: ±7.45; Phase complete.

Phase 2; $n = 1$: $A_\phi = 12$, $A_A = 11$, $A_B = 13$.

Calculation of 2 S.E. Limits

For Effects: $\pm 2\sqrt{\dfrac{2}{n}}(s) = \pm 7.45$

For CIM: $\pm 2\sqrt{\dfrac{2}{3n}}(s) = \pm 4.32$

$^*f_{3,n} = 0.51$; $n = 4$

Table 11-16

Single-Variable EVOP Worksheet; Phase 2, Cycle 1

1-Variable Design

$A_A = 11 \quad A_\phi = 12 \quad A_B = 13$

Cycle $n = 1$; $(t = 9)$
Response: Forecast Error Squared

Project: 9-04-A
Phase: 2
Date: January 5, 19--

Calculation of Averages

Operating Conditions	ϕ	A	B
Current Forecast (A_i)	12	11	13
Current Observation $[Y(t)]$	16	16	16
Current Error $= [A_i - Y(t)]^2$ #	16	25	9
(1) Previous Cycle Error Sum	-	-	-
(2) Previous Cycle Error Average	-	-	-
(3) Current Error #	16	25	9
(4) Differences (2) - (3)	-	-	-
(5) New Error Sum (1) + (3)	16	25	9
(6) New Error Average $Y_i = (5/n)$	16	25	9

Calculation of Standard Deviation

***Prior estimate of σ from
Phase 1, $n = 4$: 5.27

Previous Sum(s) = -

Previous Average(s) = -

New(s) = Range $\times f_{3,n}^{\;*}$ = -

Range = -

New Sum(s) = -

New Average(s) = $\dfrac{\text{New Sum(s)}}{n-1}$

Calculation of Effects

Phase Mean $= \frac{1}{3}(Y_\phi + \bar{Y}_A + \bar{Y}_B) = 16.67$

A Effect $= (Y_B - Y_A) = -16.00$

(CIM) Change in Mean Effects = Phase Mean - Y_ϕ = 0.67

Calculation of 2 S.E. Limits

For Effects: $\pm 2\sqrt{\frac{2}{n}}(s)^{***} = \pm 14.90$

For CIM: $\pm 2\sqrt{\frac{2}{3n}}(s)^{***} = \pm 8.59$

$^*f_{3,n} = -$; $n = -$

Table 11-17

Single-Variable EVOP Worksheet; Phase 2, Cycle 2

1-Variable Design

$A_A = 11$ $A_\phi = 12$ $A_B = 13$

Cycle $n = 2$; $(t = 10)$
Response: Forecast Error Squared

Project: 9-04-A
Phase: 2
Date: January 6, 19—

Calculation of Averages

Operating Conditions	ϕ	A	B
Current Forecast (A_i)	12	11	13
Current Observation $[Y(t)]$	15	15	15
Current Error $= [A_i - Y(t)]^2$ #	9	16	4
(1) Previous Cycle Error Sum	16.00	25.00	9.00
(2) Previous Cycle Error Average	16.00	25.00	9.00
(3) Current Error #	9.00	16.00	4.00
(4) Differences (2) – (3)	+7.00	+9.00	+5.00
(5) New Error Sum (1) + (3)	25.00	41.00	13.00
(6) New Error Average $Y_i = (5,n)$	12.50	20.50	6.50

Calculation of Standard Deviation

Previous Sum(s) = –

Previous Average(s) = –

New(s) = Range $\times f_{3,n}{}^* = 1.68$

Range = 4

New Sum(s) = 1.68

New Average(s) $= \dfrac{\text{New Sum(s)}}{n-1} = 1.68$

Calculation of Effects

Phase Mean $= \frac{1}{3}(\overline{Y}_\phi + \overline{Y}_A + \overline{Y}_B) = 13.17$

A Effect $= (\overline{Y}_B - \overline{Y}_A) = -14.00**$

(CIM) Change in Mean Effect = Phase Mean – $\overline{Y}_\phi = 0.67$

**A effect out-of-limits ± 3.36; Phase 2 complete;
Phase 3, $n = 1$; $A_\phi = 13$; $A_A = 12$; $A_B = 14$

Calculation of 2 S.E. Limits

For Effects: $\pm 2\sqrt{\frac{2}{n}}(s) = \pm 3.36$

For CIM: $\pm 2\sqrt{\frac{2}{3n}}(s) = \pm 1.93$

$*f_{3,n} = 0.42$; $n = 2$

estimate of σ from the previous phase so we might as well use that figure. In Phase 2, Cycle 2, the A effect pops out of limits so a decision is made whether to change the A_i values this early in the game. In an *automatic system*, say computer controlled, the change probably would be made. If excessive changes were to be minimized, then 3 standard deviation limits might be preferred to 2.

A point of interest is the value of $\overline{Y}(t)$ when A_i changes were effected, at $t = 8$ and $t = 10$. $\overline{Y}(8)$ using Table 11–11 is 99/8, or 12.4. We shifted to an $A_{(8)}$ of 12. However, a rapid shift came at $t = 10$ where $A_{(10)}$ was made 13. $\overline{Y}(10)$ is 130/10 or exactly 13. Assuming the present average is held, then EVOP should maintain A_ϕ at 13, and A_A and A_B at 12 and 14, respectively.

11–10.　TWO-VARIABLE EXAMPLE

For updating the linear model, Equation 11–18, consider the data given in Table 11–18. A process shift is made at time period 6. The first cycle of the EVOP solution is made at $t = 6$, with forecasts being from time period 5 by

$$\hat{Y}_{(5+\tau)} = A_{(5)} + B_{(5)}(\tau)$$

The initial values used for $A_{(5)}$ and $B_{(5)}$ are 13 and 2, respectively. These then define A_ϕ and B_ϕ. Values of A_A and A_B were set at 12 and 14, and B_A and B_B at 1.5 and 2.5. The various combinations of operating conditions are given at the top-left of Cycle 1, Table 11–19 (see pages 422–423). The first cycle of course allows no (s) to be calculated so the A_i and B_i values are continued to Cycle 2.

At Cycle 2, Table 11–20, both A and B effects are found to be out of the ± 8.48-limits. Since the interaction (AB) is within these limits, both A and B are adjusted to conditions that minimize response. Actually, since both A and B effects are out of limits, interaction

Table 11–18

Time-Series Data Set for EVOP Two-Variable Problem

t	1	2	3	4	5	6	7	8
$Y(t)$	5	7	9	11	13	17	21	25

probably need not be checked. For A_i, the responses $\overline{Y}_B$ and $\overline{Y}_D$ are minimum, so A_ϕ is set to 14. Similar reasoning holds for the B_i at $\overline{Y}_C$ and $\overline{Y}_D$, so B_i is set at 2.5. Again, in Phase 2, Cycle 1, both A and B effects are out of limits, using the prior estimate of σ. This is shown in Table 11–21. Possibly no change should immediately be effected until at least another cycle has been checked. A counter-argument would be that the true process condition has a slope of 4 so changing B_ϕ to 3.0 immediately will approach this condition faster.

This same procedure would then be continued in the future as new data are gathered. It should be realized that here is an excellent *automatic self-adaptive* procedure, highly amenable to automatic computer controlled activities.

REFERENCES CITED

1. Box, G. E. P., "Evolutionary Operation: A Method for Increasing Industrial Productivity," *Applied Statistics*, Vol. 6, No. 2, June, 1957.
2. Box G. E. P., and N. R. Draper. *Evolutionary Operation.* John Wiley and Sons, Inc., New York, N.Y., 1969.
3. Eilon, S., and J. Elmaleh, "Adaptive Limits on Inventory Control," *Management Science*, Vol. 16, No. 8, April, 1970.
4. Hicks, C. G., *Fundamental Concepts in the Design of Experiments.* Holt, Rinehart and Winston, New York, N.Y., 1963.
5. Roberts, S. D., *The Development of a Self-Adaptive Forecasting Technique*, unpublished MSIE thesis, School of Industrial Engineering, Purdue University, Lafayette, Indiana, August, 1966.

FURTHER READING

Burr, I. W., *Engineering Statistics and Quality Control.* McGraw-Hill Book Co. Inc., New York, 1953.
Duncan, A. J., *Quality Control and Industrial Statistics.* Richard D. Irwin, Inc., Homewood, Illinois, 1959.
Hines, W. W., and Montgomery, D. C., *Probability and Statistics in Engineering and Management Science.* The Ronald Press Co., New York, 1972.
Roberts, S. D., and R. Reed, "The Development of a Self-Adaptive Forecasting Technique," *AIIE Transactions*, Vol. 1, No. 4, December, 1969.

PROBLEMS (See also pp. 428–429.)

1. Control charts are used to insure that a product falls within specifications. Is there any validity to designing the specifications for an $\overline{X}$-chart such that the specifications lie just outside the limits $\overline{X} \pm 3\sigma_X$? Why or why not?

Table 11-19

Two-Variable EVOP Worksheet; Phase 1, Cycle 1

$A_C = 12$
$B_C = 2.5$

$A_D = 14$
$B_D = 2.5$

$A\phi = 13$
$B\phi = 2$

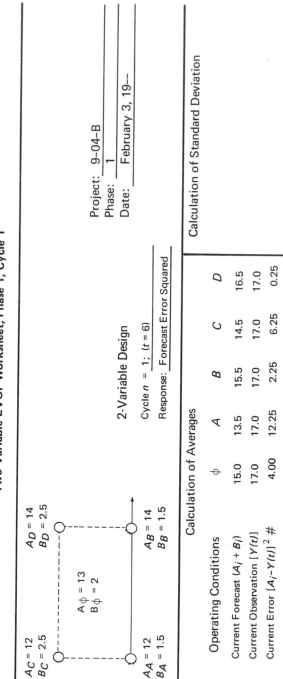

$A_A = 12$
$B_A = 1.5$

$A_B = 14$
$B_B = 1.5$

2-Variable Design

Cycle $n = 1$; $(t = 6)$

Response: Forecast Error Squared

Project: 9-04-B
Phase: 1
Date: February 3, 19—

Calculation of Averages

Operating Conditions	ϕ	A	B	C	D
Current Forecast ($A_i + B_i$)	15.0	13.5	15.5	14.5	16.5
Current Observation [$Y(t)$]	17.0	17.0	17.0	17.0	17.0
Current Error $[A_i - Y(t)]^2$ #	4.00	12.25	2.25	6.25	0.25

Calculation of Standard Deviation

(1) Previous Cycle Error Sum	–	–	–	–	–	–
(2) Previous Cycle Error Average	–	–	–	–	–	–
(3) Current Error #	–	4.00	12.25	2.25	6.25	0.25
(4) Differences (2) – (3)	–	–	–	–	–	–
(5) New Error Sum (1) + (3)	–	4.00	12.25	2.25	6.25	0.25
(6) New Error Average Y_i = (5/n)	–	4.00	12.25	2.25	6.25	0.25

Previous Sum(s) = –

Previous Average(s) = –

New (s) = Range × $f_{5,n}$* = –

Range = –

New Sum(s) = –

New Average(s) = $\dfrac{\text{New Sum(s)}}{n-1}$ = –

Calculation of 2 S.E. Limits

For Effects: $\pm \dfrac{2}{\sqrt{n}}$ (s) = –

For CIM: $\pm \dfrac{1.79}{\sqrt{n}}$ (s) = –

*$f_{5,n}$ = –; n = –

Calculation of Effects

Phase Mean = $\frac{1}{5}(\bar{Y}_\phi + \bar{Y}_A + \bar{Y}_B + \bar{Y}_C - \bar{Y}_D)$ = 5.00

A Effect = $\frac{1}{2}(\bar{Y}_B + \bar{Y}_D - \bar{Y}_A - \bar{Y}_C)$ = –8.00

B Effect = $\frac{1}{2}(\bar{Y}_C + \bar{Y}_D - \bar{Y}_A - \bar{Y}_B)$ = –4.00

(AB) Interaction = $\frac{1}{2}(\bar{Y}_B + \bar{Y}_C - \bar{Y}_A - \bar{Y}_D)$ = –2.00

(CIM) Change in Mean Effect = Phase Mean – $\bar{Y}_\phi$ = 1.00

Table 11-20

Two-Variable EVOP Worksheet; Phase 1, Cycle 2

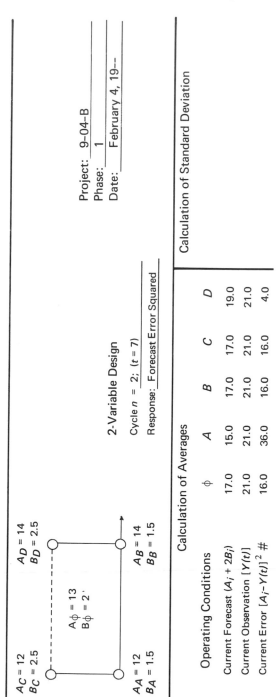

$A_C = 12$
$B_C = 2.5$

$A_D = 14$
$B_D = 2.5$

$A\phi = 13$
$B\phi = 2$'

$A_A = 12$
$B_A = 1.5$

$A_B = 14$
$B_B = 1.5$

Project: 9-04-B
Phase: 1
Date: February 4, 19--

2-Variable Design

Cycle n = 2; (t = 7)

Response: Forecast Error Squared

Calculation of Averages						Calculation of Standard Deviation
Operating Conditions	ϕ	A	B	C	D	
Current Forecast $(A_j + 2B_j)$	17.0	15.0	17.0	17.0	19.0	
Current Observation $[Y(t)]$	21.0	21.0	21.0	21.0	21.0	
Current Error $[A_j - Y(t)]^2$ #	16.0	36.0	16.0	16.0	4.0	

(1) Previous Cycle Error Sum	4.00	12.25	2.25	6.25	0.25
(2) Previous Cycle Error Average	4.00	12.25	2.25	6.25	0.25
(3) Current Error #	16.00	36.00	16.00	16.00	4.00
(4) Differences (2) – (3)	-12.00	-23.75	-13.75	-9.75	-3.75
(5) New Error Sum (1) + (3)	20.00	48.25	18.25	22.25	4.25
(6) New Error Average Y_i = (5/n)	10.00	24.13	9.13	11.13	2.13

Previous Sum(s) = –

Previous Average(s) = –

New(s) = Range $\times$ $f_{5,n}$* = 6.00

Range = 20

New Sum(s) = 6.00

New Average(s) = $\dfrac{\text{New Sum(s)}}{n-1}$ = 6.00

Calculation of Effects

Phase Mean = $\dfrac{1}{5}(\bar{Y}_\phi + \bar{Y}_A + \bar{Y}_B + \bar{Y}_C + \bar{Y}_D)$ = 11.30

A Effect = $\dfrac{1}{2}(\bar{Y}_B + \bar{Y}_D - \bar{Y}_A - \bar{Y}_C)$ = -12.00**

B Effect = $\dfrac{1}{2}(\bar{Y}_C + \bar{Y}_D - \bar{Y}_A - \bar{Y}_B)$ = -10.00**

(AB) Interaction = $\dfrac{1}{2}(\bar{Y}_B + \bar{Y}_C - \bar{Y}_A - \bar{Y}_D)$ = -3.00

(CIM) Change in Mean Effect = Phase Mean – Y_ϕ = 1.30

**A and B effects out-of-limits; ±8.48; end Phase 1.

Calculation of 2 S.E. Limits

For Effects: $\pm \dfrac{2}{\sqrt{n}}(s)$ = ±8.48

For CIM: $\pm \dfrac{1.79}{\sqrt{n}}(s)$ = ±7.62

*$f_{5,n}$ = 0.30; n = 2

Table 11-21

Two-Variable EVOP Worksheet; Phase 2, Cycle 1

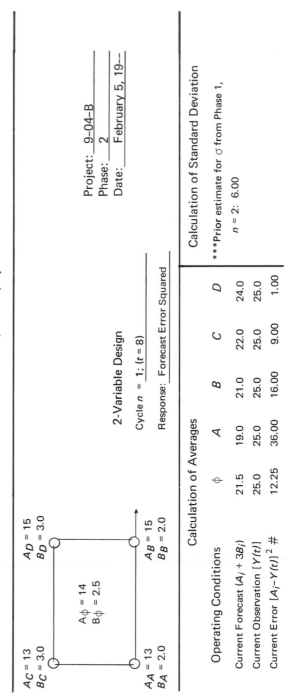

Project: __9-04-B__
Phase: __2__
Date: __February 5, 19—__

$A_C = 13$
$B_C = 3.0$

$A_D = 15$
$B_D = 3.0$

$A_\phi = 14$
$B_\phi = 2.5$

$A_B = 15$
$B_B = 2.0$

$A_A = 13$
$B_A = 2.0$

2-Variable Design

Cycle $n = 1$; $(t = 8)$

Response: Forecast Error Squared

Calculation of Averages	ϕ	A	B	C	D
Operating Conditions					
Current Forecast $(A_i + 3B_i)$	21.5	19.0	21.0	22.0	24.0
Current Observation $[Y(t)]$	25.0	25.0	25.0	25.0	25.0
Current Error $[A_i - Y(t)]^2$ #	12.25	36.00	16.00	9.00	1.00

Calculation of Standard Deviation

***Prior estimate for σ from Phase 1,
$n = 2$: 6.00

(1) Previous Cycle Error Sum	–	–	–	–	–
(2) Previous Cycle Error Average	–	–	–	–	–
(3) Current Error #	12.25	36.00	16.00	9.00	1.00
(4) Differences (2) – (3)	–	–	–	–	–
(5) New Error Sum (1) + (3)	12.25	36.00	16.00	9.00	1.00
(6) New Error Average Y_i = (5/n)	12.25	36.00	16.00	9.00	1.00

Previous Sum(s) = –

Previous Average(s) = –

New(s) = Range $\times f_{5,n}{}^*$ = –

Range = –

New Sum(s) = –

New Average(s) = $\dfrac{\text{New Sum(s)}}{n-1}$ = –

Calculation of Effects

Phase Mean = $\dfrac{1}{5}(\bar{Y}_\phi + \bar{Y}_A + \bar{Y}_B + \bar{Y}_C + \bar{Y}_D)$ = 14.85

A Effect = $\dfrac{1}{2}(\bar{Y}_B + \bar{Y}_D - \bar{Y}_A - \bar{Y}_C)$ = -14.00**

B Effect = $\dfrac{1}{2}(\bar{Y}_C + \bar{Y}_D - \bar{Y}_A - \bar{Y}_B)$ = -21.00**

(AB) Interaction = $\dfrac{1}{2}(\bar{Y}_B + \bar{Y}_C - \bar{Y}_A - \bar{Y}_D)$ = -6.00

(CIM) Change in Mean Effect = Phase Mean – $\bar{Y}_\phi$ = 2.60

**A and B effects out-of-limits, ±12.00; end Phase 2.

Calculation of 2 S.E. Limits

For Effects: $\pm \dfrac{2}{\sqrt{n}}(s)^{***}$ = ±12.00**

For CIM: $\pm \dfrac{1.79}{\sqrt{n}}(s)^{***}$ = ±10.74**

$^*f_{5,n}$ = –; n = –

2. Consider the following data:

	X_1	X_2	X_3	X_8
A	18.5	21.5	16.0	21.0
B	17.5	22.0	18.5	18.0
C	23.0	16.5	17.5	21.0
D	19.5	18.0	17.5	22.0
E	23.0	18.5	17.5	16.0
F	23.5	17.5	19.0	21.5
G	24.0	18.0	16.5	23.5
H	25.6	19.5	18.5	23.0
I	17.5	18.6	21.0	19.5
J	20.5	23.5	21.5	22.5
K	24.5	25.5	24.5	22.0
L	25.0	21.5	20.0	25.0

There are twelve samples, each with four pieces of data given.

a. The first seven samples are assumed to be in control. Calculate X-*chart* limits and plot the first 28 pieces of data. How does it look?

b. Plot the remaining 20 pieces of data and interpret your results.

3. For the data of Problem 2 use the first seven samples to generate $\bar{X}$-chart and σ-chart limits. Plot *all* applicable values and interpret.

4. Specifications for the product whose data are given in Problem 2 are 20.5 ± 3.0. Using the standard deviation, σ_X, from the first 28 pieces of data, determine the probability of the specifications being exceeded by chance causes alone. What do you recommend?

5. After analyzing a set of X-chart data the following plot is made:

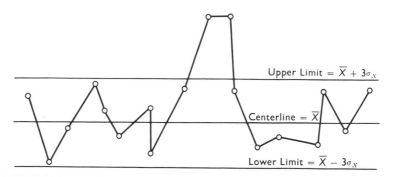

What suggestions would you make regarding the use of the chart limits if they were based on all the data given?

6. Consider the data given in Table 11–2. What is the probability of specifications being met if chance causes alone are at work and if the specifications are 5.0 to 10.0.

7. Consider the following time series data:

t	1	2	3	4	5	6	7	8	9	10	11	12
$Y(t)$	5	7	9	11	14	15	18	21	25	30	35	40

Second-order exponential smoothing (Chapter 4) is to be used to fit the equation $a_{(T)} + b_{(T)}(\tau) = \hat{Y}_{(T+\tau)}$. Use the first four pieces of data to get initial estimates of $a_{(4)}$ and $b_{(4)}$. Then use $Y_{(5)}$ through $Y_{(8)}$ to get prediction errors, assuming $\tau = 1$, on which to base error control limits. Then use these control limits to *adapt* the exponential smoothing constant, α, to the changing conditions in the remaining time periods. Start with an initial α value of 0.1.

8. Consider the one-variable EVOP case problem, with time series data given in Table 11–11. Assume the subsequent demand data are:

Time Period (t)	11	12	13	14
Demand $Y(t)$	18	17	20	19

Continue the EVOP sequence for this problem, which is originally given in Tables 11–12 through 11–17, starting with Phase 3, Cycle 1. Also starting with $A_\phi = 13$, $A_A = 12$, $A_B = 14$. The prior estimate for σ from Phase 2 is 1.68. Interpret the EVOP results.

9. Consider the two-variable EVOP case problem, with time series data given in Table 11–18. Assume that subsequent demand data are:

Time Period (t)	9	10	11
Demand $Y(t)$	29	33	37

Continue the EVOP sequence for this problem, which is originally given in Tables 11–19 through 11–21, starting with Phase 3, Cycle 1. Also start with $A_\phi = 14$, $A_A = 13$, $A_B = 15$, $B_\phi = 3.0$, $B_A = 2.5$, $B_B = 3.5$. The prior estimate for σ from Phases 2 and 1 is 6.00. Interpret the EVOP results.

12

Automated
Information Systems

I only ask for information.

CHARLES DICKENS, *David Copperfield*

12-1. NEED FOR INFORMATION

Most of the material presented so far has presupposed the existence of one important item required for analysis which frequently is not available. That item of course is data, and to be more specific, *good data*. In network planning we need good *estimates* of time and cost. Estimates are based on historical values and so past data on the time and cost of jobs or activities are a necessity. In time-series forecasting we assumed future trends for predictive purposes were represented by past historical trends of the same items for which prediction was being made. Lack of *good* historical data of course makes this problem well nigh impossible. The same arguments can be extended for the necessity of good data to allow studies to be made in the sequencing, scheduling, and inventory control areas. Of necessity in developing procedures to use in operating complex systems, simplifying assumptions frequently have to be made in order to allow analysis to be feasible. The errors encountered through problem simplification should not be compounded with poor data on which the analysis is made.

Further, information is required for management which forms the basis on which effective decisions can be made. This information may range from current operating conditions of the system to results of analysis such as realized through forecasting or economic studies.

This chapter has as its preliminary purpose the fostering of a realization in the reader that optimization may be accomplished upon some criterion but if the data on which that optimization is based are invalid from either a timely or inaccurate basis then the optimization should probably not have been attempted.

If we look back at the part titles for this text, those of *planning*, *analysis*, and *control*, we realize that good information is required in all three stages. *Rapid* determination of *timely* data can be a necessity in the *control* aspect where current operating conditions are monitored. An *automatic* information system may well prove advantageous in this case. This chapter will develop a few sound principles to provide the basis for the development of an information system. In addition, typical components of an *automated* information system will be presented to show the type of equipment that is available. Finally, one example of an automated information system will be mentioned to show a real world example of such applications with a comment on their possible advantages.

12-2. INFORMATION SYSTEMS: DEFINITIONS AND CATEGORIES

There are of course many categories of information systems. Of prime relevance to the *analysis* and *control* functions within this text would have to be *logistics* information: that is, information that will be used in the *operation* and *improvement* of the system, and that information which will indicate to management *how well* the system is operating. Even though *logistics information* is considered the key to successful attainment of the objectives discussed so far in this text, we should be cognizant of the fact that other information categories do exist. Typical might be *financial information* systems and *personnel information* systems. After presenting a few pertinent definitions we will categorize possible information systems that might interact within a total operating system such as a production facility.

A logical starting definition, one familiar to all readers, is that for *information*. The dictionary[6] defines it among others as *knowledge communicated by others or obtained by personal study or investigation*. This is not quite sufficiently bounded for our purposes. Granted, the logistics information which will form the groundwork on which our planning, analysis, and control is based frequently has to be obtained by personal study or investigation. Also, the word information implies *communication*, a flow of knowledge from one state to another, with *state* referring to both ends of the transmission, whether they be personal or machine oriented, or both. These ends may very well be any combination of the personal/computer relationship.

However, we should include somewhere in the definition, for our purposes, the word *pertinent*. Possibly the words *non-redundant* should be included. The problem with a large percentage of information systems is that the information is irrelevant, non-timely, and redundant in that the same information is repeated in many reports. A manager getting information in this fashion may not see the forest for the trees and consequently may reject *all* information. As an example consider the plight of a steel company that installed a control computer system with alarming of unusual conditions by the computer made to a typewriter. This alarm information system was based on instrumentation tolerances that were far too tight with the result that alarms were consistently being spewed out on the typewriter. The operator's only contact with the alarms thus printed was to walk over to the typewriter when the paper with alarms typed on it started covering the floor. His only action then was to rip the paper out of the typewriter, ball it up, and throw it into the garbage can unread. Obviously a little prior planning regarding when to put out alarm information would have made the difference between an alarm information system that was *beneficial* and one that had only derisory attributes.

In summation then, our formal definition of *information* as it relates to the material within the confines of this text will be:

> Pertinent, timely and non-redundant *knowledge* that is *required* for planning, analysis, and control of a particular system. This knowledge may be personally or automatically derived from system characteristics and similarly, may be transmitted either personally or automatically.

It should be mentioned that *data* are not necessarily information. Data are groups of facts from which information can be culled.

One acronym now widely accepted in the information vernacular is the MIS, or *M*anagement *I*nformation *S*ystem. Management of course connotes that the knowledge generated be geared toward management's use. Similarly, from our discussion in Chapter 1, the use of the word "system" has an implication that some synthesized grouping of components in the information system is required. This is exactly what is embodied in a management information system, and is possibly no better expressed than in a definition by Ziegler:[7]

A management information system integrates equipment, people and procedures in such a way as to deliver analysis-supporting and analytical information pertinent to management systems.

Now our earlier definition for *information* comes into play again. Since we now have an integrated package of equipment, people, and procedures, it follows that careful planning is needed to determine what is *pertinent* to what segments of the information system, and also how to eliminate redundancy in all segments of the system. These, along with *economic justification* of the information system, have to be the key points in *designing* the information system.

Frequently with rather large and complex systems the *timely* requirements for an information system might necessitate an automated system. An inventory information system for the Air Force involving millions of items could not possibly be manually reviewed, even on an exception basis, once a week or even once a month without fantastic labor costs, and undoubtedly without horrendous clerical errors. The Automation Information System (AIS) procedure in the literature is often classified as a Computer Information System (CIS). It is possible to automate modules of an information system without a computer and so the acronym AIS might be a little more applicable. We will look at some of the available *hardware* for an automated information system later in this chapter.

12–3. FUNCTION CATEGORIES

Now that we have defined rather broadly certain characteristics of information systems, let's categorize by function rather than class, knowing that our main concern is probably a logistics-type system. Dearden[3] gives a satisfactory classification of business information as:

1. Action and nonaction information.
2. Recurring and nonrecurring.
3. Documentary and nondocumentary.
4. Internal and external.
5. Historical and future.

The breakdown is probably self-evident. *Action* information refers to information for which some action needs to be taken. *Documentary* is information in some tangible written or coded form as contrasted to the *spoken* type. *External* information refers to information external to the system at hand such as the competition situation in a marketing environment. As mentioned by Dearden, the *external* and *future* information is pertinent to top-level management decision making.

The major categories of information systems are also given by Dearden[3] as:

1. Financial information.
2. Personnel information.
3. Logistics information.

Looking at these categories in light of the dichotomy of information given earlier, it is apparent that *financial information* deals with monetary aspects, primarily recurring, documentary, internal, and historical, and possibly action in nature. These very aspects of the dichotomy are those which lend themselves to automation. In fact, financial information systems are typically information systems with a large degree of data processing application.

The dichotomy of information with regard to *personnel* is the same as that for financial information and therefore in large industrial systems personnel records are largely automated.

Finally, the system most pertinent to this text, that of *logistics information*, covers areas already discussed in the text, such as forecasting from historical data, network planning data, all aspects of scheduling, inventory control, and system control. The dichotomy of information that is applicable to this category would include action, recurring, documentary, internal, and historical. However, nonrecurring items have pertinence and external factors may play a part in the logistics area, such as which external factors affect forecasting in a correlation analysis, and so on. The logistics information certainly may have a bearing on *future* conditions.

The logistics information system dichotomy lends itself to automation, especially when one thinks of the *action* considerations. However, because *process* conditions frequently have to be measured, this may become very costly. Instrumentation, for example, is a notoriously expensive component in the process control function. As we will see, though, in Section 12–7, certain off-line input consoles can allow information to be input in a manual mode by an on-the-spot operator, which later will be transmitted and analyzed automatically.

Before looking at some criteria to use in *designing* an information system, we should consider what benefits might ensue, as they should be the key to justifying the design of such a system. The best way to see potential benefits would be in the benefits actually realized in real-life systems. Therefore, at the end of Section 12–7 is presented a couple of actual applications with typical functions included. A general listing of potential benefits would include, among others:

1. If the data and information are available, then logistics techniques can be designed, implemented, and controlled. Frequently, the right data and information are not available. *Designing* an information system should insure this.

2. *Timely* information is available when needed to allow action to be taken at a most advantageous time. Immediate information on material discounts due to a manufacturer going out of business, for example, is only valid while that material is still available.

3. Management can make effective decisions due to the supporting data being the data he *needs* and also being furnished in a fashion he can understand.

4. Cost of information reporting can be reduced due to elimination of non-relevant material.

12–4. DESIGNING INFORMATION SYSTEMS

There is no doubt that this topic could have been easily and logically covered in Chapter 1 when the *systems approach* to problem solving was considered. The components of the information system should be determined and each analyzed as far as its needs for data are concerned. The interactions and redundancies should be found by synthesizing the components into a defined information system, somewhat in the fashion of developing a project network. Instead of developing a network though, the information flow should be pictured to determine the decisions required, and information needed to aid those decisions. Justification for manual, automatic, or combination systems would then be evaluated. Finally, if feasible, the information system would be implemented and continuous evaluation made (experimentation) in order to improve the information system.

Much has been written in the literature concerning the design of information systems, and in particular of management information systems. Most of this centers around the need for determining decision and information requirements, with appropriate flow charts being constructed in order to aid these steps. Also, we find stressed the need for getting those persons who will be utilizing the information system directly involved with the design of the system. One of the better seminal articles in this vein was written by Ackoff.[2] A unique feature of his article is that he pricked several pompous balloons and deflated some common misconceptions concerning management information systems.

The first of these misconceptions is that managers operate under a lack of *relevant information*. While this may be so, Ackoff stipulates correctly that the biggest problem in this vein is *too much irrelevant information*. One prime function of a management information system then, should be a *filtering* and *condensation* function.

A second misconception is that a manager needs the information he wants. Towards the end of World War II, Hitler wanted only good news about the German response to the Allied invasion. In order to tell him that Allied planes could not fly as far as certain German property, Goering stipulated that the planes were hit at extreme heights and then glided to crash in the East. Apparently this was the type of information Hitler wanted even though a competent pilot would have glided in the opposite direction so as not to land in Germany.[5] The point is that a soundly developed information system should have *convinced* Hitler that the planes were shot over Germany. Hitler might have then made the correct inference from this *correct* information that all was potentially lost and hopefully would have negotiated a settlement, saving many lives. As it was, getting information he wanted allowed him to make decisions he wanted to make, not a sound operational policy.

The third misconception claimed by Ackoff is that given the information needed, the manager's decision-making will improve. Intuition and hunches can frequently be incorrect. Scientific evaluation of the information may be required. In designing the information system, therefore, cognizance should be taken of the manager's ability to utilize the information. Information that cannot be effectively utilized is worthless. It might be that scientific computer analysis of the information prior to passing it to the manager would be worthwhile.

A fourth misconception is that *better communication* means *better operation*. Possibly this may be a correct assertion rather than a misconception. However, as Ackoff states, organizational structure needs to be investigated before determining the amount of information free flow. Those of us who went through a period of time in a nation directly attacked by another during wartime know that free flow of information to the populace is bad due to the morale factor. Conversely, situations in which information is *misrepresented* by governments can lead to credibility problems and force reactions far worse than morale feelings.

The final Ackoff misconception is that the person utilizing the information system need not understand the system, only how to use it. This is like saying an airplane pilot need know only how to fly a plane, not cope with unusual situations. An obvious point then in information system design is to get those who will utilize the system *involved* in the design of the system.

Some interesting additional points regarding the design of information systems were made by Murphy.[4] First, information should be culled to allow the managers to operate only on the *exception* type decisions. Raw data and irrelevant information are not pertinent to the manager's function. With automated information systems, routine decisions such as cyclic inventory ordering can be handled automatically. Unusual conditions such as runout or non-delivery decisions could be handled by the manager. In other words, the wheat has to be culled from the chaff.

Murphy points out another interesting design concept, that of *planned redundancy*. As mentioned earlier, information redundancy is usually non-desirable. Feeding the data from many sources can easily lead to redundancy. However, if data from several sources can be correlated, then this form of planned redundancy can lead to higher reliability of data. In other words, comparison of data received from several sources *prior* to feeding to information systems can determine invalid data or confirm the validity of data if the same redundant data are compared. However, only one set of data is fed from the computer to the information system, and this is one whose *validity is assured*. Non-valid data would then be discarded. This *planned* redundancy is pictured in Figure 12–1.

In summarizing considerations that should be made when designing information systems the following are highly prominent:

1. Flow-chart the relationships in decisions within the overall systems. Determine validity of interrelationships and correct the situation if invalid. This step of course requires the types of decisions to be determined.

2. Determine data and information relationships, leading to a determination of *required* data and *required* information—not *wanted* data and *wanted* information.

3. Determine *exception decisions* as contrasted to *routine decisions*. Information pertaining to routine situations will probably lend itself

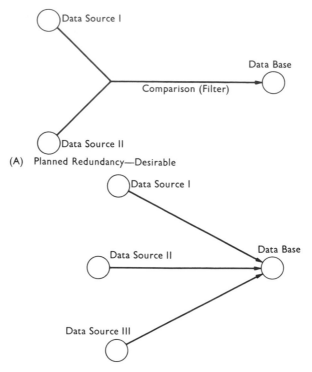

(A)   Planned Redundancy—Desirable

(B)   Potential Undesirable Redundancy

Figure 12–1. Schematic of redundant data possibilities.

to report summaries while information pertinent to exception decisions will require transmission to a decision source (manager) for action.

4. Group information and management combinations in a fashion that eliminates redundancy. This might require organizational changes and a study of existing conditions might verify the feasibility of such changes.

5. Determine feasibility of automation of the information system.

6. Determine control procedures for the information system.

In subsequent sections, we will now look briefly at items five and six, the criteria for automation of information systems and concepts of control procedures for information systems.

12–5. CRITERIA FOR AUTOMATION

Automation of information processing should never be accomplished without a sound economic justification of the automation and its related equipment. As far as the *logistics information systems* are concerned, Dearden[3] states:

The logistics systems of a manufacturing company will generally be the most adaptable to automation of all of management information systems. The reason for this is that the computer can help significantly in the solution of the critical logistics problems. The timing of information and the necessity of handling large quantities of data quickly and accurately are critical to the effective functioning of a logistics system. Prior to the development of the computer, these problems resulted in considerable inefficiencies in the typical logistics system. Further, no really effective solution was found to these problems before the development of the computer.

In general, one can utilize the same criteria regarding feasibility for automation of information systems as can be used in the justifying of control systems in discrete-item production, a topic to be covered in Chapter 13. Typical criteria would be:

1. *High volume of data.* This can be created by high volume production or high turnover of products and parts. In other words, Sears and Roebuck would have a better chance for justifying information automation than would the corner gasoline station.

2. *Rapid cyclic conditions.* If cost situations are highly affected by short time cycles, such as possibly the response to inventory runout with critical items, then automation of information aquisition might be beneficial.

3. *Large personnel group.* If the number of employees is large then the feasibility for automatic time-keeping and individual job-data tracking is apparent.

4. *Interactive information system.* When many variables interact then automation comes to the forefront in culling true information pictures from the interactive system.

5. *Repetitive information.* When information is repetitive in nature, as say in personnel reporting and in inventory reporting, automatic data processing can have great potential.

In summary, the most applicable and obvious application for automating information systems has to lie with high volume and high frequency situations. Thus, large systems will immediately be of more promise in this regard than very small systems.

12-6. INFORMATION CONTROL

As shown in the Chapter 1 introductory material, *control* is required to insure that implemented planning is accomplished as desired, and to

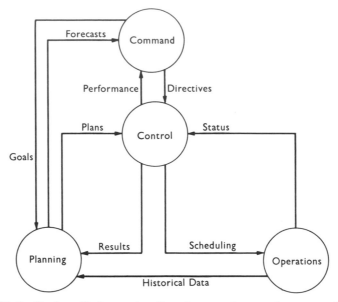

Figure 12–2. Cycles of information flow in a production logistics information system. (Courtesy of *Automation*.)

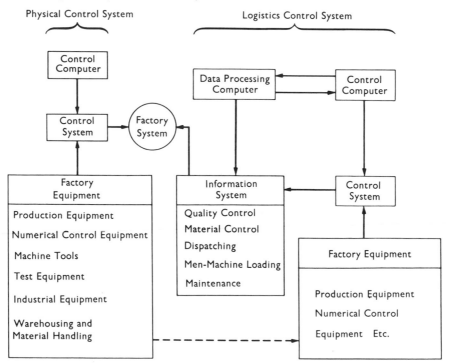

Figure 12–3. Typical relationships between physical and information control systems. (Courtesy of *Automation*.)

insure that unusual and unexpected occurrences are taken into account with the dynamic situation and of course corrected for when necessary. A flow diagram depicting this gross relationship is shown in Figure 12–2. This diagram shows the "cycles of information flow," with control being the key element. According to Abraham,[1] shortening the time between the occurrence of a specific event and the reaction to that event is the object of all management information systems. Actually, the *need* for shortening these cycles, and the *benefits* expected to accrue from this shortening is one of major tasks inherent in the *design* of information systems.

Finally, Figure 12–3 shows the *physical control* system as contrasted with an *automated information control* system for a production facility. More and more, the physical control situations, typical ones of which will be described in Chapter 13, are designed with automated information systems being interfaced with the physical control cases. Typical hardware equipment available for facilitating this automated information approach, will now be the topic for discussion in the next section.

12–7. AUTOMATION OF LOGISTICS INFORMATION SYSTEMS

There are many manufacturers now involved in the development of hardware for automating or partially automating management information systems. As mentioned previously, such systems should only be incorporated if they are justifiable on some economic scale. The following discussion will present a typical sequence of equipment, somewhat modular in characteristic, that is amenable to automation of the *logistics information* system, particularly in the production environment. The cost of such equipment of course has to be weighed against the benefits considered possible to accrue through the implementation of such equipment. In no way is the equipment described exhaustive as far as the spectrum of such equipment is concerned. The list though is quite representative of equipment available. We will start at the low end of the spectrum, as far as component complexity is concerned, and work up to a data processor that has the capability of integrating the components.

One of the first data-processing functions accomplished in production operations was that of *time-keeping*, basically the recording of employee work hours. The traditional way was, and is, for employees to clock in and out of the job using time cards and a time clock. Timekeeping clerks would then have the responsibility to record and accumulate data clocked on the time cards, primarily for pay purposes. With large employee operations the number of clerks required is considerable for such an operation. Also, the time spent by employees at clock stations waiting to find their time cards can be frustrating. In addition, it is a system prone to error as employees hurrying in or out of the plant can easily clock on the wrong card.

One possible answer is to have badge readers interfaced with some data processor. One badge reader currently being marketed is shown in Figure 12–4. Each employee has an identification badge, a normal item in most industrial operations, with an identification number that can be decoded by the automatic reader. A data processor integrating the readers can then accumulate statistics for pay purposes, by-passing the timekeeper function. Also, because the employee has his own badge at all times, the problem of the employee inserting the incorrect time card in the time clock is eliminated. Another plus is the fact that waiting time for employees is reduced as the time to pick the right time card has been eliminated.

Figure 12–4. Typical badge reader. (Courtesy of Data Pathing, Inc.)

An interesting aspect of the reader shown in Figure 12–4 is that the badge can be inserted upside down and the reader will automatically decode the inverted digits.

In the production environment, say in a job-shop situation, a worker might well perform work on several different jobs. The *time* he works on *each* job can be important for several reasons, two of which would include incentive payment and efficiency checks for management decisions. An automatic device to handle the type of information required is one step higher in order than the basic badge reader. In addition to employee identification through badge data decoding, variable information is also required indicating job and operation characteristics. Such a data collection terminal is shown in Figure 12–5. This piece of equipment has badge reading facility and will accept punched card information, which may be a job description card.

Figure 12–5. Typical data collection terminal. (Courtesy of Data Pathing, Inc.)

Variable information may be transmitted through the series of push buttons shown on the terminal's panel. Tied to a data processor, the information transmitted can be stored on magnetic tape and decoded as required for management reporting or employee remuneration purposes.

In-plant data pertinent to the internal operation of the plant requires input terminals that can accept a wide range of variable information that may pertain to quality control inspection, production conditions, inventory status, and so on. Such a terminal is shown in Figure 12–6. This device allows the worker to enter alpha-numeric data in a sequence that is indicated to the worker through a sequence of lighted panel instructions. The data are transmitted to a satellite control computer.* This same computer is programmed to direct the worker's input sequence by lighting the correct sequence steps on the input console. Since only a relatively few input buttons are required, sequencing several coded items allows a large amount of variable information to be transmitted from a relatively inexpensive piece of hardware. The

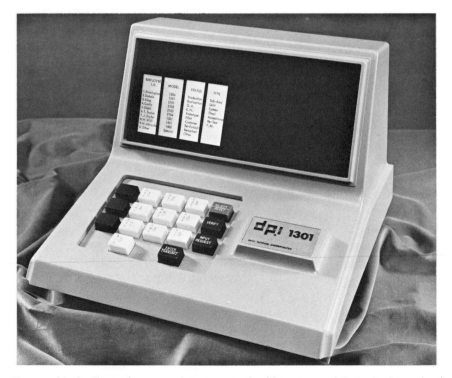

Figure 12–6. Typical source data terminal. (Courtesy of Data Pathing, Inc.)

* For control computer fundamentals see Chapter 13.

satellite computer for the source data terminals shown can handle up to forty-five such terminals. In addition to time-sharing these forty-five terminals, inputting data, and controlling sequence steps for each terminal, the control computer is able to edit the sequenced information for each input terminal and serve as a buffer to the data processor which will accept the edited data and output this data as management information, as programmed. So, for large operations, several satellite control computers may be buffered to the communications processor, which in addition to accepting coded computer information, will also accept data collection terminal information directly. A system diagram will be presented shortly.

Obviously one input device should be available to transmit input information from the various devices just discussed to those places in the operation that *need* the information. A communication processor, as shown in Figure 12–7, is the heart of the automated information

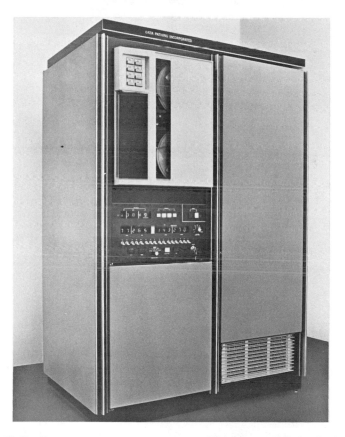

Figure 12–7. Communications processor. (Courtesy of Data Pathing, Inc.)

system. It accepts data from satellite control computers and specific terminal devices, puts them into the required report formats, and then outputs to such devices as typewriters, teletypewriters, magnetic tape storage systems, and so on. The processor shown has a capability for interfacing up to one hundred and fifty input terminals and several processors would be coupled for huge systems. With telephone carrier systems it is possible for terminal information to be carried several

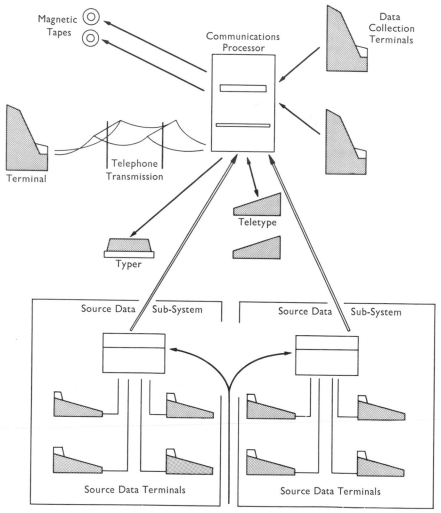

Figure 12–8. Possible hardware interface for information system. (Courtesy of Data Pathing, Inc.)

Figure 12–9. Application of automated information system at Grumman. (Courtesy of Grumman and Data Pathing, Inc.)

miles to a processor, so multiple-plant hookups are quite feasible in concept.

A schematic showing the interface of various devices is shown in Figure 12–8. As mentioned several times already, need and economic feasibility tests have to be made before such equipment is contracted for. The equipment discussed is only typical of equipment available. Hardware sophistication is such that almost any information system can be handled automatically. Only an economic evaluation, though, can pinpoint whether such systems are justified.

Finally, Figure 12–9 gives photographic representation of an installation utilizing equipment such as we have just discussed. In this *Grumman* system, 141 data input terminals communicate with 4 communications processors. Data accumulated are fed in *real time* to an IBM 360 computer system. Accomplished in the combined system operating with multi-plants are

1. Tracking of detailed parts and assemblies.
2. Collection of labor and payroll data for production areas.
3. Maintenance of timely stockroom records.
4. Tracking the fabrication of tools.
5. Maintenance of tool inventory records.

6. Establishment of standard time estimates for manufacturing.

7. Scheduling of production shops.

If the reader combines the information given in this chapter with the control digital computer overview now to be given in Chapter 13, he should have a pretty good insight into the potential for automation of both *information* and *physical* systems.

REFERENCES CITED

1. ABRAHAM, R. G., "How Data Systems Are Affecting *Decision Making*," *Automation*, Vol. 16, No. 10, October, 1969.
2. ACKOFF, RUSSELL L., "Management Misinformation Systems," *Management Science*, Vol. 14, No. 4, December, 1967.
3. DEARDEN, JOHN and McFARLAN, F. WARREN, *Management Information Systems: Text and Cases*, Richard D. Irwin, Inc., Homewood, Ill. 1966.
4. MURPHY, DENNIS J., "Designing Successful Information Systems," *Automation*, Vol. 16, No. 5, May, 1969.
5. SPEER, ALBERT, *Inside the Third Reich*, The Macmillan Company, New York, N.Y., 1970.
6. *Webster's New International Dictionary of the English Language*, G. and C. Merriam Company, Springfield, Mass. 1961.
7. ZIEGLER, J. R., "Computerized Information Systems," *Automation*, Vol. 17, No. 4, April, 1970.

FURTHER READING

BLUMENTHAL, SHERMAN C., *Management Information Systems*, Prentice-Hall, Inc., Englewood Cliffs, N.J. 1969.
KELLY, JOSEPH F., *Computerized Management Information Systems*, The Macmillan Company, New York, N.Y., 1970.

PROBLEMS

1. Discuss the types of information needed for the different categories of forecasting discussed in Chapter 3. Those categories were committee agreement, market survey, time-series analysis and correlation analysis.

2. Evaluate the feasibility for automating the information systems for each category of forecasting discussed in Problem 1.

3. Analyze the need for dynamic information systems for *production* scheduling techniques.

4. Would it seem logical that Sears and Roebuck would utilize the same approach to inventory information as would a small job-shop facility? Discuss fully both pros and cons.

5. The concept of an "information system" is rather complex. Discuss the possibility of using the "systems approach" from Chapter 1 in the design of a large-scale inventory information process.

13

Control Computer
Applications

He that gains time gains all things
SAMUEL PALMER

13-1. INTRODUCTION

We have seen that the systems planning, analysis, and control
functions can get complex for the *industrial process*. A great deal of
work has been accomplished with the use of on-line *control digital
computers*, operating in real time, to facilitate the *control* function. In
fact, the analysis function often accomplished by general purpose
computers is just as amenable to control computer application. Output
from computers can be used to facilitate the *planning* function, which
should still be under management control.

This last chapter covers the topic of *automated manufacturing*, not
by chance but by deliberate design. The complexity of the techniques
presented in forecasting, scheduling, and inventory control is often such
that they are not accepted by management. However, if these complex
functions are incorporated into a *working* computer control system
then they might be more *beneficial and acceptable*. Therefore, this
material will present a diverse grouping of control computer and
numerical control basic concepts, historical aspects, and applications,
not to make the reader an expert in the automation field, but rather to
familiarize him with some tools that should greatly facilitate the

industrial manufacturing process. In addition, if the process can be automated in part or in full by control computer, then in turn the computer can be used to tie together the planning, analysis, and control functions presented in this text. In fact, this was shown to be true on a small scale when we looked at *automated information* systems in Chapter 12.

Basically, a control digital computer has the same characteristics as a scientific or business computer, but has the added facility of being able to communicate with process instrumentation. Reading data from process instrumentation allows an evaluation of the current process status. The current status can be checked against a desired situation. The process computer can then, if programmed correctly, direct process changes in a manner designed to get the process back to the desired condition in as optimum a manner as possible. This is shown schematically in Figure 13–1.

This basic feedback operation is the heart of interactive systems planning, analysis, and control. Here is a device that can interrogate hundreds of plant conditions, monitor or control key operations, and prepare management reports concerning the process. However, the control digital computer is not restricted to just industrial plant

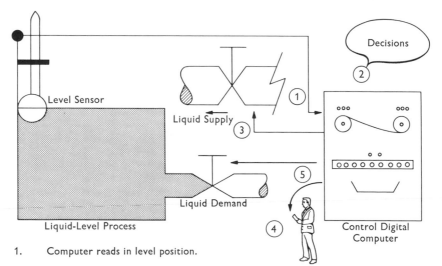

1. Computer reads in level position.
2. Computer checks against standard.
3. Computer adjusts supply, if necessary, to achieve standard level.
4 & 5. On basis of desired condition, computer sets demand valve.

Figure 13–1. Simplified schematic of control digital computer operation.

control. Airplane landing control, moon landing vehicle control, and hospital patient monitoring have all been accomplished by computer control. It is fitting, then, that this final chapter look at control digital computers, their fundamentals and past application, and then by examining current applications evaluate their potential for the future in the planning, analysis, and control areas. By 1970, some 3,000 control digital computer installations were in existence. This is remarkable, but even more so when it is realized that the first such installation was made in 1959. Over 50 percent of these installations were applied in industries with process connotations rather than discrete-item manufacturing. Little wonder then that the initial control digital computers were classified as *process computers*. Application of control digital computers have been made to such diverse areas, among others, as:[1]

1. Automotive traffic control
2. Product testing and quality control
3. Foundry control
4. Piece-part assembly
5. Warehouse control
6. Numerical control equipment interface
7. Space engineering research
8. Neurological and bio-medical research
9. Television program switching
10. Nuclear reactor control and monitoring
11. Weather forecasting
12. Freight-car process control
13. Deep sea data logging
14. Cement plant blending and kiln control
15. Utility plant start-up and control
16. Hot-strip roughing—mill control
17. Oxygen furnace control
18. Blast furnace applications
19. Nylon plant process control
20. Ethylene plant control
21. Cat-cracker operation

With such a wide spectrum of application it certainly makes sense to call the computer a *control digital* computer rather than *process* computer. The latter has connotations of both *process industries* and also could include the analog computer which has also been widely utilized in process control.

13–2. HISTORICAL NOTES

The early evolution of the control digital computer has been widely disseminated in basic digital computer texts since the control digital computer's early evolution is certainly the same as that of the usual digital computer. The traditional philosophical derivation of the digital computer from such early beginnings as cave men fooling around with notched sticks or our ancestors counting on their 10 fingers is just as applicable to the control digital computer. However, in the realistic evolution, the control digital computer has a little broader ancestry than its conventional counterpart due to the *control* aspects. A brief annotated history of industrial control leading to the control computer should be of interest.

1783: Continuous Automatic Production. Possibly the forerunner of the automated industrial facility would be Oliver Evans' flour mill. Evans' basic hypothesis was that materials handling is a link within the manufacturing process, as described by Giedion.[3]

For Oliver Evans, hoisting and transportation have another meaning. They are but links within the continuous production process; from raw material to finished goods .... At a stroke, and without forerunner in the field, Evans achieved what was to become the pivot of later mechanization.

Evans' method had no analogy in its time .... The mill could be loaded from either boats or wagons, a scale determined the weight, and a screw conveyor carried the grain inside to the point where it was raised to the top story by a bucket conveyor. It handled 300 bushels an hour ... without care of any attendant ... cleaning, grinding, and bolting ... without human intervention.

1801: Punched Card Operation. Joseph Jacquard demonstrated an automatic loom that operated through instructions from punched cards. This is always a shock to the computer specialist who has not investigated the historical aspects of his field. The card operation was mechanical in nature with pins falling through card holes actuating specific loom operations. Knitting machines also have been operated by the same principle.

1820: Difference Engine. The difference engine, built by Charles Babbage, while not really operating in the same manner as today's computers, did show that the possibility of computing machines was a reality.

1909: Production Line. The Henry Ford production line has had far-reaching connotations as regards feasibility for the automation of the production line for a particular product through the division of labor concepts. This original conveyorized line set the pace for mass production concepts.

1923: Automatic Transfer Machines. Automatic transfer machines were introduced at the Morris Engine factory in England. Transfer equipment was of course the key to a completely mechanized production line, such as is used for manufacture of engine blocks or transmission housings. According to Woollard,[15] this all happened twenty years before the Ford Motor Company set up such a system.

1946: Digital Computer. The first operational digital computer, the ENIAC, was completed at the U.S. Government proving grounds, Aberdeen, Maryland. The acronym ENIAC comes from *E*lectronic *N*umerical *I*ntegrator and *A*utomatic *C*omputer. In some ways, such as the logic philosophy, ENIAC was an extension of the desk calculator and was quite limited in capability. Obviously though, its arrival constituted a tremendous computer milestone.

1952: Numerical Control (N/C). The Massachusetts Institute of Technology in conjunction with the United States Air Force developed the first numerically controlled machine tool. A typical N/C installation is shown in Figure 13–2. Basically, the machine tool operations are directed by tape instructions, which is certainly a form of *digital computer*. One of the first applications of N/C was in the complex wing spar milling encountered in the aircraft industry. Section 13–3 will be

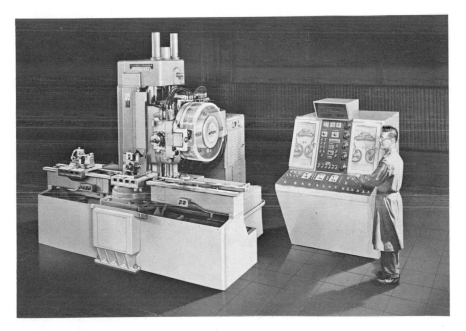

Figure 13–2. Milwaukee-matic, Model II Numerical Control Machining System. (Courtesy of the Kearny and Trecker Corporation.)

devoted, in part, to a little more detailed description of numerical control as it is such a significant milestone in the control digital computer evolution.

1959: Control Digital Computer.   The first widely publicized application of control digital computers occurred at a Texaco refinery located in Port Arthur, Texas. This new development was described by Shils[10] as follows:

Automatic remote controls in the plant long ago cut the crew requirements to three men per shift. A human operator simply can't look about at 50 recorder-controls that indicate pressure, temperature and flow; then relate the readings that indicate the level of activity of the reaction or condition of the catalyst; then calculate the complex interrelationships of the process, all in time to reset the controls to keep the plant operating at maximum efficiency . . . Texaco's RW-300 computer, on the other hand, has no difficulty doing that job every five minutes, twenty-four hours per day.

A picture of this historic Port Arthur installation is given in Figure 13–3.

1965: Production-Line Computer Control. International Business Machines developed a computer-controlled production line at their

Figure 13–3. First digital-computer-controlled process in Port Arthur, Texas. (Courtesy of the Bunker-Ramo Corporation.)

Endicott plant for manufacturing solid logic technology boards for the system 360 computer. The line was designed to use a control digital computer to supply numerical control data for N/C machines and testers, analyze feedback data and initiate appropriate action, monitor and analyze certain operations and processes, and control dispatching automatically.

1967: Integrated Manufacturing Control. Published material[14] indicates that Molins Machine Company of England developed an automatic manufacturing center combining the latest ideas in numerical control, computer scheduling, automatic handling, and machining methods tailored to the need of fully automatic control. One on-line computer is supposed to control the manufacturing process from scheduling and N/C program selection to automatic materials handling and inspection. The job shop activities are performed with hardware designed specifically for fully automatic control.

1967–? Commercial Computer-Controlled Equipment. Probably the first commercially available computer-controlled machine process was Strippit's Fabramatic hole punching and notching process, shown in Figure 13–4. The system was originally designed to allow one computer to control up to ten punching and notching machines. In 1968 Bendix demonstrated a three-axis N/C milling machine under the control of a time-shared computer 41 miles away.[5] At about the same time, the Sunstrand Corporation demonstrated a five-axis machine controlled by a digital computer. This machine performed milling, drilling, routing, and a tapping operation.[6]

The possible trend, at least from the Bendix example, is that the high first cost of digital computer control might be offset in machine-tool operations by remote time-sharing, with several companies using one control rented-time computer.

1970: Multiple-Machine Control. The last item in this historical sequence, which is not intended to be complete, but only representative, is a news release from the January, 1970, *Control Engineering*. The Japanese National Railways placed seven lathes under the *simultaneous* control of a control digital computer. Three of the lathes were reported to contain memories in which the programs were stored.

The few historical examples leading to digital computer control of complex systems have shown that an orderly sequence of events has led to today's use of control digital computers in large systems. Some of the later examples show that this application to large-scale systems is

Figure 13–4. Commercially available computer-controlled machine process. (Courtesy of Strippit Division, Houdaille Industries.)

truly *feasible*. The remainder of this chapter will be devoted to a little better insight into the application and makeup of control digital computers. A short example will be utilized to demonstrate the system planning and analysis required for *time-sharing* and *real-time* computer operation. A few case systems will be presented to show how control digital computers have been used in planning, analysis, and control activities. The immediately following section will contain a brief introduction to *numerical control* and its extension to *computer control*, as being the most simple means for introducing the concepts of discrete-item digital computer control.

13–3. NUMERICAL CONTROL/COMPUTER CONTROL

As mentioned in the control digital computer evolution material, the concepts of numerical control released in the mid 1950's certainly plays a significant role in manufacturing control. Certain digital computer control concepts can be rather easily presented as an extension of numerical control.

By its very name, *numerical control* implies *control* by some *numerical* procedure. Operator-controlled machine tools require the operator to set up the machine for the particular job to be run and then to actuate the various machine tool controls to get the job accomplished in as reasonable a time as possible. All this requires blueprint interpretation and setup calculations that can force a lengthy lead time. If a large amount of these calculations and operations can be performed *automatically* then cost savings in lead-time reduction and part rejection should be achieved. Basically, this is the *objective* of numerical control.

Instructions regarding required axial coordinates, coolant flow, tool required, and so on can be programmed *numerically* onto paper tape (or punched cards and magnetic tape for that matter). These instructions are decoded by the control unit and the machine tool is operated, or controlled, according to these instructions. Numerical control is highly adaptable to repetitive production runs and to high-cost setup operations.

In interpolating travel characteristics there are two basic types of positioning. *Point-to point* positioning refers to axial positioning that is designed to get the tool from one *point* to another required *point*, with no specific path of travel required between the points. This type of positioning is amenable to machine tool operations which require operations only at specific coordinate *points*, such as *drilling* or *punching* operations. *Continuous path* positioning, as the name implies, refers to axial travel where the path movement is specified. This may be parabolic, circular, etc., and can be approximated by a series of linear segments with coordinates of the segments themselves being specified in a *point-to-point* type of system. The differences between *point-to-point* and *continuous path* movement are shown in Figure 13–5. Possible linear interpolation for a continuous path requirement is shown in Figure 13–6. Obviously, the smaller the segment, then, the better is the approximation. With segments of the order of 1/1,000th of an inch this accuracy can be acceptable for many situations.

The advantages of numerical control have been well presented by Leone.[4] He divides them into the categories of *productivity, flexibility, quality,* and *administrative economy.* From a *productivity* point of view, savings can be justified by direct labor, setup, changeover between jobs, and reduced machining time. *Flexibility* savings can be obtained through smaller tooling costs. Also, planning and tape preparation costs can be accomplished in one location with the tapes then being available for similar machines in diverse locations. *Quality* savings can

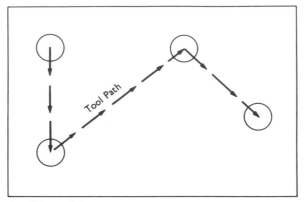

A.   Point-to-Point

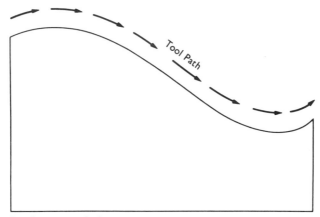

B.   Continuous Path

Figure 13–5. Point-to-point and continuous path numerical control.

be achieved through higher accuracy than is usually possible with operator control. *Repeatability* due to tape control also insures uniformity of manufacture for several parts, when needed.

Savings can be attributed for administrative economy due to reduced lead times, high ratios of good parts to total produced, minimized inspection of copies due to the fact that once a part is produced satisfactorily, all others can be almost guaranteed to meet the same specifications. These are but a few of the advantages of numerical control.

The physical elements for numerical control are shown in Figure

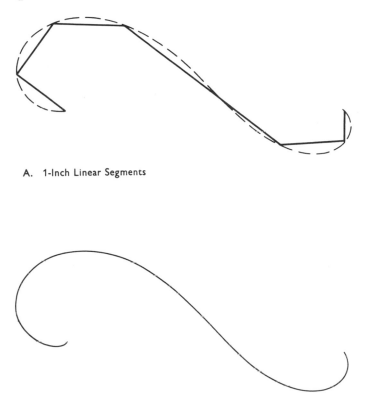

A.   1-Inch Linear Segments

B.   1/60th-Inch Linear Segments

Figure 13–6. Linear interpolation for continuous path movement.

13–7. A tape has to be prepared to direct the machine tool control. Several compiler languages are available, geared to specific machine tools. This preparation procedure therefore may be by general purpose digital computer with card input. The tape is read by a tape reader which triggers either motion actuation or actuator control. The motion actuation may be either point-to-point or may actually accomplish path interpolation. The actuation will continue until the table position coincides with that desired. Again, we see the feedback concept mentioned frequently throughout the text. The simple explanation just made covers only a single axis of motion. Complex numerical control equipment may have several axes which have to be coordinated.

Possibly the ultimate in numerical control of machine tools lies in the *machining center* concept. In fact, there has been quite a bit of con-

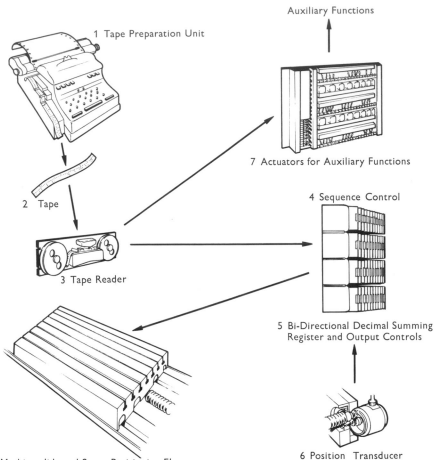

Auxiliary Functions

1 Tape Preparation Unit

7 Actuators for Auxiliary Functions

2 Tape

4 Sequence Control

3 Tape Reader

5 Bi-Directional Decimal Summing Register and Output Controls

6 Position Transducer

Machine slide and Servo Positioning Elements

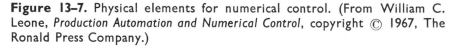

Figure 13–7. Physical elements for numerical control. (From William C. Leone, *Production Automation and Numerical Control*, copyright © 1967, The Ronald Press Company.)

troversy over whether the machine center concept or digital computer control of machine tools is the way to go. Definitions of machining center vary widely. One possibly acceptable definition would be that machining centers combine the use of two or more conventional machine tools in one piece of equipment through the use of automatic tool changers and part handling devices. Such a system is shown in Figure 13–8. The advantage of machining centers lies in their ability to handle multi-operations on a product; in essence having a production line in one piece of equipment.

Figure 13–8. Milwaukee-matic Turn-12 Machining Center. (Courtesy of The Kearny and Trecker Corporation.)

This approach may well be the key to complete plant automation, although others will certainly argue that this is not possible without control digital computer assistance. One disadvantage of conventional numerical control lies in having one control device for each machine. The machining center expands this concept to several machine operations for one controller. As an example, the manufacturer of the machine shown in Figure 13–8 claims automatic *tool changing* and automatic *workpiece* exchanging. The tool changing feature, permitting random tool selection and location, extends to 32,769 different tools. The workplace exchanging comprises off machine setup with *automated* workpiece changeover, eliminating machine downtime for workpiece setup. The linear resolution for the machine is one ten-thousandth of an inch and the rotary resolution is one-thousandth of a degree.

It is fairly apparent that numerical control can be construed as a type of *fixed program* computer control. Once the input tape is prepared, then machine actuations will be fixed by that tape. *Digital computer control* allows further flexibility through its programmed decision-making potential. Several machines, for example, could be controlled by one computer with parts being automatically directed between machines. If one machine is down, the computer could determine an alternate routing for the part manufacture and then manufacture in that sequence. Changes in part manufacture could be incorporated very easily. It is certainly not unreasonable to conceive of twenty or more machines being interconnected by one computer. An obvious fallacy with complete plant computer control is that if the computer goes down, so does the plant. The system would have to allow for the possibility of manual backup.

The statements just made are not necessarily blue-sky academic murmurings. In a 1965 article in *Automation* magazine[13] several numerical control experts, asked their opinion concerning control of numerical equipment responded with almost unanimous agreement regarding the potential of the "marriage." Typical responses were:

The idea of the entire manufacturing process being handled as a system rather than as a collection of separate quasi-independent entities is a certainty for the future.

(W. C. Leone, Rheen Electronics)

In its final concept, N/C will no longer exist as a definite step in the process since on-line computers will directly process data to individual machines on an optimized and as-required basis.

(M. H. Sluis, Pratt and Whitney)

The marriage of process computers and N/C is definitely in the future of most metal fabricating plants. When this marriage will take place is difficult to say, but if we can judge by the pace at which developments have been put into practical use, it should be within the next decade. It could happen much sooner.

(R. W. Gray, IBM Corporation)

13–4. CONTROL DIGITAL COMPUTER FUNDAMENTALS

Basically, there are but three distinct categories of digital computers: business, scientific, and control. The difference between these three categories of digital computer is apparent in the basic hardware of the computer, which in turn is necessitated by the function required from the computer. *Hardware* is defined as the physical system which makes up the computer—logic components, cabinets, central processor, etc., as differentiated from *software*, which describes the programmed functions. In conjunction with the hardware, software makes the computer an operable system.

The *business computer* has to manipulate tremendous amounts of data with relatively simple calculations. Check writing would be a typical application. The functional requirements of mass data manipulation with relatively simple calculations gives rise to a need for a computer with large amounts of backup storage in conjunction with allowing a fairly small computing memory. Disk files and tape decks are then prevalent in business computer systems with the capability of rapid transfer to the rather small core memory.

The *scientific computer* must be capable of performing highly complex calculations on problems presented to it. Production-line simulation, to facilitate optimization of the forecasting, scheduling, and inventory problem, is typical of the industrial scientific problem that would be attacked by a scientific digital computer. The fundamental requirements necessitate a large core memory to enable handling of extensive calculation requirements. A large backup storage also is required to accommodate the various sub-routines necessitated by particular problem solutions. Both scientific and business computers require very rapid input and output of data due to the characteristics of their basic applications. It should be readily apparent that a scientific and business computer can be interchangeable if the core memory is large enough, and indeed duplicity is accomplished on many machines. This interchangeability is not as feasible with a control digital computer.

The control digital computer has the same basic "central processor" as the scientific or business computer. This includes memory, logic elements, and register manipulators. The greatest functional, hardware, and software differences arise from the necessity for the control digital computer to communicate with physical processes, both in input and output mode, and also from the requirements that the control digital computer has to operate in synchronism with the time characteristics of the physical process being controlled. In other words, a control digital computer has to operate within a *real-time system*. A close-up of a typical control digital computer is shown in Figure 13–9.

Nothing externally differentiates the computer from a scientific or business installation except for the closed-circuit television and microphone communication with the line. The lack of tape decks is of course another clue. If one looks closely enough, another give-away is the fact that all but one of the cabinets to the rear of the console table are labeled *digital outputs*, indicating they contain the interface equipment between the industrial process and the control digital computer for output communication.

Figure 13–10 shows a close-up of one of many carburetor test stations, with the operator inserting a carburetor for test. According to data released in *Iron Age* magazine,[9] a General Motors facility has time-shared numerical control for 104 such test stations, which *test* and

Figure 13–9. A typical control digital computer installation. (Courtesy of General Electric and General Motors Corporations.)

adjust 20,000 carburetors a day. Every hour, the computer system prints out a listing of the number of rejects, and the reasons for the rejects. Immediate changes can then be made in manufacturing or assembling to correct problems. *Each* function of *each* test machine is monitored every quarter of a second through time-sharing techniques. The process communication system consists of 6,700 digital and 420 analog channels.

The *control* aspects of this system are interesting. Slo-Syn stepping motors can be seen in Figure 13–10. These are digital pulse-driven motors actuated through digital computer control. According to the *Iron Age* article:

Each motor controls a different machine operation. And the result is to both test and adjust the ratio of air-to-fuel flow under the full range of carburetor operation (idle, off idle, part throttle, and wide-open throttle).

For each condition, the computer compares the test value with a computer-stored digital value for mean voltage. Depending on the result, a metering screw in the carburetor is moved back or forward, until the test reading is within an allowable tolerance band. This is a form of adaptive feedback control.

Figure 13-10. Carburetor test station under digital computer control. (Courtesy of General Electric and General Motors Corporations.)

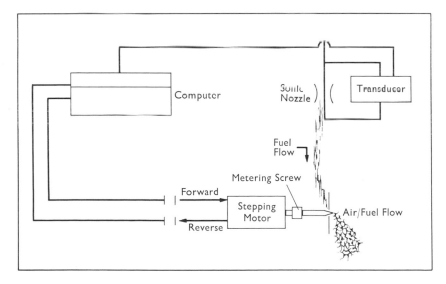

Figure 13-11. Closed-loop diagram for carburetor test line. (Reprinted from *Iron Age*, May 23, 1968, Copyrighted 1968, Chilton Co.)

The closed-loop control system is shown in Figure 13–11. It should be apparent that the overall process falls into the planning, analysis, and control feedback concepts developed in Chapter 1. Planning develops the desired condition which can be stored in the computers. Analysis comes about with the computer checking actual carburetor conditions with the planned situation. Feedback control allows adjustment of the carburetor settings until the analysis is satisfied.

13–5. REAL-TIME CONSIDERATIONS

Many hundreds of analog and digital signals may be interrogated by one control digital computer. An *analog* signal is one whose representation is *analogous* to the condition being signalled, and is usually in *voltage* form. For example, a valve position may be represented by a voltage which goes from 0 to 10 volts and which linearly represents open to closed position of the valve. A voltage level of 5 volts would then indicate that the valve is half open. A *digital* signal is one that is *discrete*, rather than *continuous* as is an analog value. Counters and relays are typical of digital instrumentation. The relay, for example, would have only two positions, open or closed, which could be input as a zero or one condition. In addition to reading in the analog and digital signals at the correct times, it may also be necessary in a control digital computer system for performance calculations to be accomplished, alarm conditions to be printed, control sensors to be adjusted, and efficiency management reports to be printed. Certain large-scale systems also incorporate business functions into the operating cycle for the control digital computer when free time is available. To this partial listing must be added a myriad of other conditions that must be considered when setting up a real-time control system.

All of the functions have to be accomplished in conjunction with the actual operation of the physical system. Therefore, a system of ordered priorities and interrupt control is required in order to allow such a complex operation to be effective. The customer bent on purchasing a control digital computer system must first determine those functions which may be applicable to computer analysis, monitoring, or control. Once a list of functions has been developed, it is necessary to determine relative priorities for the functions and minimum cycle times for each. The priority determination is necessary in case many functions have to be accomplished at the same time, thus making it mandatory that a decision be made regarding which function should be tackled first. The cycle time calculations are required in order that the ' worst-case" situation can be analyzed, to determine if all the functions can be accomplished under the "worst-case" conditions. If they cannot, certain functions will have to be deleted from the planned system. Lower-priority items are, of course, deleted first.

Entry to the system functions is made in accordance with the predetermined priorities and in accordance with the *timing* associated with each function. The timing can be rather critical in certain control situations. Monitoring of steel thickness in a rolling operation may require reading critical signals in terms of thousandths of a second in order to predict control required to prevent shear of the rolled steel. In a cement kiln operation this time requirement may be of the order of seconds, or even minutes for most control sensors. A simple flow chart for the executive routine for a cement plant control system which takes both timing and priority consideration into account is shown in Figure 13–12. The timing blocks are not really programmable as will be seen in just a minute but are given to show a complete, though trivial, system. Also, the operation blocks, such as printing alarms, themselves contain rather complex logic to allow time sharing as will be seen later in this section.

It is rather apparent that some form of system timing has to be available to the computer program to allow entry to the routines at the required time intervals. The timing device used in early control digital computers was a *digital clock.* In addition to the usual visual readout, the clock has a binary-type output, such as binary-coded-decimal, that can be interrogated by the control digital computer as it would any other digital instrument. The timing routine then consists in setting entry to the various executive control sub-routines on the basis of the clock values.

Probably the most sophisticated and most widely used timing device is the internal priority interrupt. Several levels of priority interrupt are available which automatically store intermediate computer values being currently manipulated by the program at the time of occurrence of the interrupt, transfer control to a pre-determined portion of the program, and then once action has been taken on the interrupt the intermediate values are restored and control is transferred back to the program under operation when the interrupt occurred.

The priority interrupts can be actuated by specific physical occurrences or can be triggered at specific time intervals. An example of a *physical* activation might be power failure. If the computer is powered

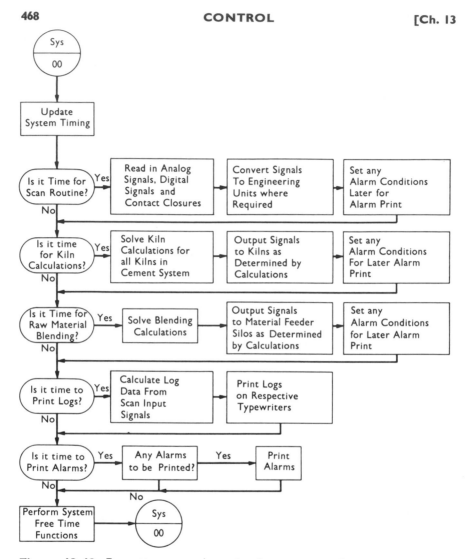

Figure 13–12. Executive control routine for a cement plant control system.

by a motor generator set with a large driving flywheel, it is possible for the main plant power to be cut to the generator set, but the flywheel will allow the generator set to supply power to the computer for a few seconds longer. If a priority interrupt is initiated by loss of line power then an orderly shutdown subroutine could be effected upon interrupt.

Similarly, interrupts can be triggered by key process changes. From a *timing* point of view, interrupts can be operated on a cycle basis, say a thousandth of a second. In this way, time counters can be maintained to allow the computer to keep track of real-time considerations, in the fashion of an internal clock. Peripheral devices, such as printers, typewriters, readers, etc., may also be connected to interrupts, thus allowing the peripherals to be buffered from the computer. Actuation of a printer interrupt, for example, could allow the next sequence of characters to be output to a printer. While actual printing is being accomplished the print interrupt would be inhibited, thus allowing the computer to accomplish other functions at the same time.

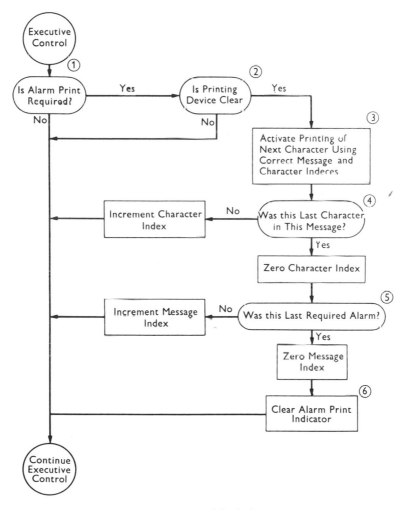

Figure 13-13. Simplified alarm routine.

The last aspect of this brief introduction to control digital computers real-time considerations is to consider the executive control system of Figure 13–12, and in particular, just the alarm print block, to show how time-sharing really works. We will assume only one classification of alarm is being programmed but several would usually be the case. Typical would be critical alarms, such as alarming conditions that impair production, non-critical alarms where previously noted critical alarms are indicated as being corrected, and so on. Also, color will not be a function. Frequently red printing may be used to indicate action required, while black indicates no action necessary. Critical alarms may require a klaxon horn to be sounded for operator warning. None of these items will be considered, though in the realistic case these and more would be prevalent.

Figure 13–13 gives a flow chart for such a simplified alarm routine. It will be assumed that entry is *not* made by priority interrupt, though this could easily be the case. Six areas of the flow chart are numbered 1 through 6. The computer procedure will be discussed by following these six areas sequentially:

1. Is alarm print required? An indicator flag will be set by the routine that finds the alarm. Such alarm-finding routines might be input scan, control calculations, etc. It may also be required that alarms can only be typed at certain times. If this is the case, another block would be required that tests an indicator set by the timing routine when this time factor is satisfied.

2. Is printing device clear? This check is the key to time-sharing. If priority interrupt were used, then interrupt would *only* occur when the device was free and this block could be bypassed. The first block of priority-interrupt alarm routine would be "Is alarm print required" but it would not be connected "program-wise" to other executive control checks as it would be entered by the *hardware* priority interrupt operations. As it stands in Figure 13–13, the printing device would be checked with a buffer program command that would take the *yes* branch only when the device was clear. *All* devices to be time-shared would have a similar buffer command to check their *free* status.

3. Printing is activated by outputting from the computer the next character. This may take the computer about 10 microseconds even though the actual printing may require a twentieth of a second with such a device as a typewriter. If the operation were not buffered then the computer would be tied up for the twentieth of a second rather than 10 millionths.

4. If the character printed were the last in the message, then the routine should be prepared to start the next message on the next entry.

5. In conjunction with step four, if no more alarms are required then entry should not be made to the routine until a new alarm is needed.
6. This last item clears any routine entrance indicator.

Exit from the alarm print routine would be to the next item in the executive control list or to a "wait" routine, waiting for the next function priority interrupt. The interesting aspect from this purely explanatory flow chart is that only *one* character is printed upon each entry. For a line printer this could be a line message. Therefore the time spent in the routine on each entry would be of the order of *microseconds*. This same approach would be used in inputting data—only one item on each entry. Thus, one pass through our simple flow chart of Figure 13–12 might be:

A. Update time counters on interrupt.
B. Input one analog, digital signal. If the scanner is tied up then this is bypassed.
C. Solve portion of kiln calculation if necessary—exit when scan or print required.
D. Solve portion of blending calculation if necessary—exit when scan or print required. (Obviously exit from *C* or *D* has to be at logical times—when one calculation iteration is solved, etc.)
E. Print one log character on log typewriter if necessary.
F. Print one alarm character on alarm typewriter if necessary.

Each pass through all the routines may take less than a thousandth of a second. All devices can be actuated at almost full speed and *simultaneously* by this method. The secret to effective *time-sharing* is effective *buffering*.

13–6. APPLICATIONS AND BENEFITS

The best way to demonstrate the potential for control digital computers in industrial applications is through a series of diversified examples, giving certain benefits for each. This will show the wide spectrum of applicability for these machines in industrial analysis and control systems. These systems will not be discussed in great detail, but rather their basic accomplishments will be presented with the thought in mind that they are representative of possibilities for a far wider grouping of *potential applications.*

Rapid Transit Control. Possibly the most benefit for the largest segment of the population from the use of control digital computers will come from their application to urban problems created by population growth. The emergence of rapid transit systems in the United States to ease the use of automobiles in population centers is a case in point.

The most advanced system is the Bay Area Rapid Transit (BART) system located in the San Francisco Bay Area. The result of an engineering consultant study for BART included the following findings for the San Francisco area:[11]

1. A system of 75 miles of double-track routes with 37 stations.
2. Trains under *advanced automatic control* with speeds up to 70 miles an hour and with *average operating speeds of 50 miles per hour, including station stops.* Headways between trains of as little as 90 seconds providing peak capacity of 30,000 seated passengers per hour in each direction.

The consultants stipulated that "it is fundamental that this rapid transit system include a fully integrated automatic control system, assuring the highest degree of safe and reliable service." Further, they stated:

The heart of the automatic control system is an *industrial type control computer.* This computer monitors the operation of the entire system by constantly checking the location and movement of all trains, announcing abnormal conditions, adjusting the stopping time at stations to meet local requirements, and performing many other system-wide control functions.

A single attendant aboard each train visually monitors the operation of the train. He normally performs no function except to observe an annunciator or display panel and watch the track for physical obstructions. The only overriding operating functions he can perform are to reduce speed or stop the train.

It need not be stated, but the speed and schedule requirements of BART just could not be safely met without a control digital computer system.

Shipboard Control. Britain's *Queen Elizabeth II* has a control digital computer aboard for several planning, analysis, and control functions. The main functions of the computer were initially planned as:[2]

1. *Data logging*—automatically recording the state of the main engines and other machinery, and printing the engine room log.
2. *Alarm scanning*—continuous automatic check on the main machinery. When any temperature or pressure departs from normal limits, the computer warns the engineers immediately.
3. *Machinery control*—continuous control of certain machinery to give increased economy and thus lower fuel consumption.
4. *Weather routing*—computing almost instantaneously, as weather reports are received, the best speed and course to minimize fuel consumption without delaying the ship.

5. *Prediction of fresh water requirements*—enabling maximum efficiency and economy in the use of the evaporating plant, which makes fresh water from sea water to maintain the ship's fresh water stocks.
6. *Inventory control*—recording of some 3,000 items of food, drink, and domestic supplies in six major stores on the ship, and reporting bonded goods unsold at the end of a voyage.

Further possibilities for computer control include navigational problems and possible customer onboard billing.

Automatic Warehousing.   The traditional approach to warehousing has been to reserve specific areas for specific raw materials or finished products.   Also, the traditional approach has utilized conventional material handling equipment to position and pick up the required items. Conventional material handling equipment is meant to imply basic up-to-date equipment such as fork-lift trucks, free and power conveyors, mechanized hand trucks, and similar items.

The trend in warehousing for a while has been to automatic warehousing with an attraction being the possibility for *random storage,* rather than specific fixed storage reserved for specific items.   Random storage allows for a balanced warehouse load to be maintained, equalizing square-footage utilization.   It has been estimated that a 20-percent reduction in volume from conventional warehouse techniques is feasible through automatic warehousing.   Further advantages include minimization of errors in order-picking, theft reduction, minimized handling damage, and increase in speed of operation.

Two interesting warehouse *case systems* are the Sara Lee bakery warehouse and Genesco's shoe operation.   The Genesco operation stores some two million pairs of shoes in its warehouse at Nashville, Tennessee.[12]   Up to 90,000 possible pairs of shoes can be stored with *one unique* combination of style, size, and width for each pair.   Reserving a particular slot in the warehouse for each combination would be ridiculous.   According to *Automation,* the basic flow procedure is as follows:

Stocks arrive at the warehouse with a punched IBM card attached to each case. These cards provide an input to the computer (IBM 7010) which assigns a suitable bin in the storage area. The computer then prints a case location label which is transmitted to the receiving platform of the warehouse. This label is attached to the case and is used to store the case in the proper bin.

The computer also controls the order-packing function for filling orders for retailers. From its memory, the computer assembles a batch of orders to be picked during an hour-long time period. The separate orders are analyzed, and the computer consolidates all shoes required, without regard to separate orders. At the same time, the computer prints out shipping labels and invoices for the packing area and prepares a master tape for a General Electric special purpose (control digital) computer that controls sorting operations. Information relating to the order is sent to accounting, so that inventory and the customers' accounts are automatically updated.

The Sara Lee bakery warehouse temperatures of -10 degrees Fahrenheit preclude wide use of operators working for long periods of time in the warehouse. The entire operation is directed by a Honeywell control digital computer which:[7]

1. Monitors the bulk storage status and use of liquid and dry ingredients.
2. Monitors and controls batch blending and mixing operations, using formulations stored in the computer's memory.
3. Computes and monitors the set points of time cycles, oven zone temperatures, speeds of oven conveyors, and other process equipment to insure uniform baking.
4. Monitors product changeovers automatically of up to 100 different selections of cakes.
5. Directs the random storage of palletized products in a holding freezer, directs order-picking on first-in, first-out basis, and assembles loads of mixed products on to pallets in an auxiliary freezer.
6. Provides records—on both tape and log sheets—of process data and accounting information.

In conclusion, it might be said that Sara Lee popularized the control digital computers somewhat in the way that Admiral Raborn did with PERT. Many Sunday newspaper supplements carried the Sara Lee story to the potential user of Sara Lee products—the housewife.

Quality Control and Inspection. One of the widest uses for control digital computers has been in the quality control and inspection areas, particularly in testing. One interesting example for quality control is found at the Plymouth Assembly Plant, Chrysler Corporation, Detroit.

International Business Machines, in their booklet "Quality Control in Automotive Assembly," discusses the complexity of quality control in the automobile plant:[8]

Complete quality control in an automotive assembly plant is complicated by several factors:

1. The great mass of data that must be handled and analyzed.
2. The wide area over which this data originates.
3. The great number of people originating this data.
4. The need for early detection of defect trends as they develop.
5. The need for quick notification to allow immediate corrective action.
6. The need for a defect summary report giving management a gage of the effectiveness of the quality control program.

There are approximately 4,000 separate defects that can be encountered during the assembly of an automobile. Assembly lines are geared to produce, during full operation, from 40 to 60 cars per hour. This production rate is often maintained two shifts per day. On the basis of this production, hypothetically 30,000 defects could be reported on a normal day.

The defect data is detected by many different inspectors spread over the entire plant floor. The defects may be repaired over this same wide area. This means that quality control data originates with as many as several hundred different people. The detection of the defect by the inspector and the repair effected by the repairman must both be reported. These reports are gathered from the actual assembly line, which often stretches a distance of several miles. The actual gathering of this quality data is complicated by the need to know the status of a defect (that is, repaired or unrepaired) as it leaves the department in which it originated. This knowledge is important to management, since it is indicative of the repair cost involved.

At a typical production rate of 40 to 60 cars per hour, failure to detect a trend for an extended period of time can create the need for repair on a large number of cars. In fact, if the defect condition lasts for only one hour, there will be enough defective cars to fill most of the repair facilities available within the factory area. It is very important, therefore, that trends be spotted as quickly as possible and that the people responsible for initiation of corrective action be notified immediately.

The quality control system requires the rapid gathering of data pertaining to specific defects and the automatic counting of defects and quick reporting of defect trends. The control digital computer in this type of system is a device that can accept quality information from remote stations, and from this information generate pertinent reports based on current system status and projected defect trends. The IBM booklet summarizes the data processing system components as:

1. *Multiple input units*, with the ability to read pre-punched cards and accept variable information (quality defects and indicative information about the car) from positions along the assembly lines.

2. *Remote typing/inquiry stations*, offering the ability to notify the proper people quickly when a defect trend develops, and allowing free access to all the information stored in the random access storage.

3. *Random access storage*, providing quick storage and retrieval of voluminous amounts of information such as the totals of the defects and the options of the cars to be built.

4. *Real-time operation*, providing direct entry of data to the computer, instantaneous processing and analysis, and immediate reaction to out-of-control conditions—for example, the automatic and timely notification that a defect trend is developing.

5. *Remote printing stations*, placed along the assembly lines to print the assembly line broadcast sheets.

In effect, the computer is used as the heart of an information inputting and reporting system, utilizing input equipment such as was discussed earlier in Chapter 12.

Discrete Manufacturing. Molins Machine Company of England has a most radical approach to computer-controlled job-shop manufacturing. Rather than integrate current numerically controlled machine tools with transfer equipment, they decided to completely redesign the manufacturing equipment to make it highly amenable to computer control.

Their "System 24" process has a series of machines, each performing a specific limited range of machining operations.[14] In this way, one highly complex N/C machine will not be tied up for long periods of time even though it will be used a relatively short period of time.

A routing conveyor delivers full bins of material to computer-selected workfixing stations, while a return conveyor sends bins, finished material, and tooling back to a workpiece center. According to Williamson, enough workpieces are fixed to standardized pallets to keep the machines running for 24 hours. Operators are needed only to fix workpieces to the pallets.

The Molins article indicates that if one of the machine tools does fail, the computer rearranges the workload to make best use of the remaining facilities. Overall, the control digital computer controls scheduling, N/C program selection, and automatic materials handling and inspection. This is quite a feat when it is considered that the job shop has always been considered one of less acceptable types of operation for centralized automation. Benefits claimed by Williamson for the "System 24" versus conventional job-shop operations include 98 percent reduction in time for repeated operations; 80 percent reduction in component costs; some 85 percent reduction in total personnel, and an 85 percent reduction in space required.

These five areas are but a few of those utilizing control digital computers. The limit of application is just about the limit of man's imagination. The same can be said regarding planning, analysis, and control for industrial systems.

REFERENCES CITED

1. BEDWORTH, DAVID D., "Discrete-Part Manufacturing Control by Digital Computer," *The Journal of Industrial Engineering*, February, 1967, Vol. XVIII, No. 2.

2. "Computer Taking Helm of New Queen Liz," *Control Engineering*, Vol. 14, No. 12, December, 1967.

3. GIEDION, SIEGFRIED, *Mechanization Takes Command*, Oxford University Press, New York, N.Y., 1948.

4. LEONE, WILLIAM C., *Production Automation and Numerical Control*, The Ronald Press Company, New York, N.Y.,1967.

5. "New Bendix N/C Series Runs by EDP," *Metalworking News*, February 12, 1968.

6. "On-Line Direct N/C by Computer Debuts," *Metalworking News*, March 4, 1968.

7. "Plant of 1970 Is Here in '64," *Factory*, February, 1964.

8. *Quality Control in Automotive Assembly*, IBM Technical Publications Department, White Plains, New York.

9. SANDFORD, J. E., "Enter—Super Quality Control Rooms." *The Iron Age*, May 23, 1968.

10. SHILS, EDWARD B., *Automation and Industrial Relations*, Holt, Rinehart and Winston, Inc., New York, N.Y., 1963.

11. *The Composite Report Bay Area Rapid Transit May 1962*, submitted to the city of San Francisco by Parsons—Brinckerhoff—Tudor—Bechtel, General Engineering Consultants.

12. "Warehousing Shoes Under Computer Control,"*Automation*,Vol.12,July1965.

13. WILBURN, Julian E., "Future Marriage of N/C and Computer Control," *Automation*, Vol. 13, No. 1, January 1966.

14. WILLIAMSON, D. T. N., "Integrated Manufacturing Control," *Control Engineering*, Vol. XIV, No. 9, September, 1967.

15. WOOLLARD, FRANK G., "Automation in Engineering Production," in *The Push-Button World*, edited by E. M. Hugh-Jones, University of Oklahoma Press, Norman, Okla., 1956.

PROBLEMS

1. Perform a literature search to enable you to evaluate the feasibility for control digital computer application in one or more of the following areas:

A. Cement plant control.

B. Steel plant control.

C. Automobile manufacturing control.

D. Traffic control.

E. Testing and inspection.

F. Shipboard control.

G. Real-time data processing.

H. Railroad applications.

I. Discrete-item manufacturing.

2. Classify those discrete-item manufacturing functions you feel have the most potential benefits accruing from control digital computer application. Justify your findings.

3. Comment on the statement: "All types of computer, including scientific and business, will one day fall into the classification of control digital computers."

4. What advantages would be realized if the statement in Problem 3 is correct? What disadvantages?

5. Evaluate the benefits to be achieved through the use of a control digital computer in an integrated manufacturing system (Molins) versus those benefits accruing through the use of N/C machine centers.

6. Assuming costs can be reduced through the use of integrated circuitry, what do you feel would be the justification for a control digital computer in "every home," other than benefiting the computer manufacturers.

APPENDIX

A

Areas and Ordinates of the Normal Curve

Table A-1

Areas of the Normal Curve

Z	0.00	0.01	0.02	0.03	0.04	Z
0.0	0.500 00	0.503 99	0.507 98	0.511 97	0.515 95	0.0
0.1	0.539 83	0.543 79	0.547 76	0.551 72	0.555 67	0.1
0.2	0.579 26	0.583 17	0.587 06	0.590 95	0.594 83	0.2
0.3	0.617 91	0.621 72	0.625 51	0.629 30	0.633 07	0.3
0.4	0.655 42	0.659 10	0.662 76	0.666 40	0.670 03	0.4
0.5	0.691 46	0.694 97	0.698 47	0.701 94	0.705 40	0.5
0.6	0.725 75	0.729 07	0.732 37	0.735 65	0.738 91	0.6
0.7	0.758 03	0.761 15	0.764 24	0.767 30	0.770 35	0.7
0.8	0.788 14	0.791 03	0.793 89	0.796 73	0.799 54	0.8
0.9	0.815 94	0.818 59	0.821 21	0.823 81	0.826 39	0.9
1.0	0.841 34	0.843 75	0.846 13	0.848 49	0.850 83	1.0
1.1	0.864 33	0.866 50	0.868 64	0.870 76	0.872 85	1.1
1.2	0.884 93	0.886 86	0.888 77	0.890 65	0.892 51	1.2
1.3	0.903 20	0.904 90	0.906 58	0.908 24	0.909 88	1.3
1.4	0.919 24	0.920 73	0.922 19	0.923 64	0.925 06	1.4
1.5	0.933 19	0.934 48	0.935 74	0.936 99	0.938 22	1.5
1.6	0.945 20	0.946 30	0.947 38	0.948 45	0.949 50	1.6
1.7	0.955 43	0.956 37	0.957 28	0.958 18	0.959 07	1.7
1.8	0.964 07	0.964 85	0.965 62	0.966 37	0.967 11	1.8
1.9	0.971 28	0.971 93	0.972 57	0.973 20	0.973 81	1.9
2.0	0.977 25	0.977 78	0.978 31	0.978 82	0.979 32	2.0
2.1	0.982 14	0.982 57	0.983 00	0.983 41	0.983 82	2.1
2.2	0.986 10	0.986 45	0.986 79	0.987 13	0.987 45	2.2
2.3	0.989 28	0.989 56	0.989 83	0.990 10	0.990 36	2.3
2.4	0.991 80	0.992 02	0.992 24	0.992 45	0.992 66	2.4
2.5	0.993 79	0.993 96	0.994 13	0.994 30	0.994 46	2.5
2.6	0.995 34	0.995 47	0.995 60	0.995 73	0.995 85	2.6
2.7	0.996 53	0.996 64	0.996 74	0.996 83	0.996 93	2.7
2.8	0.997 44	0.997 52	0.997 60	0.997 67	0.997 74	2.8
2.9	0.998 13	0.998 19	0.998 25	0.998 31	0.998 36	2.9
3.0	0.998 65	0.998 69	0.998 74	0.998 78	0.998 82	3.0
3.1	0.999 03	0.999 06	0.999 10	0.999 13	0.999 16	3.1
3.2	0.999 31	0.999 34	0.999 36	0.999 38	0.999 40	3.2
3.3	0.999 52	0.999 53	0.999 55	0.999 57	0.999 58	3.3
3.4	0.999 66	0.999 68	0.999 69	0.999 70	0.999 71	3.4
3.5	0.999 77	0.999 78	0.999 78	0.999 79	0.999 80	3.5
3.6	0.999 84	0.999 85	0.999 85	0.999 86	0.999 86	3.6
3.7	0.999 89	0.999 90	0.999 90	0.999 90	0.999 91	3.7
3.8	0.999 93	0.999 93	0.999 93	0.999 94	0.999 94	3.8
3.9	0.999 95	0.999 95	0.999 96	0.999 96	0.999 96	3.9

Table A-1—*Continued*

z	0.05	0.06	0.07	0.08	0.09	z
0.0	0.519 94	0.523 92	0.527 90	0.531 88	0.535 86	0.0
0.1	0.559 62	0.563 56	0.567 49	0.571 42	0.575 34	0.1
0.2	0.598 71	0.602 57	0.606 42	0.610 26	0.614 09	0.2
0.3	0.636 83	0.640 58	0.644 31	0.648 03	0.651 73	0.3
0.4	0.673 64	0.677 24	0.680 82	0.684 38	0.687 93	0.4
0.5	0.708 84	0.712 26	0.715 66	0.719 04	0.722 40	0.5
0.6	0.742 15	0.745 37	0.748 57	0.751 75	0.754 90	0.6
0.7	0.773 37	0.776 37	0.779 35	0.782 30	0.785 23	0.7
0.8	0.802 34	0.805 10	0.807 85	0.810 57	0.813 27	0.8
0.9	0.828 94	0.831 47	0.833 97	0.836 46	0.838 91	0.9
1.0	0.853 14	0.855 43	0.857 69	0.859 93	0.862 14	1.0
1.1	0.874 93	0.876 97	0.879 00	0.881 00	0.882 97	1.1
1.2	0.894 35	0.896 16	0.897 96	0.899 73	0.901 47	1.2
1.3	0.911 49	0.913 08	0.914 65	0.916 21	0.917 73	1.3
1.4	0.926 47	0.927 85	0.929 22	0.930 56	0.931 89	1.4
1.5	0.939 43	0.940 62	0.941 79	0.942 95	0.944 08	1.5
1.6	0.950 53	0.951 54	0.952 54	0.953 52	0.954 48	1.6
1.7	0.959 94	0.960 80	0.961 64	0.962 46	0.963 27	1.7
1.8	0.967 84	0.968 56	0.969 26	0.969 95	0.970 62	1.8
1.9	0.974 41	0.975 00	0.975 58	0.976 15	0.976 70	1.9
2.0	0.979 82	0.980 30	0.980 77	0.981 24	0.981 69	2.0
2.1	0.984 22	0.984 61	0.985 00	0.985 37	0.985 74	2.1
2.2	0.987 78	0.988 09	0.988 40	0.988 70	0.988 99	2.2
2.3	0.990 61	0.990 86	0.991 11	0.991 34	0.991 58	2.3
2.4	0.992 86	0.993 05	0.993 24	0.993 43	0.993 61	2.4
2.5	0.994 61	0.994 77	0.994 92	0.995 06	0.995 20	2.5
2.6	0.995 98	0.996 09	0.996 21	0.996 32	0.996 43	2.6
2.7	0.997 02	0.997 11	0.997 20	0.997 28	0.997 36	2.7
2.8	0.997 81	0.997 88	0.997 95	0.998 01	0.998 07	2.8
2.9	0.998 41	0.998 46	0.998 51	0.998 56	0.998 61	2.9
3.0	0.998 86	0.998 89	0.998 93	0.998 97	0.999 00	3.0
3.1	0.999 18	0.999 21	0.999 24	0.999 26	0.999 29	3.1
3.2	0.999 42	0.999 44	0.999 46	0.999 48	0.999 50	3.2
3.3	0.999 60	0.999 61	0.999 62	0.999 64	0.999 65	3.3
3.4	0.999 72	0.999 73	0.999 74	0.999 75	0.999 76	3.4
3.5	0.999 81	0.999 81	0.999 82	0.999 83	0.999 83	3.5
3.6	0.999 87	0.999 87	0.999 88	0.999 88	0.999 89	3.6
3.7	0.999 91	0.999 92	0.999 92	0.999 92	0.999 92	3.7
3.8	0.999 94	0.999 94	0.999 95	0.999 95	0.999 95	3.8
3.9	0.999 96	0.999 96	0.999 96	0.999 97	0.999 97	3.9

Table A-2

Ordinates of the Normal Curve

Z	0.00	0.01	0.02	0.03	0.04	Z
0.0	0.398 94	0.398 92	0.398 86	0.398 76	0.398 62	0.0
0.1	0.396 95	0.396 54	0.396 08	0.395 59	0.395 05	0.1
0.2	0.391 04	0.390 24	0.389 40	0.388 53	0.387 62	0.2
0.3	0.381 39	0.380 23	0.379 03	0.377 80	0.376 54	0.3
0.4	0.368 27	0.366 78	0.365 26	0.363 71	0.362 13	0.4
0.5	0.352 07	0.350 29	0.348 49	0.346 67	0.344 82	0.5
0.6	0.333 22	0.331 21	0.329 18	0.327 13	0.325 06	0.6
0.7	0.312 25	0.310 06	0.307 85	0.305 63	0.303 39	0.7
0.8	0.289 69	0.287 37	0.285 04	0.282 69	0.280 34	0.8
0.9	0.266 09	0.263 69	0.261 29	0.258 88	0.256 47	0.9
1.0	0.241 97	0.239 55	0.237 13	0.234 71	0.232 30	1.0
1.1	0.217 85	0.215 46	0.213 07	0.210 69	0.208 31	1.1
1.2	0.194 19	0.191 86	0.189 54	0.187 24	0.184 94	1.2
1.3	0.171 37	0.169 15	0.166 94	0.164 74	0.162 56	1.3
1.4	0.149 73	0.147 64	0.145 56	0.143 50	0.141 46	1.4
1.5	0.129 52	0.127 58	0.125 66	0.123 76	0.121 88	1.5
1.6	0.110 92	0.109 15	0.107 41	0.105 68	0.103 96	1.6
1.7	0.094 05	0.092 46	0.090 89	0.089 33	0.087 80	1.7
1.8	0.078 95	0.077 54	0.076 14	0.074 77	0.073 41	1.8
1.9	0.065 62	0.064 38	0.063 16	0.061 95	0.060 77	1.9
2.0	0.053 99	0.052 92	0.051 86	0.050 82	0.049 80	2.0
2.1	0.043 98	0.043 07	0.042 17	0.041 28	0.040 41	2.1
2.2	0.035 47	0.034 70	0.033 94	0.033 19	0.032 46	2.2
2.3	0.028 33	0.027 68	0.027 05	0.026 43	0.025 82	2.3
2.4	0.022 39	0.021 86	0.021 34	0.020 83	0.020 33	2.4
2.5	0.017 53	0.017 09	0.016 67	0.016 25	0.015 85	2.5
2.6	0.013 58	0.013 23	0.012 89	0.012 56	0.012 23	2.6
2.7	0.010 42	0.010 14	0.009 87	0.009 61	0.009 35	2.7
2.8	0.007 92	0.007 70	0.007 48	0.007 27	0.007 07	2.8
2.9	0.005 95	0.005 78	0.005 62	0.005 45	0.005 30	2.9
3.0	0.004 43	0.004 30	0.004 17	0.004 05	0.003 93	3.0
3.1	0.003 27	0.003 17	0.003 07	0.002 98	0.002 88	3.1
3.2	0.002 38	0.002 31	0.002 24	0.002 16	0.002 10	3.2
3.3	0.001 72	0.001 67	0.001 61	0.001 56	0.001 51	3.3
3.4	0.001 23	0.001 19	0.001 15	0.001 11	0.001 07	3.4
3.5	0.000 87	0.000 84	0.000 81	0.000 79	0.000 76	3.5
3.6	0.000 61	0.000 59	0.000 57	0.000 55	0.000 53	3.6
3.7	0.000 42	0.000 41	0.000 39	0.000 38	0.000 37	3.7
3.8	0.000 29	0.000 28	0.000 27	0.000 26	0.000 25	3.8
3.9	0.000 20	0.000 19	0.000 18	0.000 18	0.000 17	3.9

Table A-2—Continued

Z	0.05	0.06	0.07	0.08	0.09	Z
0.0	0.398 44	0.398 22	0.397 97	0.397 67	0.397 33	0.0
0.1	0.394 48	0.393 87	0.393 22	0.392 53	0.391 81	0.1
0.2	0.386 67	0.385 68	0.384 66	0.383 61	0.382 51	0.2
0.3	0.375 24	0.373 91	0.372 55	0.371 15	0.369 73	0.3
0.4	0.360 53	0.358 89	0.357 23	0.355 53	0.353 81	0.4
0.5	0.342 94	0.341 05	0.339 12	0.337 18	0.335 21	0.5
0.6	0.322 97	0.320 86	0.318 74	0.316 59	0.314 43	0.6
0.7	0.301 14	0.298 87	0.296 59	0.294 31	0.292 00	0.7
0.8	0.277 99	0.275 62	0.273 24	0.270 86	0.268 48	0.8
0.9	0.254 06	0.251 64	0.249 23	0.246 81	0.244 39	0.9
1.0	0.229 88	0.227 47	0.225 06	0.222 65	0.220 25	1.0
1.1	0.205 94	0.203 57	0.201 21	0.198 86	0.196 52	1.1
1.2	0.182 65	0.180 37	0.178 10	0.175 85	0.173 60	1.2
1.3	0.160 38	0.158 22	0.156 08	0.153 95	0.151 83	1.3
1.4	0.139 43	0.137 42	0.135 42	0.133 44	0.131 47	1.4
1.5	0.120 01	0.118 16	0.116 32	0.114 50	0.112 70	1.5
1.6	0.102 27	0.100 59	0.098 93	0.097 28	0.095 66	1.6
1.7	0.086 28	0.084 78	0.083 29	0.081 83	0.080 38	1.7
1.8	0.072 06	0.070 74	0.069 43	0.068 14	0.066 87	1.8
1.9	0.059 59	0.058 44	0.057 30	0.056 18	0.055 08	1.9
2.0	0.048 79	0.047 80	0.046 82	0.045 86	0.044 91	2.0
2.1	0.039 55	0.038 71	0.037 88	0.037 06	0.036 26	2.1
2.2	0.031 74	0.031 03	0.030 34	0.029 65	0.028 98	2.2
2.3	0.025 22	0.024 63	0.024 06	0.023 49	0.022 94	2.3
2.4	0.019 84	0.019 36	0.018 89	0.018 42	0.017 97	2.4
2.5	0.015 45	0.015 06	0.014 68	0.014 31	0.013 94	2.5
2.6	0.011 91	0.011 60	0.011 30	0.011 00	0.010 71	2.6
2.7	0.009 09	0.008 85	0.008 61	0.008 37	0.008 14	2.7
2.8	0.006 87	0.006 68	0.006 49	0.006 31	0.006 13	2.8
2.9	0.005 14	0.004 99	0.004 85	0.004 70	0.004 57	2.9
3.0	0.003 81	0.003 70	0.003 58	0.003 48	0.003 37	3.0
3.1	0.002 79	0.002 71	0.002 62	0.002 54	0.002 46	3.1
3.2	0.002 03	0.001 96	0.001 90	0.001 84	0.001 78	3.2
3.3	0.001 46	0.001 41	0.001 36	0.001 32	0.001 27	3.3
3.4	0.001 04	0.001 00	0.000 97	0.000 94	0.000 90	3.4
3.5	0.000 73	0.000 71	0.000 68	0.000 66	0.000 63	3.5
3.6	0.000 51	0.000 49	0.000 47	0.000 46	0.000 44	3.6
3.7	0.000 35	0.000 34	0.000 33	0.000 31	0.000 30	3.7
3.8	0.000 24	0.000 23	0.000 22	0.000 21	0.000 21	3.8
3.9	0.000 16	0.000 16	0.000 15	0.000 14	0.000 14	3.9

B

Random Numbers

Table B-1

Random Digits

10480	15011	01536	02011	81647	91646	69179	14194	62590
22368	46573	25595	85393	30995	89198	27982	53402	93965
24130	48360	22527	97265	76393	64809	15179	24830	49340
42167	93093	06243	61680	07856	16376	39440	53537	71341
37570	39975	81837	16656	06121	91782	60468	81305	49684
77921	06907	11008	42751	27756	53498	18602	70659	90655
99562	72905	56420	69994	98872	31016	71194	18738	44013
96301	91977	05463	07972	18876	20922	94595	56869	69014
89579	14342	63661	10281	17453	18103	57740	84378	25331
85475	36857	53342	53988	53060	59533	38867	62300	08158
28918	69578	88231	33276	70997	79936	56865	05859	90106
63553	40961	48235	03427	49626	69445	18663	72695	52180
09429	93969	52636	92737	88974	33488	36320	17617	30015
10365	61129	87529	85689	48237	52267	67689	93394	01511
07119	97336	71048	08178	77233	13916	47564	81056	97735
51085	12765	51821	51259	77452	16308	60756	92144	49442
02368	21382	52404	60268	89368	19885	55322	44819	01188
01011	54092	33362	94904	31273	04146	18594	29852	71585
52162	53916	46369	58586	23216	14513	83149	98736	23495
07056	97628	33787	09998	42698	06691	76988	13602	51851
48663	91245	85828	14346	09172	30168	90229	04734	59193
54164	58492	22421	74103	47070	25306	76468	26384	58151
32639	32363	05597	24200	13363	38005	94342	28728	35806
29334	27001	87637	87308	58731	00256	45834	15398	46557
02488	33062	28834	07351	19731	92420	60952	61280	50001
81525	72295	04839	96423	24878	82651	66566	14778	76797
29676	20591	68086	26432	46901	20849	89768	81536	86645
00742	57392	39064	66432	84673	40027	32832	61362	98947
05366	04213	25669	26422	44407	44048	37937	63904	45766
91921	26418	64117	94305	26766	25940	39972	22209	71500
00582	04711	87917	77341	42206	35126	74087	99547	81817
00725	69884	62797	56170	86324	88072	76222	36086	84637
69011	65795	95876	55293	18988	27354	26575	08625	40801
25976	57948	29888	88604	67917	48708	18912	82271	65424
09763	83473	73577	12908	30883	18317	28290	35797	05998

Table B-1—*Continued*

91567	42595	27958	30134	04024	86385	29880	99730	55536
17955	56349	90999	49127	20044	59931	06115	20542	18059
46503	18584	18845	49618	02304	51038	20655	58727	28168
92157	89634	94824	78171	84610	82834	09922	25417	44137
14577	62765	35605	81263	39667	47358	56873	56307	61607
98427	07523	33362	64270	01638	92477	66969	98420	04880
34914	63976	88720	82765	34476	17032	87589	40836	32427
70060	28277	39475	46473	23219	53416	94970	25832	69975
53976	54914	06990	67245	68350	82948	11398	42878	80287
76072	29515	40980	07391	58745	25774	22987	80059	39911
90725	52210	83974	29992	65831	38857	50490	83765	55657
64364	67412	33339	31926	14883	24413	59744	92351	97473
08962	00358	31662	25388	61642	34072	81249	35648	56891
95012	68379	93526	70765	10592	04542	76463	54328	02349
15664	10493	20492	38391	91132	21999	59516	81652	27195

C

Third-Order
Exponential Smoothing

AN APPROACH TO SECOND-ORDER POLYNOMIAL FIT

Fitting a first-order polynomial by exponential smoothing in Chapter 4 was accomplished by considering the expected lag of first-order smoothing to the data and also the second-order smoothing lag to the first-order smoothed values. A similar approach can be made to fitting a second-order polynomial with the addition of third-order exponential smoothing $\hat{Y}(t), 3$ which smooths the second-order smoothed statistics.

Let

$$\hat{Y}(t), 1 = \text{first-order smoothing at time } t$$

and

$$\hat{Y}(t), 2 = \text{second-order smoothing at time } t$$

and

$$Y(t) = \text{data value at time } t; \qquad Y(t) = a + bt + ct^2$$

Then

$$\hat{Y}(t), 1 = \alpha Y(t) + \beta \hat{Y}(t-1), 1 = \alpha Y(t) + \alpha\beta Y(t-1) \\ + \alpha\beta^2 Y(t-2) + \cdots$$

Similarly,

$$\hat{Y}(t-1), 1 = \alpha Y(t-1) + \alpha\beta Y(t-2) + \alpha\beta^2 Y(t-2) + \cdots$$

so

$$[\hat{Y}(t), 1 - \hat{Y}(t-1), 1] = \alpha[Y(t) - Y(t-1)] + \alpha\beta[Y(t-1)$$
$$-Y(t-2)] + \alpha\beta^2[Y(t-2) - Y(t-3)] + \cdots \quad \text{(C-1)}$$

If it is assumed that *lag* is defined as

$$\text{lag} = L'(t) = [Y(t) - \hat{Y}(t), 1] \quad \text{(C-2)}$$

then

$$L'(t) = Y(t) - \alpha Y(t) - \beta\hat{Y}(t-1), 1$$
$$L'(t) = \beta[Y(t) - \hat{Y}(t-1), 1];$$

since $\beta = (1 - \alpha)$

$$L'(t) = \beta[Y(t) - \hat{Y}(t), 1 + \hat{Y}(t), 1 - \hat{Y}(t-1), 1]$$

but, $(Y(t) - \hat{Y}(t), 1)$ is defined as $L'(t)$, from Equation C–2; so

$$[L'(t) - \beta L'(t)] = \beta[\hat{Y}(t), 1 - \hat{Y}(t-1), 1]$$

and

$$\underline{L'(t) = \left(\frac{\beta}{\alpha}\right)[\hat{Y}(t), 1 - \hat{Y}(t-1), 1]} \quad \text{(C-3)}$$

However, Equation C–1 gives $[\hat{Y}(t), 1 - \hat{Y}(t-1), 1]$ as

$$\alpha[Y(t) - Y(t-1)] + \alpha\beta[Y(t-1) - Y(t-2)] + \alpha\beta^2[Y(t-2)$$
$$- Y(t-3)] + \cdots$$

Since $Y(t) = a + bt + ct^2$, then Equation C–1 can be rewritten by the following manipulation:

$$[Y(t) - Y(t-1)] = a + bt + ct^2 - a - b(t-1) - c(t-1)^2$$
$$= [b + c(2t-1)]$$

And, in general,

$$[Y(t-i) - Y(t-i-1)] = b + c[2t - 2i - 1]$$

Equation C–1 can now be stated as

$$[\hat{Y}(t), 1 - \hat{Y}(t-1), 1] = \alpha[b + c(2t-1)] + \alpha\beta[b + c(2t-3)]$$
$$+ \alpha\beta^2[b + c(2t-5)] + \cdots = \frac{\alpha[b + 2tc]}{(1-\beta)} - \frac{c(1+\beta)}{\alpha}$$
$$= \left[b + c\left(2t - \frac{(1+\beta)}{\alpha}\right)\right]$$

Equation C–3 now can be written

$$L'(t) = \left(\frac{\beta}{\alpha}\right)\left[b + c\left(2t - \frac{(1 + \beta)}{\alpha}\right)\right] \tag{C-4}$$

and at $t = 0$, for initial conditions:

$$L'(0) = \left(\frac{\beta}{\alpha}\right)\left(b - c\frac{(1 + \beta)}{\alpha}\right)$$

And since $L'(0) = Y(0) - \hat{Y}(0)$, 1 by definition,

$$\hat{Y}(0), 1 = Y(0) - \frac{\beta}{\alpha}[\hat{b}(0)] + \frac{(1 + \beta)\beta}{\alpha^2}[\hat{c}(0)]$$

and Equation 4–15 is proved.

Equation 4–16 now falls out a little more simply. Similarly to $L'(t)$, define

$$L^2(t) - Y(t) - \hat{Y}(t), 2 \tag{C-5}$$

therefore,

$$L^2(t) = [Y(t) - \hat{Y}(t), 1] + [\hat{Y}(t), 1 - \hat{Y}(t), 2], \quad \text{and:}$$

$$L^2(t) = L'(t) + [\hat{Y}(t), 1 - \hat{Y}(t), 2] \tag{C-6}$$

lt is known that $\hat{Y}(t), 1 - \alpha Y(t) + \alpha\beta Y(t - 1) + \alpha\beta^2 Y(t - 2) + \cdots$, and that $\hat{Y}(t), 2 = \alpha \hat{Y}(t), 1 + \alpha\beta \hat{Y}(t - 1), 1 + \alpha\beta^2 \hat{Y}(t - 2), 1 + \cdots$, so then

$$[\hat{Y}(t), 1 - \hat{Y}(t), 2] = \alpha[L'(t) + \beta L'(t - 1) + \beta^2 L'(t - 2) + \cdots]$$

From Equation C–4, it was shown that

$$L'(t) = \left(\frac{\beta}{\alpha}\right)\left[b + c\left(2t - \frac{(1 + \beta)}{\alpha}\right)\right]$$

So $\alpha[L'(t) + \beta L'(t - 1) + \beta^2 L'(t - 2) + \cdots]$ reduces to

$$(\beta)(b)[1 + \beta + \beta^2 + \cdots] - \frac{\beta(1 + \beta)}{\alpha}c[1 + \beta + \beta^2 + \cdots]$$

$$+ 2\beta c[t + (t - 1)\beta + (t - 2)\beta^2 + \cdots]$$

and since we will evaluate at $t = 0$, this evolves to

$$\left(\frac{\beta}{\alpha}\right)(b) - \frac{\beta(1 + \beta)}{\alpha^2}(c) - \frac{2\beta^2(c)}{\alpha^2}$$

or

$$[\hat{Y}(0), 1 - \hat{Y}(0), 2] = \left\{\frac{\beta}{\alpha}(b) - \frac{(c)\beta}{\alpha^2}(1 + 3\beta)]\right\}$$

Knowing $L^2(0) = L'(0) + [\hat{Y}(0), 1 - \hat{Y}(0), 2]$ from Equation C–6, it follows that

$$L^2(0) = L'(0) + \left\{ \frac{\beta}{\alpha}(b) - \frac{\beta}{\alpha^2}[1 + 3\beta] \right\}$$

and knowing

$$L'(0) = \left(\frac{\beta}{\alpha}\right)\left[b - c\,\frac{(1 + \beta)}{\alpha} \right]$$

it is seen that

$$L^2(0) = 2\left(\frac{\beta}{\alpha}\right) b - \frac{2\beta(c)}{\alpha^2}(1 + 2\beta)$$

Finally, since $L^2(0) = Y(0) - \hat{Y}(0)$, 2 by definition,

$$\hat{Y}(0),\, 2 = Y(0) - 2\,\frac{(\beta)}{\alpha}[\hat{b}(0)] + \frac{2\beta(1 + 2\beta)}{\alpha^2}[\hat{c}(0)]$$

and Equation 4–16 is proved.

In exactly the same fashion, by defining

$$L^3(t) = [Y(t) - \hat{Y}^3(t)] = [Y(t) - \hat{Y}^2(t)] + [\hat{Y}^2(t) - \hat{Y}^3(t)]$$

so

$$L^3(t) = L^2(t) + [\hat{Y}^2(t) - \hat{Y}^3(t)]$$

algebraic manipulation will evolve Equation 4–17:

$$\hat{Y}(0),\, 3 = Y(0) - 3\left(\frac{\beta}{\alpha}\right)[\hat{b}(0)] + \frac{3\beta(1 + 3\beta)}{\alpha^2}[\hat{c}(0)]$$

Equations 4–15 through 4–17, of course, give the initial conditions for the three orders of smoothing. If they are now written as a function of t, and using the end point of the fitted line $a + bt + ct^2$, $Y(t)$, as the estimate $\hat{a}(t)$ we get

$$\hat{Y}(t),\, 1 = \hat{a}(t) - \left(\frac{\beta}{\alpha}\right)[\hat{b}(t)] + \frac{\beta(1 + \beta)}{\alpha^2}[\hat{c}(t)] \tag{C–7}$$

$$\hat{Y}(t),\, 2 = \hat{a}(t) - \left(\frac{2\beta}{\alpha}\right)[\hat{b}(t)] + \left[\frac{2\beta(1 + 2\beta)}{\alpha^2}\right][\hat{c}(t)] \tag{C–8}$$

$$\hat{Y}(t),\, 3 = \hat{a}(t) - \left(\frac{3\beta}{\alpha}\right)[\hat{b}(t)] + \left[\frac{3\beta(1 + 3\beta)}{\alpha^2}\right][\hat{c}(t)] \tag{C–9}$$

Now, at time t the object of interest is to calculate the three coefficients in terms of the three orders of smoothing. Solving the three equations,

C–7 through C-9, simultaneously for $\hat{a}(t)$, $\hat{b}(t)$, and $\hat{c}(t)$ in terms of $\hat{Y}(t)$, 1; $\hat{Y}(t)$, 2; and $\hat{Y}(t)$, 3 will do this. Solving for $\hat{b}(t)$ in Equation C–7 gives

$$\hat{b}(t) = \left[\frac{\alpha}{\beta}\right]\left[\hat{a}(t) - \hat{Y}(t), 1 + \frac{\beta(1 + \beta)}{\alpha^2}\hat{c}(t)\right]$$

If this is now substituted into Equations C–8 and C–9, we find

$$\hat{a}(t) = 2\,\hat{Y}(t), 1 - \hat{Y}(t), 2 + \left(\frac{2\beta^2}{\alpha^2}\right)\hat{c}(t) \qquad (C\text{–}10)$$

from C–8 and

$$2\hat{a}(t) = 3\,\hat{Y}(t), 1 - \hat{Y}(t), 3 + \left(\frac{6\beta^2}{\alpha^2}\right)\hat{c}(t) \qquad (C\text{–}11)$$

from C–9. Substituting Equation C–10 into C–11 gives

$$\hat{c}(t) = \left[\frac{\alpha^2}{2\beta^2}\right][\,\hat{Y}(t), 1 - 2\,\hat{Y}(t), 2 + \hat{Y}(t), 3]$$

and Equation 4–14 is proven.

If $\hat{c}(t)$ is now substituted back into Equation C–10,

$$\hat{a}(t) = 2\,\hat{Y}(t), 1 - \hat{Y}(t), 2 + \hat{Y}(t), 1 - 2\hat{Y}(t), 2 + \hat{Y}(t), 3$$

so,

$$\hat{a}(t) = 3\,\hat{Y}(t), 1 - 3\hat{Y}(t), 2 + \hat{Y}(t), 3$$

and Equation 4–12 is proven.

Lastly, if $\hat{c}(t)$ and $\hat{a}(t)$ are now substituted into Equation C–7, it is found that

$$\hat{Y}(t), 1 - 3\hat{Y}(t), 1 - 3\hat{Y}(t), 2 + \hat{Y}(t), 3 - \left(\frac{\beta}{\alpha}\right)\hat{b}(t) +$$

$$\frac{(1 + \beta)}{2\beta}[\,\hat{Y}(t), 1 - 2\hat{Y}(t), 2 + \hat{Y}(t), 3]$$

which simplifies to

$$\hat{b}(t) = \left[\frac{\alpha}{2\beta^2}\right][\,\hat{Y}(t), 1 \cdot (1 + 5\beta) - \hat{Y}(t), 2 \cdot (2 + 8\beta) + \hat{Y}(t), 3 \cdot (1 + 3\beta)]$$

and Equation 4–13 is proven.

D

Comments on Some Pert Assumptions

In the discussion of PERT in Chapter 2, it was pointed out that several assumptions are made that may, or may not, be valid. Two key assumptions will be discussed a little further in this section. These concern the use of the *Central Limit Theorem* in evolving a *critical path* probability distribution from its activity distributions and the use of approximations for the mean and variance of the beta distribution in estimating distribution characteristics for the individual activities.

CENTRAL LIMIT THEOREM

Let $X = x_1 + x_2 + \cdots + x_n$, where $x_1, x_2, \ldots, x_n$ are identically distributed *independent* random variables each having mean μ and variance σ^2. The distribution of the *sum* of the random variables, $x_1 + x_2 + \cdots + x_n$, approaches the normal distribution with mean $n\mu$ and $n\sigma^2$. The theorem is found to be rather powerful when it is realized that the sum of the random variables will be approximately normal even though the individual distribution of the random variables may be completely non-normal. The traditional empirical way of showing that the Central Limit Theorem does work is to use the distributions generated when independent dice are thrown and their values obtained are summed. The distributions of the *individual* dies are certainly non-normal, being uniform in distribution. For example, if a die with four sides numbered 1, 2, 3 and 4 for simplicity, can be thrown with each side having an equal probability of occurrence it follows that each die has the following distribution characteristics, where $P(x_i)$ designates the probability of x_i occurring:

X_i	$P(X_i)$	$X_iP(X_i)$	$X_i^2P(X_i)$
1	1/4	1/4	1/4
2	1/4	2/4	4/4
3	1/4	3/4	9/4
4	1/4	4/4	16/4
		10/4	30/4

The mean of the distribution is

$$\mu = \sum_{i=1}^{4} X_iP(X_i) = 10/4 = 2.5$$

and the variance is

$$\sigma^2 = \sum_{i=1}^{4} X_i^2P(X_i) - \left[\sum_{i=1}^{4} X_iP(X_i)\right]^2$$

which evolves to

$$\sigma^2 = 30/4 - (10/4)^2 = 1.25$$

Plotting the probability distribution of course reveals the traditional uniform distribution:

$P(X_i) = 1/4$

X_i

Now, what happens if four dice are thrown, and their results are summed? The probability distribution characteristics are as follow:

X_i	$P(X_i)$	$X_iP(X_i)$	$X_i^2P(X_i)$
4	1/256	4/256	16/256
5	4/256	20/256	100/256
6	10/256	60/256	360/256
7	20/256	140/256	980/256
8	31/256	248/256	1984/256
9	40/256	360/256	3240/256
10	44/256	440/256	4400/256
11	40/256	440/256	4840/256
12	31/256	372/256	4464/256
13	20/256	260/256	3380/256
14	10/256	140/256	1960/256
15	4/256	60/256	900/256
16	1/256	16/256	256/256
		2560/256	26,880/256

The mean turns out to be $2560/256 = 10$, and the variance is

$$[26,880/256 - (2560/256)^2] = \frac{1280}{256} = 5.$$

A plot of $P(X_i)$ versus X_i reveals that the distribution is approaching the familiar bell-shaped curve of the normal distribution:

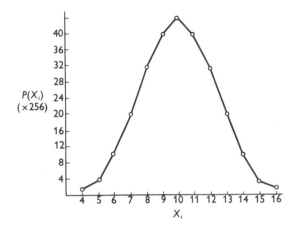

Also, it is seen from the calculations that the expected mean with the sum of four dice is four times that of one die and similarly with the variance relationship.

As an aside, the probabilities for the sums of n dice can be found recursively, once the probabilities of one die are known.

$$P_{(n)}(X) = \left[\sum_{Y=\alpha}^{\beta} P_{(n-1)}(Y) \right][1/m]$$

where $P_{(n)}(X)$ is probability of X with n dice;

    X is the sum of the faces of n dice, $X = n, n+1, \ldots, (m)(n)$;

    α is *maximum* of $(X - m)$, $(n - 1)$;

    β is *minimum* of $(X - 1)$; $m(n - 1)$;

    m is the number of faces on one die; and

    n is the number of dice being summed.

For example, consider the probabilities just given for four dice, each with four faces. If the probability of getting an 8 with five dice were desired:

$$\alpha = \text{maximum of } (8 - 4), \quad (5 - 1) = 4$$

$$\beta = \text{minimum of } (8 - 1), \quad 4(5 - 1) = 7$$

so,

$$P_{(5)}(8) = \left[\sum_{Y=4}^{7} P_{(4)}(Y) \right][1/m]$$

which from the given probabilities for 4 dice is

$$[1/256 + 4/256 + 10/256 + 20/256][1/4] = 35/1024$$

This can be verified when it is realized that there will be

1. five combinations of dice having the combination 11114.
2. twenty combinations of dice having the combination 11123.
3. ten combinations of dice having the combination 11222.

The three different number combinations are the only ones feasible summing to 8, and the number of combinations is 35.

In evaluating the PERT use of the Central Limit Theorem, in all probability there will be sufficient activities on the critical path to justify the use of the Central Limit Theorem, assuming *independence* of activity distributions. It is doubtful that adjacent time distributions would be truly independent. The longest time for a preceding activity should have some bearing, it would seem, on the shortest time of the succeeding activity. It would be truly difficult for an estimator to divorce completely in his mind succeeding activity time distributions, when an overall project time may be desired. In the actual accomplishment of activities, it would be rare if all physical characteristics were separated. In addition, it is not anticipated that all activities will have the same distribution characteristics as specified by the Central Limit Theorem, though the theorem is satisfactory if the activity variances are relatively close.

ACTIVITY BETA DISTRIBUTION ASSUMPTION AND APPROXIMATIONS

As mentioned in Chapter 2, the beta distribution is unimodal, with finite endpoints. Whether the beta distribution represents a general activity distribution is subject to debate. The finite endpoints are, of course, reasonable. Intuitively it is quite plausible that most tasks would be unimodal in characteristic, with some variation around that single peak. However, even if the activity distribution is unimodal and has finite endpoints, the beta distribution may not be appropriate. For example, triangular and uniform distributions are unimodal, with finite endpoints. MacCrimmon and Ryavic* analyzed such

---

* K. R. MacCrimmon and C. A. Ryavic, *An Analytical Study of the PERT Assumptions*, Memorandum PM-3408-PR, The Rand Corporation, Santa Monica, California, December, 1962.

possibilities with a quasi-uniform and a quasi-delta distribution. The worst absolute error was found to be a function of m, the modal estimate, and had a value, as a *proportion* of the *range*, of $(1 - 2m)/3$, where m could lie between 0 and 1. A 33-percent error could be realized. The variance had a worst-case absolute error, as a proportion of the range, of $1/36$.

Even though the activity distribution might follow the beta, errors can, of course, be made by using the PERT mean and standard deviation estimates:

$$\mu_p = \frac{a + 4m + b}{6} \qquad \text{[PERT mean]}$$

$$\sigma_p = \frac{b - a}{6} \quad \text{[PERT standard deviation]}$$

where a is optimistic time estimate,
m is modal estimate, and
b is worst-case time estimate.

Richmond* shows that the theoretical formulas for the mean and variance of the beta distribution are

$$\mu_T = \frac{\alpha + 1}{\alpha + \beta + 2}$$

$$\sigma_T{}^2 = \frac{(\alpha + 1)(\beta + 1)}{(\alpha + \beta + 2)^2(\alpha + \beta + 3)}$$

with the mode $m = \alpha/(\alpha + \beta)$.

To get a relationship between the PERT and theoretical values, it is convenient to set $a = 0$ and $b = 1$. All results can then be a function of the range, $b - a$. The PERT mean can now be written:

$$\mu_p = \frac{4m + 1}{6} = \frac{\dfrac{(4)(\alpha)}{\alpha + \beta} + 1}{6} = \frac{5\alpha + \beta}{6(\alpha + \beta)}$$

This can be evaluated against the beta mean:

$$\mu_T = \frac{\alpha + 1}{\alpha + \beta + 2}$$

---

* S. B. Richmond. *Operations Research for Management Decisions*, New York, The Ronald Press Co., 1968.

Richmond compared statistics for various α and β relationships.

1. $\alpha = 1$, $\beta = 3$:
$$\mu_p = \mu_T = 1/3$$
$$\sigma_p{}^2 = 1/36$$
$$\sigma_T{}^2 = 1/32$$

2. $\alpha = \beta = 1$:
$$\mu_p = \mu_T = 1/2$$
$$\sigma_p{}^2 = 1/36$$
$$\sigma_T{}^2 = 1/20$$

3. $\alpha = \beta = 2$:
$$\mu_p = \mu_T = 1/2$$
$$\sigma_p{}^2 = 1/36$$
$$\sigma_T{}^2 = 1/28$$

These are all quite reasonable approximations. What if we shift the mode considerably to one side, say $\alpha = 1$, $\beta = 9$, such that the true $m = 1/10$:

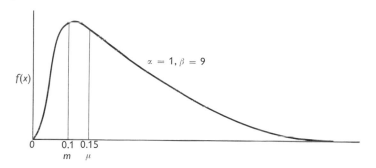

The true mean value is 1/6 by

$$\frac{\alpha + 1}{\alpha + \beta + 2}.$$

The PERT approximations give

$$\mu_p = \frac{a + 4m + b}{6}; \qquad \mu = \frac{1.4}{6} = 0.23$$

The PERT $\sigma_p{}^2$ is, of course, 1/36. The beta $\sigma_T{}^2$ is:

$$\sigma_T{}^2 = \frac{(2)(10)}{(12)^2(13)} = \frac{20}{1872} = \frac{1}{94}$$

The mean is a fair approximation but the variance is rather terrible. However, this was a somewhat unlikely distribution being skewed considerably.

In summary, MacCrimmon and Ryavic contend that the PERT assumptions are dangerous. Richmond, however, feels they are reasonably well justified. If the activity distributions tend to be symmetrical, it is probable that errors made with the assumptions will be relatively slight.

Index